THE SCIENCES
GCSE Grade Booster

P. E. Donovan
P. A. Fryer
J. J. Brennan

Schofield & Sims Ltd.

0 7217 4623 3

First printed 1994

Schofield & Sims Ltd.
Dogley Mill
Fenay Bridge
Huddersfield
HD8 0NQ
England

Designed by Armitage Typo/Graphics
Printed in Great Britain by Scotprint Ltd., Musselburgh

Contents

Introduction

This Sciences Grade Booster is written to help you revise in the last part of your GCSE course. It is not intended as a textbook and you should use a text and/or your notes to check details. You should also read your syllabus to see if there are any sections you can omit.

The book is arranged in such a way that it will be convenient for revision. Throughout you will find headings and subheadings in the margin, with definitions, explanations, equations, examples, etc., to the right of the margin. Use a card with the book to expose the keyword in the margin, but keep the right-hand side covered. Then try to recall the material on the right. By careful lowering of the card, you can allow yourself to see just enough of the writing to prompt you.

Remember that there are several aspects of the GCSE Science course not covered or only touched on in a book like this. One such aspect is laboratory skills on which you will be assessed, but which is still likely to appear in written exam papers. You need to study your practical note book and experiment sheets.

Acknowledgements

The authors would like to thank colleagues at Bradford and Ilkley Community College, and friends, for their helpful suggestions and guidance.

Special thanks go to:

MATERIALS AND THEIR PROPERTIES
Roger Sutcliffe for his assistance in preparing the earth science chapter.

PHYSICAL PROCESSES
(i)   Bill Ross who kindly read and made constructive suggestions on the original manuscript
(ii)   Mrs Halina Reid and Tim Tyne for their efforts in regard to the presentation of the Physics material
(iii)   Dr. Martin Dickinson of the School of Engineering, Humberside University, for a very careful reading of the final draft.

P. E. Donovan
P. A. Fryer
J. J. Brennan

Symbols

To save space the following notation has been adopted:

~   denotes 'of the order of', i.e. to the nearest power of ten.

≃   denotes 'is approximately equal to'.

=   denotes 'is equal to'.

>   denotes 'is greater than'.

≥   denotes 'is greater than or equal to'.

<   denotes 'is less than'.

≤   denotes 'is less than or equal to'.

∴   denotes 'therefore'.

∝   denotes 'varies directly as'.

The Sciences

Life and Living Processes

1 Life Processes and Cells °

Characteristics of Living Organisms Living organisms are composed of units called *cells*. All living organisms must be capable of carrying out the following processes:

Movement, altering position.

Respiration, releasing energy within a cell.

Nutrition, obtaining food.

Irritability, responding to stimuli.

Growth, increasing mass.

Excretion, removing waste products from cells.

Reproduction, producing new individuals.

Unicellular Organisms Some organisms are composed of only one cell. This cell must be capable of carrying out *all* of the above processes. The *amoeba* is an example of a unicellular organism.

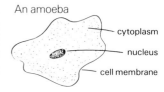

An amoeba

cytoplasm

nucleus

cell membrane

(Note: The ability to draw and correctly label a diagram is a good indication of your knowledge of that organism or structure. Practise drawing diagrams.)

Multicellular organisms In organisms which are composed of more than one cell, the cells may become specialised to carry out a particular process.

Tissues Similar cells which perform a particular function are known as tissues. Examples of tissues include:

a) Connective Tissue This tissue supports, connects and protects organs in the body. It includes: blood, bone and cartilage.

b) Epithelial Tissue This tissue covers or lines structures in the body. It includes the epidermis of the skin.

Organs Several tissues may join together to form an organ. The stomach is composed of epithelial, muscular, nervous and connective tissues.

Systems Several organs may work together to form a system. The digestive system is composed of many organs, including the stomach, intestines, liver and pancreas. An individual is composed of many systems working together, e.g. the digestive, nervous, reproductive and excretory systems in humans.

Animal Cells The following structures in animal cells may be seen using a light microscope.

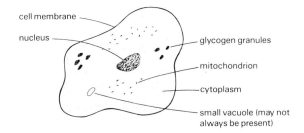

Cell Membrane The cell membrane controls the entry and exit of materials within the cell. It is *selectively permeable,* i.e. it allows some substances to enter and leave the cell, but not others. The cell membrane is composed of protein and fat, and encloses the cytoplasm and the other contents of the cell. It may be folded to increase the surface area of the cell.

Nucleus The nucleus contains the genetic material of the cell. This is carried on genes on the chromosomes in the nucleus. It controls all the cell's activities and is responsible for cell division.

Glycogen Granules Glycogen granules form the main food store in animal cells which is used to provide energy.

Cytoplasm Cytoplasm is a jelly-like substance surrounded by the cell membrane. It provides the medium in which chemical reactions take place in the cell. Cytoplasm is composed of 70%-90% water.

Small Vacuole The small vacuoles may contain food or excess water. They are not permanent structures in animal cells.

Mito-chondria Mitochondria appear as small dots under the light microscope. They form the sites for the production of *ATP* (adenosine triphosphate) which provides energy for the cell. Cells which require large amounts of energy, e.g. liver and muscle cells, have large numbers of mitochondria in them.

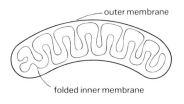

A mitochondrion as seen under an electron microscope

The folded inner membrane provides a very large surface area on which chemical reactions can take place.

Plant Cells

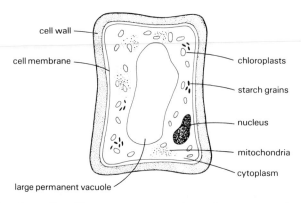

Cell Wall
The cell wall gives support to the cell and to the plant. It is made from *cellulose*, which is a carbohydrate. It is permeable to water and solutes.

Chloroplasts
Chloroplasts contain the green pigment *chlorophyll*. This traps light energy and converts it to chemical energy during *photosynthesis.* Plants require the mineral *magnesium* to make chlorophyll.

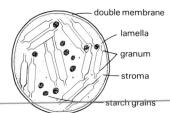

A chloroplast as seen under an electron microscope

Starch Grains
Starch grains form the main food store in plant cells. They are built up from *glucose molecules* which are made during photosynthesis, and are used by the plant to provide energy.

Large Vacuole
The large vacuole contains *cell sap* which is a watery fluid containing dissolved sugars. It is always present in a plant cell.

Comparison of Plant and Animal Cells	Structure	Plant	Animal
	Cell membrane	✔	✔
	Cell wall	✔	✕
	Cytoplasm	✔	✔
	Nucleus	✔	✔
	Mitochondria	✔	✔
	Chloroplasts	✔	✕
	Starch granules	✔	✕
	Glycogen granules	✕	✔
	Permanent vacuole	✔	✕

Specialisation of Cells

Red Blood Cell

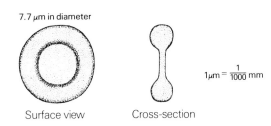

7.7 μm in diameter

$1 \mu m = \frac{1}{1000}$ mm

Surface view   Cross-section

The red blood cell is a biconcave disc. This shape increases the surface area of the cell. The cell does not contain a nucleus but is filled with a red pigment called *haemoglobin*. Haemoglobin combines with oxygen to form *oxyhaemoglobin*.

Reproductive Cells   In humans, the reproductive cells contain only 23 chromosomes in their nuclei. Other body cells contain 46 chromosomes in their nuclei.

Egg   The reproductive cell in a female is called an egg.

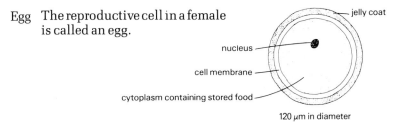

jelly coat

nucleus

cell membrane

cytoplasm containing stored food

120 μm in diameter

Sperm   The reproductive cell in a male is called a sperm.

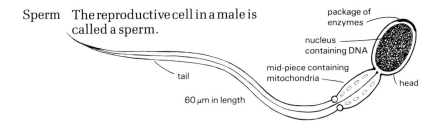

package of enzymes

nucleus containing DNA

mid-piece containing mitochondria

tail

head

60 μm in length

Guard Cells   Guard cells are found in the leaves of plants. They control the opening and closing of pores in the leaf. The pores, or *stomata*, allow gases to enter and leave the leaf.

chloroplast

vacuole

stoma

guard cell

epidermal cell of leaf

nucleus

9

2 Body Systems

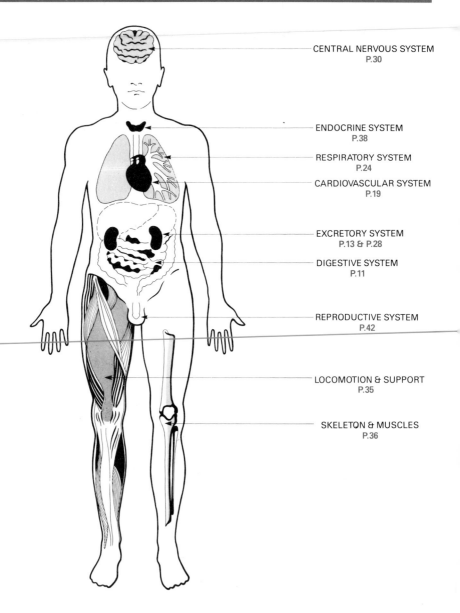

CENTRAL NERVOUS SYSTEM
P.30

ENDOCRINE SYSTEM
P.38

RESPIRATORY SYSTEM
P.24

CARDIOVASCULAR SYSTEM
P.19

EXCRETORY SYSTEM
P.13 & P.28

DIGESTIVE SYSTEM
P.11

REPRODUCTIVE SYSTEM
P.42

LOCOMOTION & SUPPORT
P.35

SKELETON & MUSCLES
P.36

The processes which keep humans alive are carried out by many systems within the body. These are composed of organs which work together to perform specific tasks.

The Digestive System

Digestion Most of the food we eat is in the form of large insoluble compounds of carbohydrates, proteins and fats. These are too large to pass into the blood to be carried to the cells. They must be broken down into the simple soluble molecules from which they have been built. This process is called digestion.

The Digestive System Digestion takes place in the digestive system and involves physical processes, e.g. chewing, and chemical processes, e.g. the action of enzymes.

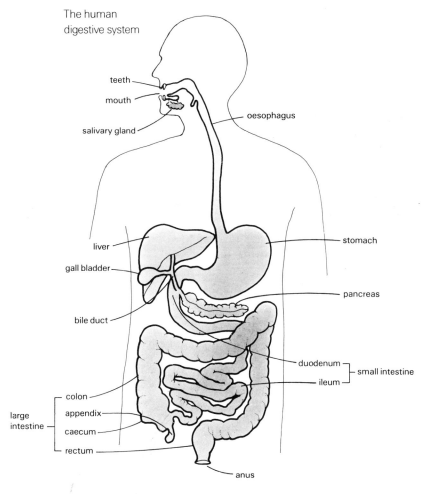

The human digestive system

teeth
mouth
salivary gland
oesophagus
liver
gall bladder
bile duct
stomach
pancreas
duodenum ⎱ small intestine
ileum ⎰
large intestine ⎱ colon
appendix
caecum
rectum ⎰
anus

11

Mouth The process of digestion begins in the mouth. The tongue helps to move food around the mouth and helps in swallowing. It contains taste-buds which can taste soluble particles.

Teeth Teeth cut and tear food into small particles. This increases the surface area over which enzymes can act. Humans have two sets of teeth. Milk-teeth emerge between the ages of six months and two years. There are twenty milk-teeth and all of them are lost between six and twelve years. Permanent teeth emerge between the ages of six years and adulthood. There are thirty-two permanent teeth and they consist of:

8 incisors – chisel-shaped for cutting
4 canines – pointed for tearing and cutting
8 premolars] – these have flattened surfaces
12 molars } which are uneven. They are used
for grinding and chewing. (page 49)

Salivary Glands Salivary glands secrete a liquid called *saliva*. This softens, moistens and lubricates food. It has a slightly alkaline pH of between pH7 and pH8, which helps to neutralise acid in the mouth. Saliva contains a carbohydrase enzyme called *amylase* which starts the digestion of starch to glucose.

Enzymes Enzymes are special proteins which act as biological catalysts in cells. They change the rates of reaction, but remain unchanged themselves at the end of the reaction.

Amylase breaks down starch $\xrightarrow{\text{to}}$ glucose.
Pepsin breaks down protein $\xrightarrow{\text{to}}$ amino-acids.
Lipase breaks down fats and oils $\xrightarrow{\text{to}}$ to fatty acids and glycerol.

Oesophagus The oesophagus is a muscular tube which connects the mouth to the stomach. Goblet cells in the walls secrete mucus to lubricate the food. Muscular contractions, known as *peristalsis*, move the food towards the stomach. Peristalsis is responsible for the movement of food through the whole of the digestive system.

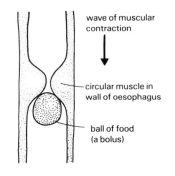

wave of muscular contraction

circular muscle in wall of oesophagus

ball of food (a bolus)

Stomach The stomach is a muscular bag with an extensively folded inner surface. This increases the surface area over which food in the stomach can come into contact with gastric juice. The breakdown of proteins into amino-acids starts in the stomach.

Protease A protease is an enzyme which acts on proteins. Pepsin is a protease produced in the stomach. It is released from cells in the stomach wall as an inactive substance called pepsinogen. This prevents the pepsin from breaking down the protein in the cell membranes of the stomach cells.

Hydro-chloric Acid Hydrochloric acid is produced by cells in the stomach wall. It activates pepsinogen by changing it to pepsin. Pepsin works best in acidic conditions (pH1) provided by the hydrochloric acid. Any bacteria present on the food arriving in the stomach are killed by the acid.

Mucus Mucus forms a thick covering on the inside surface of the stomach. This protects the cells from the hydrochloric acid and protease. Mucus lubricates the food as it passes through the stomach. Stress, poor diet, smoking or infrequent meals may lead to insufficient mucus being produced. Stomach ulcers can then develop as the stomach cells are digested. Water, alcohol and some painkillers can be absorbed into the bloodstream through the stomach walls.

The Small Intestine The function of the small intestine is to:
1. complete digestion;
2. absorb the products of digestion into the bloodstream.

Duodenum The first part of the small intestine, the duodenum receives:
1. food from the stomach;
2. pancreatic juice from the pancreas;
3. bile from the liver.

Pancreatic Juice Pancreatic juice contains enzymes which complete the breakdown of food. Carbohydrases break down starch to glucose. Proteases break down protein to amino-acids. Lipases break down fats to fatty acids and glycerol. Pancreatic juice also contains sodium hydrogencarbonate (sodium bicarbonate). This has a pH of 7-8 and neutralises the acid from the stomach. It also provides the optimum pH for the action of enzymes from the pancreas.

Bile Bile is an excretory product produced in the liver from the breakdown of old red blood cells. It emulsifies fats, i.e. it splits up large droplets of fat into smaller droplets of fat. This increases the surface area on which lipase can work and so speeds up the digestion of fat. Bile is *not* an enzyme.

Absorption Absorption is the process by which small, soluble particles of food must move out of the digestive system and enter the bloodstream. The particles can then be carried to the cells of the body.

13

Villi   The internal surface of the small intestine is greatly folded into structures called villi. They increase the surface area over which digested food can be absorbed. Within each villus are blood capillaries and lymphatic vessels. The wall of each villus is composed of a single layer of cells. These features help absorption to take place quickly.

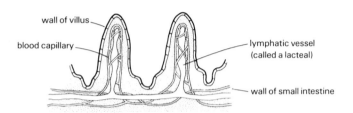

wall of villus

blood capillary

lymphatic vessel (called a lacteal)

wall of small intestine

Glucose and amino-acids pass into the blood capillaries. These eventually lead to the liver. Fatty acids and glycerol pass into the lymphatic vessels. These drain into the blood in the neck. This ensures that products of fat digestion are added to the bloodstream gradually. Absorption occurs by diffusion and by active transport.

The Liver   The liver regulates blood sugar level. Glucose from the villi in the small intestine arrives at the liver in the hepatic portal vein. Excess glucose is removed from the blood and is converted into glycogen in the liver cells. Glycogen is stored in liver cells and muscle cells. This reaction is controlled by hormones from the pancreas.

Deamination of Amino-Acids   Amino-acids are carried to the liver from the small intestine by the hepatic portal vein. Excess amino-acids are broken down in liver cells to form ammonia, which is converted to urea. This contains nitrogen and is excreted by the kidneys in urine.

Manufacture of Bile   Old red blood cells are broken down in the liver. Bile is formed from the haemoglobin pigment. It passes into the gall-bladder, where it is stored. Bile leaves the gall-bladder through the bile duct and passes into the duodenum.

Storage   The liver can store iron, which it obtains from the breakdown of haemoglobin, and also vitamins A and D. The liver also stores glycogen.

Removal of Toxins   Toxins, e.g. alcohol and drugs, are broken down in the liver into harmless compounds. Excessive amounts of toxins can destroy liver cells.

The Large The large intestine has a folded internal surface with many
Intestine mucus-producing cells (goblet cells). Water is absorbed from
the material arriving in the large intestine from the small
intestine. The water is returned to the blood. Bacteria are
present in the large intestine. These bacteria manufacture
vitamin K and help to break down some of the fibre in the diet.

Egestion Egestion is the removal of undigested food from the digestive
system. When most of the water has been removed from the
material in the large intestine, it is known as faeces. Faeces
consist of: roughage or fibre, bacteria, mucus, dead cells, some
water.

Defaecation Peristalsis moves the faeces into the rectum. Muscular
contractions increase and the faeces are expelled from the body
through the anus.

Food and Diet

Why we Food provides the raw materials that we need to build tissues.
need Food It provides the raw materials with which to make and replace
essential chemicals, e.g. enzymes and hormones. It provides
energy for all the reactions which take place in the body.

Balanced A balanced diet is composed of the following substances:
Diet   Carbohydrates

Proteins

Fats and Oils

Vitamins

Minerals

Roughage

Water

A balanced diet must have all of these substances in the correct
proportions.

1. Carbo- Carbohydrates are composed of the elements carbon, hydrogen
hydrates and oxygen. They provide us with energy – approx. 17 kJ/g.

Glucose Glucose is the smallest and simplest carbohydrate. It is a
soluble sugar which is manufactured by plants during
photosynthesis. Fruit and sugar-cane are two sources of
glucose. Glucose is the source of energy used by cells in
respiration.

Starch Starch is a large carbohydrate molecule formed from glucose molecules joining together. It is insoluble. It is made in plants from glucose and is used to store energy. Starch is obtained from many foods, including rice, potatoes and bread.

Glycogen Glycogen is a large, insoluble carbohydrate molecule formed from glucose molecules. It is found in animal cells. Glucose is converted to glycogen in the liver and is stored as glycogen in liver and muscle cells.

Cellulose Cellulose is a very large, insoluble carbohydrate. It is found only in plants and it forms the cell walls. It cannot be digested by humans and forms roughage which helps to keep food moving through the digestive system and reduces the risk of developing bowel cancer.

Constipation Constipation is caused by a shortage of roughage in the diet. Undigested food in the large intestine becomes compacted because large amounts of water are reabsorbed from it. Roughage, or fibre, enables the muscles of the large intestine to grip the food and move it quickly through to the rectum.

2. Proteins Proteins are composed of the elements carbon, hydrogen, oxygen and nitrogen. They may also contain sulphur and phosphorus. Proteins are required for the growth and repair of tissue. They are also required for the manufacture of enzymes. Foods rich in protein include fish, lean meat, milk, eggs and soya beans.

Amino-Acids Amino-acids are the small units from which proteins are built. They are used to build the proteins required by the body.

Non-essential Amino-Acids Non-essential amino-acids do not have to be obtained from the diet. They can be made, or *synthesised*, in the cells.

Essential Amino-Acids Essential amino-acids can be obtained only from food. Animal protein is a rich source of essential amino-acids.

Excess Amino-Acids The presence of nitrogen in the amino-acid molecules means that excess amino-acids cannot be stored in the body.
In the liver, nitrogen is removed from the molecules and is converted into ammonia. This is highly toxic and so it is converted to urea, which is less toxic to the body. Urea is removed from the blood by the kidneys.
The remainder of the amino-acid molecule is converted to glycogen and is stored in the liver cells.
A daily intake of essential amino-acids is required to produce the proteins necessary for healthy tissues.

3. Fats and Oils Fats and oils are composed of the elements carbon, hydrogen and oxygen. These elements are found in a different proportion from those in carbohydrates. Fatty foods provide energy – approx. 39 kJ/g. They also provide insulation and protection, and they are necessary for the manufacture of vitamin D.

Fatty Acids and Glycerol Fatty acids and glycerol are the units from which fats and oils are built. *Saturated* fatty acids are obtained mainly from animal products, e.g. beef, pork, butter, milk and eggs. *Unsaturated* fatty acids are found mainly in plant products, e.g. olive oil and peanut oil. *Polyunsaturated* fatty acids are obtained from corn oil, sesame oil and soya bean oil. Unsaturated and especially polyunsaturated fatty acids are believed to lower the level of cholesterol in the blood.

Heart Disease Heart disease may be caused by a high cholesterol level in the blood. Cholesterol is a saturated fat which is made in the body and is also found in animal tissues, e.g. meat and eggs. It builds up on the walls of blood vessels and may restrict blood flow to the heart cells. These cells may then die.

Obesity Obesity is an increase in weight which occurs when the energy intake from food exceeds the body's energy output. It places additional strain on the heart and may increase the chance of developing coronary heart disease.

4. Vitamins Vitamins are organic substances which are required in very small amounts to maintain body reactions and growth.

Vitamin A Vitamin A is obtained from fish liver oil, milk, butter, yellow vegetables, and carrots. It maintains healthy skin, bones and teeth and it prevents night blindness. Vitamin A can be stored in the liver.

Vitamin C Citrus fruits, tomatoes, potatoes and green vegetables are rich sources of vitamin C. It is necessary for healthy skin and blood vessels and helps to prevent scurvy. Heating destroys vitamin C.

Vitamin D Vitamin D is obtained from fish liver oil, egg yolk and milk. It is required for the absorption of calcium from the intestine. It can be manufactured in the fatty tissue under the skin in the presence of sunlight and it can be stored in the liver. Deficiency of vitamin D can lead to rickets.

Vitamin K Green vegetables, liver and eggs provide vitamin K in the diet. It can be produced by bacteria living in the large intestine and is essential for blood clotting.

17

5. Minerals Minerals are inorganic substances required by the body.

Iron Iron is obtained from meat, especially liver, egg yolk, beans, nuts and cereals. It is essential for the manufacture of haemoglobin in red blood cells. Lack of iron in the diet leads to anaemia, which is a deficiency of haemoglobin in the red blood cells. Iron can be stored in the liver.

Calcium Milk, egg yolk, fish and green vegetables are sources of calcium. It is required for blood clotting, bone formation and muscle and nerve activity. Vitamin D is necessary for absorption of calcium.

Iodine Iodine is obtained from seafood, cod-liver oil and table salt. It is required for the manufacture of the thyroid hormone, thyroxine. This hormone regulates the level of activity in body cells and also controls growth of the skeleton and brain. Deficiency of iodine can lead to a swelling of the thyroid gland in the neck. This is known as a goitre.

Fluorine Fluorine is obtained mainly from drinking water and from fluoride toothpaste. It forms part of the teeth and bones. It prevents tooth decay if taken in the correct concentrations.

6. Roughage Roughage is composed mainly of cellulose from plants. Cellulose cannot be digested by humans and provides bulk which enables the muscles of the digestive system to grip the food and push it along by peristalsis. Lack of roughage or fibre in the diet can cause constipation and may cause cancer of the large intestine or the bowel.

Foods which are rich in fibre include wholemeal bread, bran and such unprocessed foods as brown rice, brown pasta. Processing removes most of the fibre from the food.

7. Water Water is obtained from the food eaten and by drinking.
It is required for many purposes:

(i) to form solutions to carry nutrients and gases into cells and to carry waste products out of cells;

(ii) chemical reactions, e.g. the manufacture of enzymes and hormones requires water;

(iii) temperature regulation involving the production of sweat;

(iv) lubrication of moving parts of the body and of substances moving through the body.

Most excess water is removed from the blood by the kidneys. We also lose water from our bodies in sweat, faeces and when we breathe out.

The Cardiovascular System

Transport in Mammals Transport in mammals is carried out by the circulatory system.

Circulatory System The circulatory system is composed of the heart, blood vessels and blood.

The diagram shows how it works

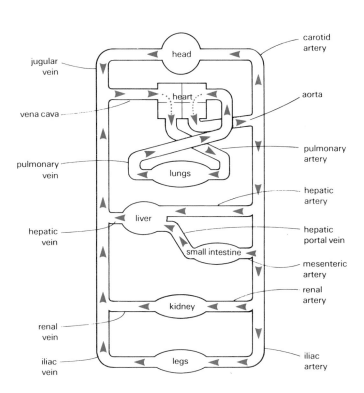

Double Circulation Blood enters and leaves the heart twice on its journey around the body.

Pulmonary Circulation Blood is pumped from the
Heart ──to──→ Lungs ──to──→ Heart

Systemic Circulation Blood is pumped from the
Heart ──to──→ Body ──to──→ Heart

Structure of the Heart

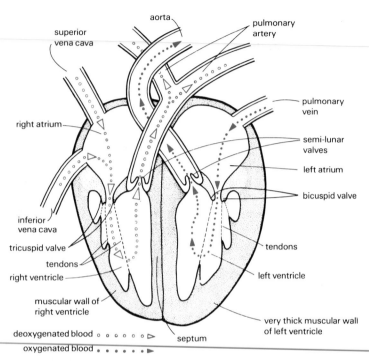

The following labels appear on the diagram:

- aorta
- superior vena cava
- pulmonary artery
- pulmonary vein
- right atrium
- semi-lunar valves
- left atrium
- bicuspid valve
- inferior vena cava
- tricuspid valve
- tendons
- tendons
- right ventricle
- left ventricle
- muscular wall of right ventricle
- very thick muscular wall of left ventricle
- deoxygenated blood ○ ○ ○ ○ ○ ○ ▷
- septum
- oxygenated blood • • • • • • ▶

The Heart The heart is responsible for pumping blood around the body. It pumps blood to the lungs, where it can collect oxygen and lose carbon dioxide. The oxygenated blood returns to the heart from the lungs. It is then pumped around the body and returns to the heart.

Venae Cavae The venae cavae are large veins which carry deoxygenated blood into the right side of the heart from the organs of the body.

Right Atrium The right atrium is the upper chamber on the right side of the heart. It receives deoxygenated blood from the body. It contracts when full of blood and pushes the blood into the right ventricle.

Tricuspid Valves The tricuspid valves are flaps of tissue which separate the right atrium from the right ventricle. When open, the valves allow blood to flow from the atrium to the ventricle. When closed, they prevent blood from flowing back into the atrium when the ventricle contracts.

Right Ventricle The right ventricle is the lower chamber on the right side of the heart. When it is full of blood, its walls contract and blood is pushed up into the pulmonary artery.

Pulmonary Artery	The pulmonary artery carries blood from the right ventricle to the lungs. Valves in the artery prevent blood from flowing back into the ventricle.
Pulmonary Vein	The pulmonary vein carries oxygenated blood from the lungs to the heart.
Left Atrium	The left atrium receives blood from the pulmonary vein. When the atrium is full of blood, its walls contract and blood is forced into the ventricle.
Bicuspid Valves	The bicuspid valves separate the left atrium and ventricle. They close when the ventricle is full of blood and prevent the blood from flowing back into the atrium when the ventricle contracts.
Left Ventricle	The left ventricle is the lower chamber on the left side of the heart. It receives oxygenated blood from the left atrium. Its muscular walls are very thick in order to pump the blood all round the body. When the walls contract, blood is forced out of the heart under high pressure.
Aorta	The aorta is the large muscular artery which carries oxygenated blood from the heart to the organs of the body. As it reaches each organ, it branches to form arteries.
Health of the Heart	Heart disease can result from combinations of several factors. These include:
1. High Cholesterol Level	Most cholesterol in the blood comes from saturated fats in the diet. Cholesterol may be deposited on the walls of arteries. This may narrow the passageway for blood and damage the tissues in the artery.
2. High Blood Pressure	When blood pressure is high, the heart muscle has to use more energy to pump blood round the body. This may cause the heart to become bigger and so require more oxygen. If the oxygen demand is not met, angina or chest pains may result. This weakens the heart muscle.
3. Blockage in a Coronary Artery	A heart attack may be caused by a blockage in one of the coronary arteries. This results in some of the heart muscle dying and so the heart is weakened.
4. Smoking	Nicotine, a drug in tobacco, causes the blood vessels to constrict by stimulating the release of several hormones into the blood. The heart, therefore, has to pump harder to move blood round the body.
5. Lack of Exercise	Regular exercise strengthens the muscles of blood vessels and the heart. The heart becomes more efficient at pumping blood round the body. Lack of exercise weakens the muscle and the heart becomes less efficient.
6. Heredity	The incidence of heart disease tends to increase in some families, due to genetic factors.

Blood Blood is composed of: plasma, red blood cells, white blood cells and platelets.

Plasma Plasma is a fluid consisting mainly of water in which blood cells float. It contains dissolved sugars, amino-acids, urea, hormones and minerals. Blood proteins, e.g. *fibrinogen*, which is required for blood clotting, are also found in plasma.

Red Blood Cells (Erythrocytes) Red blood cells are the most common type of blood cell. They are made in the bone marrow and spleen. The red colour is caused by a pigment called *haemoglobin*, which contains iron. Haemoglobin combines with molecules of oxygen to form a compound called *oxyhaemoglobin*. This compound carries oxygen round the body to cells which need it. When it reaches these cells, the oxyhaemoglobin breaks down into *oxygen* and *haemoglobin*, and the oxygen can then diffuse out of the capillary and into the cells.

Structure of Red Blood Cell Red blood cells do not contain a nucleus. This allows the cells to carry more haemoglobin. This shape also gives the cell a large surface area for absorption of oxygen. When red blood cells die, they are broken down in the liver and spleen. Iron is removed

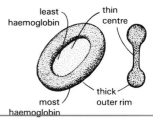

and stored until it is needed to make new haemoglobin. The remainder of the haemoglobin molecule is converted to *bile salts* and is stored in the gall bladder.

White Blood Cells White blood cells are made in the bone marrow and lymph glands. They engulf and destroy bacteria and produce *antibodies*.

a) Phagocytes Phagocytes engulf and destroy bacteria by *phagocytosis*. They can squeeze out of the capillaries and move between cells to destroy bacteria.

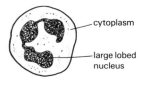

b) Lymphocytes Lymphocytes are manufactured in the lymph glands. These glands are found in the neck, the groin, under the arms, and in many other parts of the body. The cells recognise foreign organisms in the body and destroy them by producing antibodies.

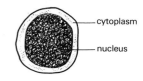

Platelets Platelets are made in the bone marrow. They are small fragments of cytoplasm enclosed in a membrane. They do not have a nucleus. Platelets are necessary for the clotting of blood.

Blood Vessels Blood is carried around the body in blood vessels. The main blood vessels are arteries, capillaries and veins.

Arteries Arteries carry blood *away* from the heart to organs in the body. Blood flows under *high pressure* in the arteries. Inside an organ, the artery divides into smaller and smaller vessels called arterioles. These divide further to form capillaries.

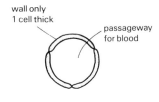

Cross-section of an artery

Capillaries Capillaries form tiny, narrow vessels which branch extensively throughout an organ. They ensure that all cells of the body are in very close contact with a supply of blood. Substances in the blood, e.g. oxygen and glucose, can diffuse easily through the thin wall of

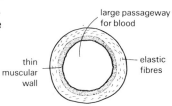

Cross-section of a capillary

the capillary and into the cells surrounding it. Substances from the cells, e.g. carbon dioxide and other waste products, can diffuse into the capillary and be carried away in the blood. Capillaries then join to form larger vessels called *venules*. These join together as they leave an organ to form a vein.

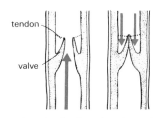

Cross-section of a vein

Veins Veins carry blood *towards* the heart from organs in the body. Blood in veins flows under *low pressure*. *Valves* are present in the veins to prevent the blood from flowing back and moving away from the heart due to the low pressure.

Longitudinal section through veins to show valves

23

The Respiratory System

Structure and Function of the Respiratory System

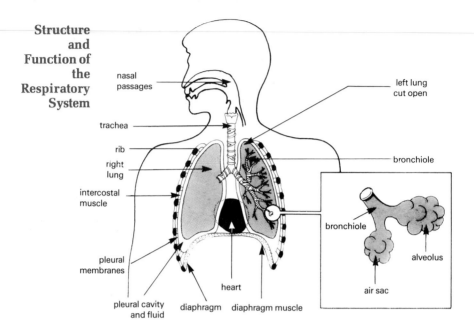

Nasal Passages
: The nasal passages filter the air as it passes through them. Air is warmed as it passes over the surface of the many blood vessels in the nasal passages. *Mucus* traps any dust particles. It is produced by goblet cells which line the passages. It also moistens the air. Small hairs called *cilia* beat backwards and forwards constantly and sweep the mucus and dirt towards the oesophagus, where it is swallowed.

Trachea
: The trachea carries air to the lungs. It is supported by rings of cartilage which prevent it from collapsing each time we breathe out. The trachea is lined with cilia and goblet cells. These trap any dust particles and sweep them up to the oesophagus.

Bronchus
: One bronchus leads into each lung. They are formed when the trachea divides into two as it reaches the lungs. They are supported by rings of cartilage.

Bronchioles
: Inside each lung, the bronchus divides into finer and finer branches called bronchioles. These end in tiny, elastic air sacs called *alveoli*.

Lungs
: The lungs contain bronchi, bronchioles and alveoli. They have a very good blood supply and provide a large surface area for gas exchange.

24

Rib-Cage The rib-cage surrounds and protects the lungs. It is attached to the spine at the back and to the sternum at the front. The spaces between the rib bones contain the intercostal muscles. When these contract and relax, they raise and lower the rib-cage.

Diaphragm The diaphragm is a sheet of muscle which separates the thorax (chest) from the abdomen. It is attached by muscles to the body wall. When these muscles are relaxed, the diaphragm curves up into the thorax. When the muscles contract, the diaphragm is pulled down and flattened.

Pleural The pleural cavity is a space between the rib-cage and the
Cavity and lungs. It is enclosed between the pleural membranes. It protects
Membranes the lungs from being damaged by friction as the rib-cage moves up and down.

Gas Alveoli are the sites of gas exchange in the lungs. They form
Exchange in the respiratory surfaces, and allow oxygen and carbon dioxide
the Lungs to move in and out of the lungs.

Absorption
of Oxygen in
the Alveoli

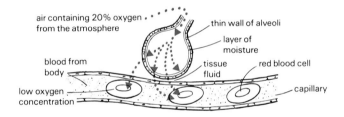

Movement of Air containing 20% oxygen is drawn into the alveoli. Oxygen
Oxygen dissolves in the layer of moisture lining each alveolus (a). Blood in the capillaries surrounding each alveolus has a very low concentration of oxygen in the red blood cells. Oxygen diffuses from the area of high concentration in the alveolus to the area of low concentration in the red blood cells. It passes in solution through the cells in the wall of the alveolus (b), through the tissue fluid (c) which separates the alveolus from the capillary, through the cells which make the wall of the capillary (d), into the red blood cell (e). Oxygen combines with haemoglobin in the red blood cells to form oxyhaemoglobin.

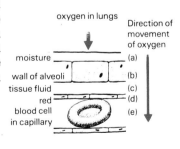

Movement of Carbon Dioxide Blood arriving in the lungs from the body has a high concentration of carbon dioxide in it. Most carbon dioxide is carried in the blood plasma as hydrogen carbonate ions. Air inside the lungs has a low concentration of carbon dioxide. Carbon dioxide diffuses from an area of high concentration in the blood to an area of low concentration in the alveoli. The movement is similar to that of oxygen but it takes place in the *opposite direction.*

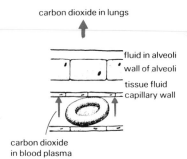

carbon dioxide in lungs

fluid in alveoli
wall of alveoli
tissue fluid
capillary wall

carbon dioxide in blood plasma

Inhaled Air Air which is breathed into the lungs contains the following gases (approximate volumes):

Nitrogen	79%
Oxygen	20%
Carbon dioxide	0.03%
Water vapour	1%

Exhaled Air Air which is breathed out of the lungs contains the following gases (approximate volumes):

Nitrogen	79%
Oxygen	15%
Carbon dioxide	4%
Water vapour	saturated

Oxygen diffuses from the inhaled air in the lungs, through the walls of the alveoli into the blood capillaries outside the alveoli. It diffuses into the red blood cells and is carried to respiring cells in the body.

Carbon dioxide, produced by respiring cells, is carried to the alveoli by the blood. The carbon dioxide diffuses out of the blood, through the walls of the alveoli and is then breathed out of the lungs.

Respiration Respiration is a chemical reaction in which glucose is broken down in a cell and energy is released. It takes place in the mitochondria and is controlled by enzymes. Respiration takes place in *all* living organisms *all* the time. In humans, oxygen is required for respiration and this type of respiration is called aerobic. Some organisms respire in the absence of oxygen and this type is called anaerobic respiration. Yeast, a fungus, respires anaerobically. It uses glucose as a source of energy but instead of carbon dioxide and water being produced as waste products, carbon dioxide and alcohol are produced.

Role of the Lungs The lungs regulate the concentrations of oxygen and carbon dioxide in the blood. They remove some excess water from the blood in exhaled air.

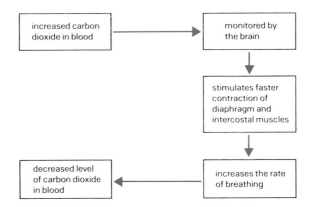

The Effects of Smoking Tobacco smoke contains at least 1000 constituents. Many of these are harmful.

Tar Tar contains carcinogenic substances which may lead to lung cancer.

Smoke Particles Smoke particles stop the beating of cilia in the bronchial tubes inside the lungs. The irritation that the particles cause increases the production of mucus from goblet cells, and this gradually destroys the cells of the alveoli, leading to emphysema. Emphysema is a disease which decreases the surface area over which gas exchange can take place because the alveoli are destroyed.

Nicotine Nicotine is a drug in tobacco, to which smokers become addicted. It stimulates the release of hormones which cause blood vessels to constrict. This results in the heart having to work harder to pump blood round the body. This puts extra strain on the heart and can lead to coronary heart disease. Nicotine also increases the concentration of fatty acids in the blood. The red blood cells may become sticky and clump together to form clots inside blood vessels.

Carbon Monoxide Carbon monoxide in tobacco smoke combines readily with haemoglobin and so decreases the oxygen-carrying capacity of the blood. It damages the walls of arteries and increases the risk of their becoming narrow. This leads to strokes and heart attacks.

27

The Urinary System

Structure of the Urinary System

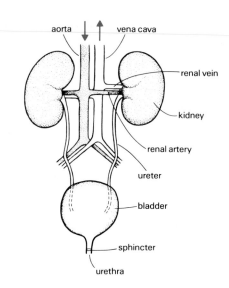

Role of the Kidneys   Urea is filtered out of the blood by the kidneys. It is removed from the body in the urine. Excess salts, e.g. sodium chloride, are removed from the blood and passed out of the body in the urine. The pH of blood is about 7.3. The kidneys maintain the pH of the blood by removing ions which would cause the blood to become acidic.

Osmoregulation is the control of the water content of the blood. It is carried out by the urinary system.

Internal Structure of a Kidney

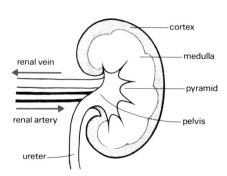

Inside each kidney there are between one and two million structures called *nephrons*. Nephrons are responsible for: (i) filtering the blood; and (ii) reabsorbing materials which are required by the body, back into the blood.

Filtration In the nephron, the blood is filtered to remove waste products, e.g. urea, excess water and excess salt.

Reabsorption The nephron then reabsorbs substances which the body requires, e.g. glucose, amino acids and some water. These are absorbed back into the blood.

Waste substances remain in the nephron and pass into the bladder as a liquid called URINE. It is stored there until it is expelled from the body.

Water is lost from the blood in approximately the following volumes:

Urine	– 700 cm^3 per day
Faeces	– 150 cm^3 per day
Sweat	– 500 cm^3 per day
Exhaled Breath	– 400 cm^3 per day

Water is gained by:

Eating and drinking	– 1400 cm^3 per day
Respiration	– 350 cm^3 per day

Dialysis In dialysis, blood is filtered artificially using a machine. This happens if the kidneys have been damaged by injury or disease. A kidney machine is used to filter the blood.

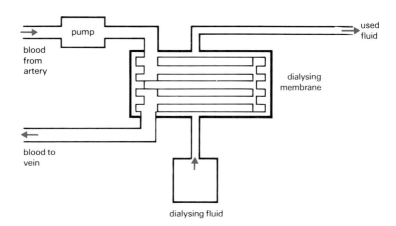

Dialysis is required regularly until a healthy kidney can be transplanted from a kidney donor. Waste substances are filtered out of the blood as it passes over the dialysing membrane. The filtered and cleaned blood is then returned to the body.

The Nervous System

The Nervous System The nervous system is responsible for:
(i) detecting stimuli, using sense organs (receptors);
(ii) responding to the stimuli, using muscles or glands (effectors).

Structure The nervous system is composed of:
(i) the Central Nervous System (CNS) which is composed of the brain and spinal cord;
(ii) nerves or neurones, which carry electrical impulses to and from the CNS.

The diagram shows how it works.

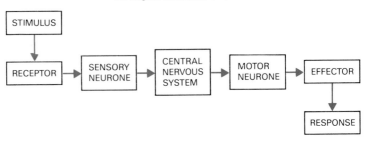

Sensory Neurones

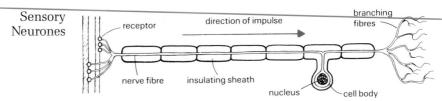

Sensory neurones carry impulses from sense organs to the brain or spinal cord.

The Brain The brain regulates, co-ordinates and integrates all the information that it receives from the sense organs.

Motor Neurones

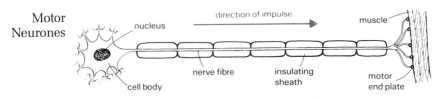

Motor neurones carry impulses from the brain and spinal cord to muscles or glands.

Receptors

1. The Eye The function of the eye is to focus light rays on to receptor cells, which then convert the light energy into electrical energy. Electrical impulses are carried from the eye to the brain by the optic nerve.

Structure of the Eye

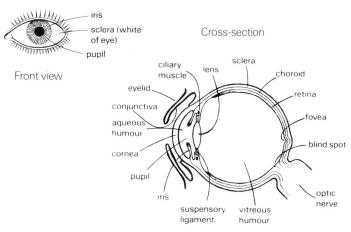

Conjunctiva The conjunctiva is a thin, transparent membrane that protects the front of the eye and lines the eyelids. Tears from the tear glands are moved over the surface of the cornea by blinking the eyelids. Tears keep the surface of the eye moist. They also contain an enzyme which kills bacteria.

Cornea The cornea is the transparent cover over the front of the eye. It protects the eye, and it also bends the light rays as they pass into the eye.

Iris and Pupil The iris contains circular and radial muscles which can contract and relax to change the size of the pupil in the middle. This regulates the amount of light entering the eye.

a) In dim light, the radial muscles of the iris contract. This increases the size of the pupil, and so more light can enter the eye.

b) In bright light, the circular muscles of the iris contract. This decreases the size of the pupil. It protects the eye by limiting the amount of light entering.

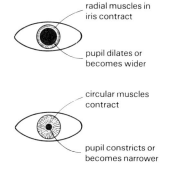

31

The Lens, Ciliary Muscle and Suspensory Ligament The lens is a transparent, biconvex disc which is made from protein. It is held in position by the suspensory ligaments. These in turn are attached to the ciliary muscle. The ciliary muscle alters the shape of the lens for near and far vision, and this alteration is called *accommodation*.

Accommodation When the ciliary muscle relaxes, the suspensory ligaments are pulled taut. This in turn pulls the lens into a long, thin shape. Light rays which enter the eye from a distant object are focused by the lens on to the retina. When the ciliary muscle contracts, the suspensory ligaments slacken. The lens now forms a shorter, fatter shape. Light rays entering the eye from a near object are bent by the lens and focused on to the retina.

Aqueous Humour Aqueous humour is a watery fluid which fills the space in the eye in front of the lens. It provides the lens and cornea with food and oxygen, and removes waste products from them. It also helps to bend the light rays as they pass through.

Vitreous Humour The vitreous humour is a jelly-like substance which fills the eyeball behind the lens. It helps to keep the shape of the eyeball and to support the retina. It can also bend light rays slightly.

Retina The retina is the innermost layer of the eye. It is composed of light-sensitive cells which detect light and colour. Light energy detected by the cells is converted into nerve impulses which are sent to the brain along the optic nerve. The light-sensitive cells in the retina are called cones and rods.

Cones Cones are stimulated by light of high intensity. They can also detect colour. The highest concentration of cones is found at the fovea (a small depression in the retina), and it is on this area that light rays are focused by the lens, to give a clear, sharp image.

Rods Rods are stimulated by light of low intensity. They are specialised for night-vision. The rods contain a pigment called *visual purple* which allows them to function. Vitamin A is required by the rods to make this pigment.

Blind Spot The blind spot is an area of the retina which does not contain rods or cones. Nerve fibres from the rods and cones in the retina leave the eye at this point and enter the optic nerve. Light rays falling on the blind spot cannot be detected by the brain.

Choroid The choroid is the middle layer of the eye. It contains many blood vessels which supply the retina with food and oxygen and remove waste products. The cells of the choroid contain a dark pigment which absorbs light rays in the eye and prevents them from being reflected back out of the eye.

Sclera The sclera is the tough, white outer covering of the eye.

2. The Ear   The ear converts the vibration of air waves into electrical impulses. The brain converts these impulses into the sensation of sound. The ear is also responsible for balance. The position of the head in relation to the rest of the body is detected by cells in the inner ear. These send impulses to the cerebellum in the brain.

Structure of the Ear

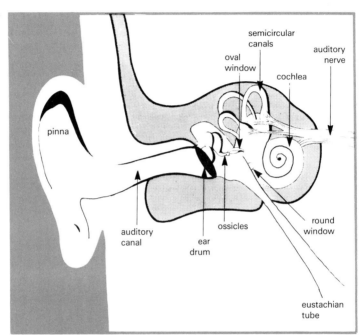

Outer Ear

Pinna   This is a flap of cartilage and skin which helps to collect the sound waves.

Auditory Canal   Sound waves pass along the canal to the middle ear. Cells in the wall secrete wax which protects the middle ear. (page 51)

Ear Drum   This is formed from a thin sheet of tissue. When sound waves hit it, it vibrates.

Middle Ear   This is an air-filled space containing three bones or ossicles which connects the outer and inner ears.

Ossicles   Vibration of the ear drum causes these bones to vibrate. These vibrations are passed to the inner ear.

Eustachian Tube   This is a small passageway which links the middle ear to the throat. Swallowing helps to balance the pressure between the outer and middle ears.

33

Inner Ear The structures in the inner ear are filled with fluid.

Oval Window The ossicles of the middle ear are in contact with the membrane of the oval window. When the ossicles vibrate, the vibrations are passed through the membrane to the fluid in the cochlea which lies on the other side of the oval window.

Cochlea This is a fluid-filled coiled tube which is connected to the middle ear by the oval window. As vibrations pass into the fluid, it moves over sensory cells in the wall of the cochlea. These cells transmit nerve impulses to the brain.

Round Window This membrane-covered opening in the wall of the cochlea prevents the pressure in the fluid of the cochlea from building up too much due to large vibrations.

Semicircular Canals These fluid filled canals lie at right angles to each other. They are responsible for balance. Sensory cells in the ampulla of each canal relay information to the brain about the position of the head. As the head changes position, the fluid in the canals moves over the sensory cells and the brain uses this information to maintain balance.

Auditory Nerve This sensory nerve carries nerve impulses to the brain from the inner ear.

Deafness This can be caused by anything which interferes with the entry of sound waves into the ear, their transmission to the inner ear, or a fault in the sensory cells of the cochlea.

Common Causes Wax can block the auditory canal and prevent sound waves reaching the middle ear.

Objects can be pushed into the canal.

Osteosclerosis is a disease of the bones of the middle ear in which they fuse together and so cannot vibrate.

Blockage of the Eustachian tube by mucus, e.g. during a cold, can cause pressure to build up in the middle ear, resulting in deafness and earache.

Damage to the auditory nerve or to the sensory cells of the inner ear may prevent impulses from reaching the brain.

Exposure to high levels of noise may result in permanent damage to the ears, causing total or partial deafness.

Glue ear is a common condition in children. Fluid accumulates in the middle ear and impairs hearing. It is usually caused by an infection, e.g. a cold.

3. Skin Skin contains many receptors which can respond to several stimuli. These include: (i) touch; (ii) pressure; (iii) temperature.

Locomotion and Support

Animals Movement and support in animals is provided by the muscles and skeleton. The types of skeleton found in animals form three main groups.

Hydrostatic Skeleton Animals such as earthworms have a hydrostatic skeleton. In this type of skeleton, layers of circular and longitudinal muscles surround a fluid. When the muscles contract and relax, they put pressure on the fluid which causes movement.

Exoskeleton Arthropods such as insects and crustaceans have an exoskeleton. This is composed of a hard protein called *chitin* which is laid down on the outside of the animal's body.

Invertebrates are animals which have either a hydrostatic skeleton or an exoskeleton.

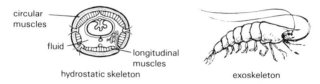

circular muscles
fluid
longitudinal muscles
hydrostatic skeleton

exoskeleton

Endoskeleton Humans have an internal skeleton which is called an endoskeleton. It is made from bones – which are composed of protein, and calcium and phosphate ions – and also from cartilage. Cartilage is softer than bone and is more flexible. It is composed of protein and elastic fibres.

Animals which have an internal skeleton are called *vertebrates*.

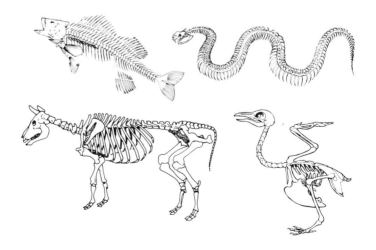

Structure of the Human Skeleton The skeleton is a living tissue and so it requires a good blood supply to provide nutrients and to remove waste products. The human skeleton is composed of bone and cartilage.

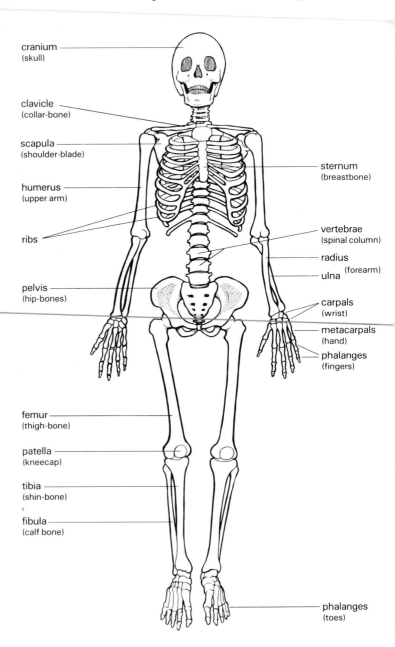

cranium
(skull)

clavicle
(collar-bone)

scapula
(shoulder-blade)

humerus
(upper arm)

ribs

pelvis
(hip-bones)

sternum
(breastbone)

vertebrae
(spinal column)

radius
(forearm)
ulna

carpals
(wrist)

metacarpals
(hand)

phalanges
(fingers)

femur
(thigh-bone)

patella
(kneecap)

tibia
(shin-bone)

fibula
(calf bone)

phalanges
(toes)

Functions of the Human Skeleton The human skeleton performs protective and supportive functions, helps movement, anchors muscles and makes blood cells and platelets.

Protection The skeleton provides protection for the soft organs of the body. The rib-cage protects the heart and lungs and the skull protects the brain and sense organs in the head. It prevents damage by friction or pressure.

Support Support of the body is provided by the skeleton. It holds the body upright against the pull of gravity.

Manufacture of Blood Cells Red and white blood cells and platelets are manufactured by the long bones in the skeleton.

Movement The skeleton helps the body to move by allowing the attachment of muscles. Muscles can contract and relax and pull against the skeleton. This results in movement. Joints in the skeleton give flexibility and allow a wide range of movements.

Muscles There are three types of muscle tissue found in humans. The type concerned with movement of the body is called *skeletal muscle*.

Skeletal Muscle Skeletal muscles are attached to the skeleton. They are arranged in pairs called *antagonistic muscles*. Together, each pair of muscles is responsible for the movement of a particular bone at a joint. Antagonistic muscles work by acting in the opposite way to each other. When one member of a pair contracts, the other member must relax. Any muscle can only become shorter by contracting, or return to its original length by relaxing. Skeletal muscle is also known as voluntary muscle because it is under conscious control.

Smooth Muscle Smooth muscle is not attached to the skeleton. It is found in the internal organs of the body. Smooth muscle is found in the walls of the alimentary canal. Smooth muscle contractions called peristalsis are responsible for moving food through the digestive system. Contraction of smooth muscle occurs without conscious control.

Cardiac Muscle Cardiac muscle is found in the heart. The muscle can contract and relax rapidly and continuously without tiring.

Ligaments and Tendons Movement of the skeleton occurs at joints between bones. Bones are held together by tough elastic tissues called *ligaments*. Muscles which move bones are attached to the surface of the bone by very strong inelastic tissues called *tendons*.

The Endocrine System and Homeostasis

Homeostasis The regulation and maintenance of a constant internal environment is very important for the efficient working of cells. This process is called homeostasis. Many organs are involved in ensuring that the composition of the blood is kept more or less constant.

Lungs The lungs regulate the concentrations of oxygen and carbon dioxide in the blood. They remove some excess water from the blood in exhaled air.

Liver The liver regulates the concentration of glucose in the blood. It removes excess amino-acids from the blood and converts them to urea and glycogen.

Blood arriving at the liver in the hepatic portal vein contains a high concentration of glucose and amino-acids. The amount of glucose in the blood must be carefully regulated by the liver.

Blood Sugar Regulation Glucose arriving in the liver can be: (i) broken down into carbon dioxide and water during respiration in the liver cell; (ii) converted into glycogen and stored in the liver; (iii) converted into fat and stored under the skin; (iv) allowed to leave the liver in the blood, to be carried to other body cells.

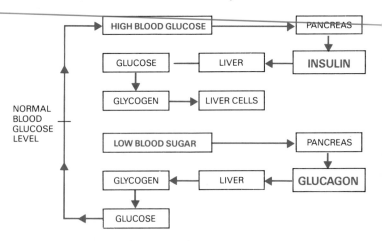

The amount of glucose which the liver leaves in the blood is controlled by hormones produced by the pancreas.

These hormones are called insulin and glucagon, and the diagram above shows how they act together to keep the level of glucose in the blood constant. This is an example of negative feedback.

The level of glucose dissolved in the blood plasma cannot be allowed to change. If the plasma contains too much glucose, then water from the cells surrounding the capillaries moves out of the cells by osmosis and into the capillaries. The cells become dehydrated and the volume of blood increases.

If the plasma does not contain enough glucose, the body cells will not receive sufficient glucose for respiration to take place.

Hormones from the pancreas pass into the blood and are carried to the liver. If the level of glucose in the plasma is too high, the pancreas is stimulated to release *insulin*. This hormone causes liver cells to absorb glucose from the blood plasma and to convert it into glycogen, which can then be stored in the liver.

If the level of glucose in the plasma is too low, then the pancreas is stimulated to release *glucagon*. This hormone stimulates the liver cells to break down stored glycogen into glucose. The glucose is released into the blood and so the blood-sugar level rises. The level of glucose in the blood is kept constant by negative feedback.

Diabetes mellitus Diabetes mellitus is a disease which results from insufficient insulin being produced by the special cells in the pancreas called the *islets of Langerhans*. The blood-sugar level of people suffering from diabetes increases. This high level of blood sugar is called hyperglycaemia. Diabetes results in some glucose being present in urine. The condition can be controlled by regular injections of insulin and by careful regulation of the diet.

Kidneys The kidneys regulate the amount of water in blood. They remove urea and other waste products, e.g. salts, from the blood, and they also control the pH of the blood.

The amount of water lost from the blood in the kidneys is controlled by the hypothalamus in the brain.

Osmo-regulation If too much water has been lost from the blood, the hypothalamus stops the kidneys from excreting water. If the blood contains too much water, the hypothalamus causes the kidneys to remove water from the blood and form dilute urine. The hypothalamus regulates the kidneys by causing the pituitary gland to secrete, or stop secreting, a hormone called anti-diuretic hormone (ADH). Negative feedback ensures that too much water is not removed from the blood.

39

Skin The skin helps to remove some excess water and salts from the blood through the sweat glands. It controls the loss of heat from the body surfaces and helps to maintain the blood at a constant temperature, i.e. 37°C.

High Blood Temperature When the body temperature rises, blood capillaries in the skin become wider. This is called *vasodilation*. Vasodilation increases the blood supply to the surface of the body and heat can be lost by radiation and convection.

Sweating When sweating occurs, the blood supply to the capillaries around the sweat glands is increased. Cells in the glands remove water and salt from the blood. These pass out on to the surface of the skin via the sweat ducts and sweat pores. Evaporation of sweat removes heat from the body. The temperature of the blood is monitored by the hypothalamus in the brain.

Low Blood Temperature When the body temperature falls, blood capillaries in the skin become narrower. This is called *vasoconstriction*. Vasoconstriction decreases the blood supply to the surface of the skin. Blood is diverted along shunt vessels which lie deep in the dermis. The blood is kept away from the body surface and so does not lose heat. Sweating is stopped and no water is removed from the capillaries, so less heat is lost.

Fat Layers of fat under the skin increase the insulation of the body.

Hairs Hairs on the skin can be raised by the contraction of the erector muscles. This traps an insulating layer of air around the body which slows down heat loss.

Shivering Shivering involves fast muscle contraction which releases heat energy. This heat is transferred to the blood.

Hypo-thermia Hypothermia results in a lowering of the body temperature. It occurs when the body temperature starts to fall due to extreme cold or exposure. The hypothalamus stops working. Body temperature continues to fall and this may lead to death.

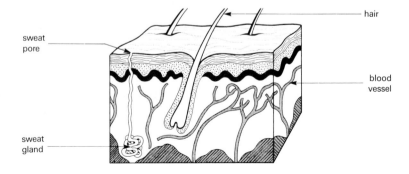

Endocrine System The endocrine system is composed of several glands which produce secretions called *hormones*. The hormones are released into the bloodstream. They travel to target organs.

Hormones

Gland	Hormone	Target Organ
Pancreas	a) Insulin b) Glucagon	Liver Liver
Adrenal	Adrenalin	Heart and many organs
Ovaries and Testes	Sex Hormones	Many organs

Insulin Insulin is produced by the pancreas. It travels to the liver. Under the influence of insulin, liver cells remove glucose from the blood in the liver. Glucose is converted to glycogen and stored in the liver cells. The level of glucose in the blood falls.

Glucagon Glucagon is also produced by the pancreas and travels to the liver. It causes glycogen, which is stored in the liver cells, to be broken down into glucose. The glucose passes into the bloodstream and the level of glucose in the blood rises.

Adrenalin Adrenalin is a hormone produced by the adrenal glands. It brings about a response known as the 'fight or flight' reaction. This prepares the body to respond to any dangerous situation quickly. The heart rate increases to pump blood around the body more quickly. The breathing rate increases to bring more oxygen into the body and to remove carbon dioxide more quickly. The pupils in the eyes dilate (i.e. become wider) to allow more light into the eye. Blood is diverted to the muscles to ensure that they can respond quickly to any danger.

Reproductive Hormones Reproductive hormones are produced by the ovaries and testes. They are responsible for the changes that occur in the body at puberty. The hormones are also responsible for the maturation and release of eggs, the production of sperm, and for the preparation for, and maintenance of, pregnancy.

Hormones can be given to women to treat infertility. The hormones stimulate the ovary to release an egg. This treatment is necessary if the woman is unable to produce any or enough reproductive hormones herself.

Hormones can also be used to prevent ovulation or the release of an egg from the ovary. These hormones are taken in the contraceptive pill or they can be implanted under the skin.

The Reproductive System

Sexual Reproduction Sexual reproduction involves the joining together or fusion of two *gametes* or sex cells. Gametes are normally produced by two separate individuals.

Male Gamete A male gamete is called a sperm or spermatozoon. Millions of sperm are produced at one time. They are small and very mobile. They have no stored food and so they must rely on a supply of energy from the fluid in which they swim. They are approximately 60 μm long.

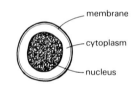

Female Gamete A female gamete is called an egg or ovum (plural: ova). Very few eggs are produced at one time. An egg is large – approximately 120 μm in diameter – since it contains stored food to nourish the cells of the embryo until the placenta forms. Eggs cannot swim, but they are moved along by the beating of cilia which line the Fallopian tubes.

Structure of the Female Reproductive System

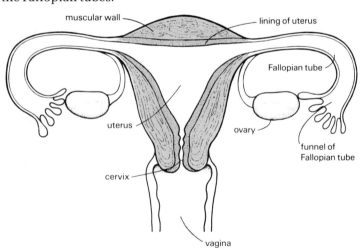

Ovary The two ovaries contain *follicles*. Approximately every 28 days one of the follicles matures and releases an egg. This is called *ovulation*. The ovaries produce the female reproductive hormones oestrogen and progesterone.

Fallopian Tubes The Fallopian tubes connect the uterus with the ovaries. When an egg is released from the ovary, it is drawn into the funnel of the Fallopian tube. This is lined with cilia, which beat and move the egg towards the uterus. Fertilisation occurs in the Fallopian tube if the egg meets a sperm.

Uterus The uterus receives the fertilised egg. It nourishes and protects the developing embryo. Its muscular wall contracts to deliver the baby at birth.

Cervix The cervix is the neck or opening into the uterus. It widens or *dilates* to allow a baby to leave the uterus.

Vagina The vagina is the passageway connecting the uterus to the outside of the body.

The Menstrual Cycle The menstrual cycle is a series of changes which occur in the lining of the uterus. These changes are controlled by the pituitary gland and by oestrogen and progesterone. The cycle lasts on average for 28 days.

Oestrogen Oestrogen causes the lining of the uterus to thicken. It controls the *secondary sexual characteristics*, i.e. the changes that occur in the body at puberty. (page 48)

Progesterone Progesterone maintains the thick lining of the uterus.

Diagram of the Menstrual Cycle

lining thickening   blood supply increases   lining breaking down

Graafian follicle maturing   ovulation – egg released from follicle   Yellow Body developing   Yellow Body disintegrating

oestrogen   progesterone

menstruation   copulation could result in fertilisation   menstruation

days 1 2 3 4 5 6 7 8 9 10 11 12 13 14 15 16 17 18 19 20 21 22 23 24 25 26 27 28 1 2 3 4 5

beginning of menstruation   end of menstruation

Structure of the Male Reproductive System

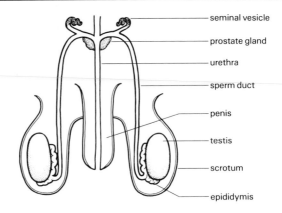

- seminal vesicle
- prostate gland
- urethra
- sperm duct
- penis
- testis
- scrotum
- epididymis

Scrotum The scrotum is a bag of skin which contains the testes. The development of sperm occurs best at a temperature of about 35°C, so the testes are suspended in the scrotum outside the body to keep them cool.

Testes The testes manufacture sperm or male gametes. About 300 million sperm are made each day.

Testosterone Testosterone is the main male reproductive hormone. It is produced by the testes and is responsible for: (i) secondary sexual characteristics, e.g. deep voice, muscle growth, body hair; (ii) development of male reproductive organs.

Epididymis Sperm are stored in the epididymis until they become mature. If sperm are not passed out of the male during *ejaculation*, they are reabsorbed by the body.

Sperm Duct The sperm duct propels the sperm towards the urethra during ejaculation. Removing a section of the duct – *vasectomy* – prevents the sperm from entering the urethra. After a vasectomy sperm production continues normally but the sperm are reabsorbed by the body.

Seminal Vesicle The seminal vesicles secrete an alkaline, sugar-rich fluid. The sugar provides an energy source for the sperm, which they use for movement.

Prostate Gland The prostate gland secretes an alkaline fluid which helps sperm to move easily. Sperm plus secretions are called *semen*.

Urethra The urethra forms a passageway for semen or urine. It passes through the penis to the outside of the body.

Penis The penis is composed of spongy tissue which becomes filled with blood and results in the penis becoming erect. The contraction of muscles in the wall expel the semen from the urethra during ejaculation.

Sexual Intercourse During sexual intercourse, the erect penis of the male is placed inside the vagina of the female. Sperm are released into the vagina during ejaculation. Sperm swim up through the cervix, through the uterus, and into the Fallopian tubes.

Fertilisation If one sperm meets an egg, fertilisation may result. One sperm breaks through the membrane of the egg. The nucleus of the sperm fuses with the nucleus of the egg to produce a *zygote*, or fertilised egg. No other sperm can penetrate the egg because of a protective layer which the egg secretes around itself.

Twins If two eggs are released by the ovary, and they are each fertilised in the Fallopian tubes, two zygotes will result. These will develop into *non-identical* twins.

If one egg is fertilised by one sperm, the fertilised egg or zygote starts to develop. If, at this stage, the zygote splits into two, each half will continue to develop and grow separately. This results in *identical* twins.

Development and Pregnancy The zygote continues to develop as it passes along the Fallopian tube. It forms a ball of cells.

Implantation Implantation takes place 7-8 days after fertilisation. The zygote reaches the uterus and buries itself in the thick vascular lining. This provides it with food and oxygen for growth.

Artificial Insemination Several eggs ripen in the ovary and are removed from the woman. They are then placed in a solution of the male's sperm. Fertilisation may occur and cell division starts. The eggs are replaced in the uterus for implantation and growth. Not all the eggs may survive.

Pregnancy

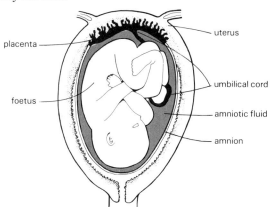

Amnion The amnion is a thin membrane that surrounds the foetus. It encloses the amniotic cavity.

Amniotic Fluid   Amniotic fluid fills the amniotic cavity. The foetus floats in the liquid. The fluid protects the foetus by acting as a shock absorber.

Umbilical Cord   The umbilical cord carries the umbilical artery and vein from the foetus to the placenta.

Placenta   The placenta develops from the growing embryo. The placenta is greatly folded, has a very good blood supply and is thin-walled to speed up movement across its surface. It allows nutrients and oxygen to pass from the mother's bloodstream into the foetus's bloodstream. The placenta allows waste products, e.g. carbon dioxide, to leave the foetus's blood and pass into the mother's blood. The blood of the mother and the foetus never mix because: (i) the blood groups may be different; (ii) the mother's blood is at a much higher pressure than that of the foetus and would damage the foetus's blood vessels.

Alcohol and Drugs   Alcohol and drugs can pass through the placenta from the mother to the foetus. Alcohol slows down growth and may result in deformities in the baby. Many drugs cause defects in the developing foetus.

Smoking   This results in a low infant birth weight. The mother's blood contains less oxygen than normal, so the foetus will be deprived of oxygen for respiration. Babies born to mothers who smoke have an increased incidence of bronchitis and pneumonia in early life.

Rubella   The rubella or German measles virus can cross over the placenta, from the mother to the foetus. If this happens in the first three months of pregnancy, the baby can be born blind, deaf, and mentally and physically handicapped.

Birth   The development and growth of the foetus in the uterus lasts for nine months. This is called the *gestation period*. At the end of this period, waves of muscular contractions occur in the uterus. These contractions gradually push the baby out of the uterus through the cervix, which dilates to allow the baby through. When the baby has been delivered, the contractions continue so the placenta (or afterbirth) can be expelled.

Changes   Several changes take place in the baby just after birth.

Breathing   In the uterus, oxygen was supplied to the foetus from the mother by way of the placenta. Carbon dioxide was removed from the foetus's bloodstream and passed into the mother's. The lungs of the foetus were filled with fluid because they are not used for gas exchange in the uterus. After birth, the fluid is absorbed by the lungs, which are then inflated so that gas exchange can be carried out.

Circulation As the lungs of the foetus do not function, blood from the right side of the heart does not need to be pumped to the lungs. The blood is pumped through an opening in the wall between the two atria to the left side of the heart, and is then pumped round the body. After birth, the opening is closed so that blood must be pumped to the lungs to be oxygenated.

Lactation During pregnancy, the *mammary glands* produce milk. At birth, the sucking action of the baby stimulates the glands to release the milk. Milk contains high levels of fat to provide energy, protein for growth, and vitamins and minerals.

Advantages of Breast-Feeding Breast-feeding establishes contact between the mother and child. Nutrients in the mother's milk are better suited to the child than those from cow's milk. Breast milk contains antibodies which protect the baby during its first few months. Fewer breast-fed babies suffer from allergies. Sucking helps the development of the teeth and jaw.

Birth Control Birth control involves regulating: (i) the *number* of children born; (ii) *when* children are born.

Methods of Contraception The differing methods of contraception stop conception taking place by: (i) preventing fertilisation; (ii) preventing the development of eggs; (iii) preventing implantation of a fertilised egg in the uterus.

Barrier Methods Barrier methods keep the eggs and sperm apart so that fertilisation cannot take place.

Condom A condom is a rubber sheath which fits over the penis and prevents sperm entering the vagina during intercourse. It can provide protection against sexually-transmitted diseases, such as syphilis, gonorrhoea and AIDS.

Diaphragm The diaphragm is a rubber cap which fits over the neck of the uterus. It prevents sperm from entering the uterus.

Chemical Methods Chemical methods prevent ovulation. The most common method is the contraceptive pill.

Contraceptive pill The contraceptive pill ('the pill') is taken every day for three weeks in each menstrual cycle. It contains chemicals identical to oestrogen and progesterone. The levels of these chemicals prevent an egg from being released from the ovary.

Intra-uterine Devices (IUDs) Intra-uterine devices, or IUDs, are tiny structures which are placed inside the uterus. They prevent a fertilised egg from implanting in the wall of the uterus.

Sterilisation   Sterilisation is a permanent method of contraception. In the male, the sperm ducts are cut so that sperm cannot leave the testes. In the female, the Fallopian tubes are cut so that eggs cannot reach the uterus.

Sexually-Transmitted Diseases   These diseases may be spread from one person to another during sexual contact.

Syphilis   Syphilis is a disease which is caused by a bacterium. The bacteria cause sores and fever and may cause blindness and insanity. Syphilis can be passed across the placenta from a mother to her child.

Gonorrhoea   Gonorrhoea is caused by a bacterium. The bacteria cause inflammation of the urinary tract, and if not treated can result in sterility and death. It can be passed to a new-born baby from the vagina of the mother during birth. It can infect the eyes of the baby and lead to blindness. Both gonorrhoea and syphilis can be treated with penicillin.

AIDS   Acquired Immune Deficiency Syndrome (AIDS) is caused by a virus. The virus can be spread by sexual contact or by the exchange of body fluids, such as blood or semen. The virus attacks lymphocytes in the blood and so the body's immunity to infection is lowered. AIDS can therefore be spread by any body fluid which may contain lymphocytes.

Adolescence   This is the time when a human's reproductive organs become mature. The body begins to change due to the effect of the sex hormones and to show features known as *secondary sexual characteristics*. In females these include:

(i) the release of eggs from the ovaries and the onset of the menstrual cycle
(ii) the development of breasts
(iii) growth of pubic and underarm hair.

In males:

(i) the testes produce sperm
(ii) muscle growth increases and the voice deepens
(iii) body hair grows.

3 Lifestyle and Health

Diet A balanced diet is essential to good health (see page 15), but there are many other factors which affect the health of the body.

Malnutrition Malnutrition is the result of an unbalanced diet.

Starvation A shortage of energy-rich foods in the diet causes starvation, e.g. marasmus. It results in the body's energy stores being used up. In extreme cases, the body tissues, e.g. the muscles, are broken down to provide energy.

Tooth Decay (Dental Caries) Bacteria which live naturally in the mouth break down sugar on the teeth and produce an acid. This can cause decay by softening the enamel and eventually destroying it. The softer dentine is then destroyed, exposing the nerves in the pulp.

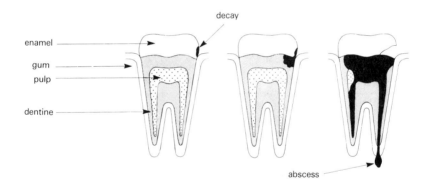

Bacteria may destroy the pulp and the inside of the tooth dies. The dead tissue and bacteria form pus which may gather inside the tooth and form an abscess. The tooth may have to be removed and the infection treated with antibiotics.

Bacteria and acid can build up on the surface of the tooth, particularly around the edge of the gums, to form plaque. This can damage the gum and the tooth becomes loose and will eventually fall out.

Regular brushing and visits to the dentist can prevent the build up of plaque and prevent the loss of teeth by decay.

Smoking Tobacco smoke contains many chemicals which can lead to cancer, lung disease and heart disease. (See pages 21 and 27.)

49

Alcohol   Alcohol is a poison which is broken down in the body by the liver. Excessive drinking of alcohol can cause liver and brain damage.
Excessive drinking has many social consequences e.g. increased road accidents, violence, poverty in families where money is spent on alcohol instead of on food and housing.

Drugs   Alcohol and tobacco are drugs which are legal to use. Many drugs are illegal because they are considered to be harmful. These include:

Cannabis   This is regarded as a 'soft' drug as it is not particularly harmful. It has a relaxing effect on the body.

Heroin   This is a 'hard' drug derived from the opium poppy. In the form of morphine it is used as a medicine to reduce pain but it is an illegal drug because it may lead to addiction and dependency. It is injected into the veins or smoked. Repeated injections damage veins and the use of dirty needles can spread diseases such as AIDS and hepatitis.

Cocaine   This drug, and crack which is derived from it, comes from the coca plant. It makes the user feel confident and happy but has a relatively short effect. Crack is very addictive.

Solvents   Commonly used substances, e.g. petrol, lighter fuel and cleaning fluids, produce vapours. When these are inhaled, they have a relaxing effect on the body. They damage the brain and liver and can kill even if used only once.

Ecstasy   This is an amphetamine-based drug which can produce hallucinations and a feeling of euphoria. Some users experience severe sweating, which may lead to dehydration, blurred vision and nausea. Death can also occur.

Micro-organisms and Disease

Bacteria   These micro-organisms can enter the body through openings, e.g. nose and mouth or through damaged skin. Inside the body they divide rapidly – one bacterium can divide into two in only twenty minutes. Large numbers of bacteria release toxins into the blood which produce the symptoms of disease.

Bacteria can cause many infectious diseases, such as salmonella, diphtheria, tuberculosis, typhoid and cholera.

The bacteria can spread quickly through a population, particularly if there is an inadequate water purification system and sewage treatment system.

Viruses   Viruses cannot reproduce until they enter a living cell. Inside the cell they reproduce rapidly and then spread to infect other cells when the cell ruptures. They can be difficult to destroy because they are hidden inside the body cells. Viruses can cause polio, measles, German measles and AIDS.

Fungi   Diseases caused by fungi include athlete's foot, ringworm and thrush.

Protozoa   These single celled organisms are often passed into the blood by carriers or vectors. The protozoan which causes malaria lives inside the salivary glands of a mosquito. When the mosquito bites a victim, some protozoa may be injected into the bloodstream and cause the disease in humans.

Useful Micro-organisms   Although many micro-organisms are harmful, many others are extremely useful.

Bacteria   Those present in the large intestine produce Vitamin K which is required for blood clotting. Some bacteria produce enzymes for use in detergents and important medicines, e.g. insulin. They are very important in the decomposition of sewage and the production of biogas which can be used as fuel. They are also used in the production of cheese, yogurt and vinegar.

Fungi   Some fungi produce antibiotics, e.g. penicillin. They are used in baking (yeast) and to produce alcohol. They are very important in the decomposition of dead organisms.

Defence against Disease

Skin   Undamaged skin provides a barrier to the entry of micro-organisms.

Acid   Hydrochloric acid, secreted by the stomach, destroys most bacteria which enter through the mouth.

Enzymes   Tears contain an enzyme which destroys any bacteria that come into contact with the surface of the eye. This enzyme is called lysosyme.

Wax   The ears secrete a sticky, acidic wax which kills and traps bacteria.

Mucus   Openings in the body, e.g. nasal passages, vagina, anus and penis, secrete mucus which traps bacteria and prevents them passing into the body. In the nasal passages hairs called cilia sweep the mucus and bacteria away from the lungs. (See page 24.)

Blood Clotting If the skin is damaged, bacteria can quickly enter broken blood vessels. Blood clotting seals the broken vessels and prevents the entry of bacteria as well as preventing excessive loss of blood. The formation of a scab protects the new skin underneath until it has completely regrown.

Immunity Antibodies in the blood enable the body to become immune or resistant to bacteria or toxins which may enter the body.

Passive Immunity During development in the uterus, antibodies from the mother may cross the placenta into the blood of the foetus. These provide immunity for a short time after birth against diseases such as polio. The antibodies, however, eventually break down and immunity to the disease is lost.

Injected Antibodies Antibodies may be given by injection to destroy bacteria already present in the blood. This is used against diphtheria and tetanus bacteria. It can provide protection only for a short time.

Active Immunity Immunisation is the injection of small amounts of antigen or vaccine into the body. The antigens stimulate lymphocytes to produce antibodies to destroy them. This type of immunity provides long-term protection because the lymphocytes 'remember' the foreign antigen and, if it ever re-enters the body, the lymphocytes can quickly produce antibodies to destroy it. (page 22)

Plant Systems

Structure of a Plant

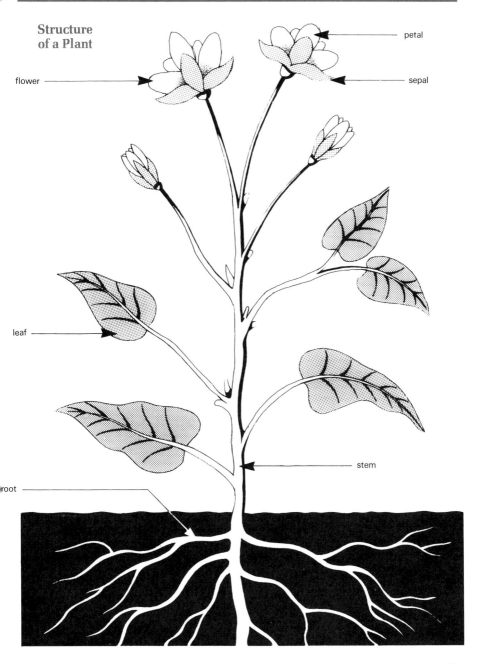

flower

petal

sepal

leaf

stem

root

Photosynthesis and Plant Nutrition

Photo- Photosynthesis is the process by which green plants
synthesis manufacture their food. It is a chemical reaction controlled by
enzymes, which takes place in the chloroplasts in the cell.
Chloroplasts contain the green pigment called chlorophyll.
Most photosynthesis takes place in the leaves. These are
specially adapted to allow photosynthesis to take place.

Leaves Leaves are thin to allow quick diffusion of gases. They provide a
large surface area for the absorption of light. They are well
supplied with *xylem* and *phloem* to allow quick transport of
substances in and out of the leaf. They have pores called
stomata to allow the entry and exit of gases.

**Structure of
a Leaf**

**a) External
Features**

**b) Cross-
section as
seen under a
Light
Microscope**

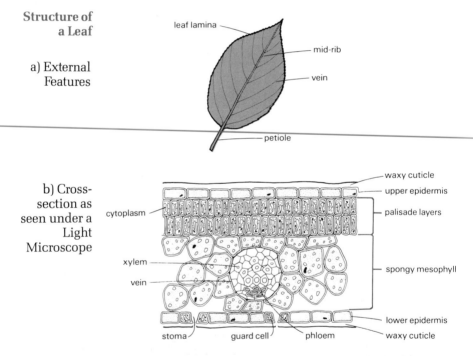

Chloroplasts Chloroplasts are small, green structures found in cells in the
leaf and stem. They contain a green pigment called
chlorophyll. This traps light energy and converts it to chemical
energy. Most chloroplasts are found in the upper sections of the
palisade cells. Here, they can absorb most light. Chemical
energy made in photosynthesis is stored in starch molecules.

54

Requirements for Photosynthesis	Photosynthesis requires the presence of light, carbon dioxide, water and chlorophyll.

$$Carbon\ Dioxide\ +\ Water\ \xrightarrow[Chlorophyll]{Light\ Energy}\ Glucose\ +\ Oxygen.$$

$$6CO_2\ +\ 6H_2O\ \longrightarrow\ C_6H_{12}O_6\ +\ 6O_2$$

1. Carbon Dioxide	Carbon dioxide is absorbed from the atmosphere by the leaf. It moves by diffusion through the stomata. From here, it diffuses through the air spaces in the spongy mesophyll to the palisade cells. It passes through the cell membranes into the cytoplasm.
2. Water	Water travels up through the plant in the xylem vessels. When it reaches the veins in the leaves, it moves by osmosis from the xylem to the palisade cells.
Chlorophyll	Chlorophyll is a green pigment found on the lamellae of the chloroplasts. It absorbs *light energy* and converts it into *chemical energy*. The energy is used to combine the carbon dioxide and water molecules to form glucose.
Products of Photosynthesis	Photosynthesis produces glucose and oxygen.
1. Glucose	Glucose is manufactured mainly in the palisade cells. It moves into the phloem and is then carried to other parts of the plant. Any glucose remaining in the leaves is converted to starch and is stored in the cytoplasm.
2. Oxygen	Oxygen is a waste product of photosynthesis. It moves from the palisade cells by *diffusion*, and passes down through the air spaces to the stomata in the lower epidermis. From here, it diffuses out into the atmosphere.
Limiting Factors on the Rate of Photosynthesis	The rate at which photosynthesis takes place is controlled by several limiting factors. Photosynthesis depends on: a) light intensity; b) carbon dioxide concentration; c) temperature.
Light Intensity	High light intensity will result in a high rate of photosynthesis. The high rate will continue only if there is sufficient carbon dioxide in the atmosphere and if the temperature is high enough. The availability of light is the most important factor controlling the rate of photosynthesis.
Carbon Dioxide Concentration	Providing there is sufficient light, the greater the carbon dioxide concentration, the greater the rate of photosynthesis.

Temperature Photosynthesis is a chemical reaction controlled by enzymes. Enzymes work best at an optimum temperature. If the temperature is kept at the optimum value and there is sufficient light and carbon dioxide, then the rate of photosynthesis will be high.

Nutrients and Minerals In addition to light and water, healthy plants require a number of different substances for their nutrition.

Glucose Glucose is manufactured by the plant during photosynthesis. It can then be converted into the other carbohydrates which the plant needs, and also the proteins and fats required by the cells.

Starch Starch is an insoluble carbohydrate which is used as a food store in plant cells.

Cellulose Cellulose is a large carbohydrate which is used to make plant cell walls.

Protein Plants need protein to manufacture many substances, including cell membranes and enzymes. Proteins contain the elements carbon, hydrogen and oxygen which they can obtain from carbohydrates. They also contain nitrogen.

Nitrogen Plants can absorb nitrogen from the soil as nitrate salts. They are absorbed in solution through the roots by active transport and by diffusion. Bacteria living in root nodules on some plant roots, e.g. pea and bean plants, can manufacture nitrates for use by the plant.

Magnesium Magnesium forms part of the chlorophyll molecule. A shortage of magnesium results in yellow leaves, or *chlorosis*.

Phosphorus Phosphorus is present in some proteins and in ATP (adenosine triphosphate), which stores energy in cells. Shortage of phosphorus results in stunted growth.

Iron Iron is required to manufacture chlorophyll. A shortage of iron results in yellow leaves.

Potassium Potassium is required for the chemical reactions which take place in photosynthesis and respiration in plant cells. Shortage leads to yellowing of leaves and premature death.

Calcium Calcium is required for the formation of new cells and a shortage will result in poor growth.

Trace Elements Minute amounts of other minerals (e.g. sodium, manganese and copper) are often required for healthy plants. These are called trace elements.

Transport in Plants

Transport Water and nutrients move from the soil into the plant by *osmosis*.
Movement of Water moves from small spaces surrounding the soil particles
Water into structures on the root called *root hairs*.

Root Hairs Root hairs help to anchor the plant in the soil, but more importantly they increase the surface area of the root for absorption. They carry the water to the xylem vessels in the centre of the root and these then carry the water up the stem to the leaves. Dissolved minerals are also absorbed.

Internal Structure of a Root

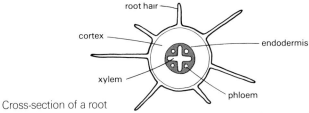

Cross-section of a root

Xylem Vessels Xylem vessels carry water from the roots to the leaves. The walls of the vessels are made of lignin which is impermeable to water. Small holes in the walls allow water to move out of the vessels into the cells of the root, stem and leaves.

Phloem Soluble sugars which are made in the leaves by photosynthesis are carried to growing parts of the plant and respiring cells by the phloem. Excess sugar is carried to storage regions and converted to starch.

Internal Structure of a Stem

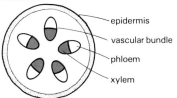

Cross-section of a stem

Transpiration Water is constantly evaporating from the cells in the mesophyll layers of the leaf into the air spaces surrounding them. Water vapour then moves out of the leaf through the stomata. This is called transpiration.

The rate at which transpiration takes place depends on:

1. Wind Fast air movement over the surfaces of a leaf increases the rate of transpiration.

2. Temperature High temperature increases the rate at which water evaporates from the leaf.

3. Humidity High humidity decreases the rate of transpiration by preventing rapid evaporation of water into the air.

Gas Exchange in Plants

Gas Exchange Gas exchange in plants occurs mainly in the leaves. It is brought about by diffusion through the stomata in the leaves. The overall movement of gases in and out of a leaf depends on whether photosynthesis is taking place. Plants are living organisms and so respiration must take place in their cells to provide energy necessary for life. This takes place constantly.

Gas Exchange during Photo-synthesis Occurs in light.

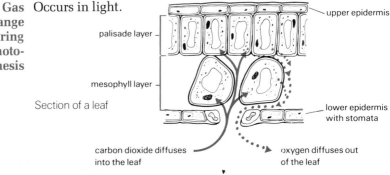

palisade layer

mesophyll layer

Section of a leaf

upper epidermis

lower epidermis with stomata

carbon dioxide diffuses into the leaf

oxygen diffuses out of the leaf

Gas Exchange during Respiration Occurs all the time.

palisade layer

mesophyll layer

Section of a leaf

upper epidermis

lower epidermis with stomata

oxygen diffuses into the leaf

carbon dioxide diffuses out of the leaf

Oxygen diffuses in through the stomata of a leaf from the atmosphere and enters the cells where respiration is taking place. It reacts with glucose in the cells to produce energy. Carbon dioxide and water vapour are produced as waste products and these diffuse out of the cells and then leave the leaf via the stomata.

When light energy is available to green plants, photosynthesis will take place. Carbon dioxide gas diffuses in through the stomata and then into the palisade cells. Here it reacts with water in the chloroplasts to form glucose. Oxygen is produced as a waste product. This diffuses out of the palisade cells and then out of the leaf through the stomata. When the rate of photosynthesis is high, the stomata open wide to allow diffusion of gases to proceed quickly.

Response in Plants

Sensitivity Plants and animals respond to stimuli from their environment. *Receptors* are used to detect the stimuli. A response to a stimulus is usually brought about by an *effector*. Effectors include nerves, muscles and, in plants, hormones.

Light and Gravity Light and gravity are two stimuli to which plants respond. *Phototropism* is a response to light. *Geotropism* is a response to gravity.

Phototropism Phototropism involves growth in response to light. Stems of plants grow towards light and are said to be positively phototropic. Roots of plants grow away from light and are said to be negatively phototropic. Stems will grow towards light if it comes from one direction, i.e. stems bend towards a light source.

Geotropism Geotropism involves growth in response to gravity. Shoots of plants grow away from the pull of gravity, i.e. upwards. They are negatively geotropic. Roots of plants grow towards the pull of gravity, i.e. downwards. They are positively geotropic.

Plant Hormones *Auxins* are growth hormones found in plants. They are produced in the shoot tips and are transported throughout the plant to the roots.

When a shoot is illuminated from above, auxins move down through the shoot uniformly. The cells in the shoot will grow at the same rate and so the shoot will grow upwards, towards the light.

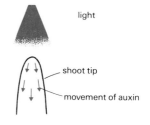

light

shoot tip

movement of auxin

When a shoot is lit from one side, it bends and grows towards the light. More auxin passes down through the cells on the shaded side of the shoot. These cells grow faster and so the shoot bends.

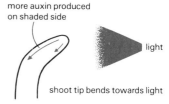

more auxin produced on shaded side

light

shoot tip bends towards light

If the shoot tip is removed, the shoot does not grow. Auxins, therefore, are produced only in the tip of a shoot. Some plant hormones are often used by humans to regulate or control processes in plants, e.g. 'cuttings' of plants can be stimulated to produce roots by dipping the cutting into hormones.

Support in Plants

Support Support in plants is achieved by the turgidity of their cells and by strong tissues in the cells.

Turgidity of Cells Water pressure inside plant cells helps to keep the cells rigid. If plant cells lose water, *wilting* results. Cells become *flaccid* as water is lost, and the leaves and plant droop. Wilting occurs when the plant roots cannot take up sufficient water to replace that lost by transpiration.

Cellulose The cell walls of plants are supported and strengthened by cellulose.

Lignin Lignin is woody tissue which is deposited in the cell wall. It prevents the passage of water in and out of the cells and they soon die. Xylem vessels are formed from the dead cells. They are used to transport water throughout a plant.

Stems Woody tissue is found around the inside of a stem towards the edge. This supports the stem but allows it to bend slightly.

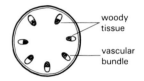

woody tissue

vascular bundle

Roots Woody tissue is found in the centre of roots. Roots are flexible in order to allow them to move through the soil.

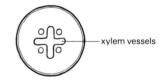

xylem vessels

Secondary Thickening This type of growth supports tall plants by thickening the stems. Cellular tissue called *cambium* divides and produces woody tissue towards the inside of a stem. New phloem is produced towards the outside.

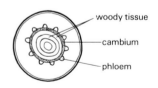

woody tissue

cambium

phloem

Non-woody Plants Some plants do not contain wood and so require other methods of support.

Ivy clings on tightly to other plants or walls. Water lilies use water to support their leaves. Sweet peas use tendrils to hold on to other plants or structures.

Reproduction in Plants

| Sexual Re-production | Sexual reproduction in plants involves the fusion of gametes. The gametes are brought together by pollination. The male gametes are carried in pollen grains. The female gametes are called eggs. Gametes are produced by the flower. |

Flower Structure

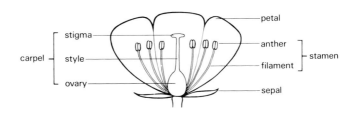

Sepals	Sepals are small green leaves which protect the flower when it is a bud.
Petals	Petals are often, but not always, brightly coloured. They are used to attract insects to the flower.
Stamen	The stamen is the male part of a flower. It consists of the anthers and the filament.
Anthers	The anthers contain four pollen sacs. In these, the pollen grains develop.
Filament	The filament holds the anthers up in the flower.
Carpel	The carpel is the female part of the flower.
Stigma	The stigma is the swollen platform on the top of the style. It secretes a sticky fluid to hold the pollen grains and to stimulate them to germinate.
Style	The style is a tube which connects the stigma to the ovary. The pollen grain grows a tube down through the style.

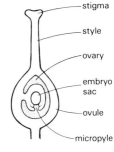

Female part of a flower

| Ovary | The ovary contains the ovule which holds female gametes in the embryo sac. The ovule forms the seed. The ovary forms the fruit. |
| Micropyle | The micropyle is a small opening which leads to the embryo sac in the ovule. |

Fertilisation A pollen grain containing the male gamete lands on the stigma. It grows a pollen tube down through the style to the ovary when it germinates. The pollen tube grows through the micropyle to the embryo sac. The male gamete moves down through the pollen tube and enters the embryo sac. It fuses with the female gamete. The fertilised egg divides many times to form an *embryo* and develops into a seed.

Methods of Pollination Pollen can be transferred from the anthers to the stigma by:

Wind Anthers project outside the flower to be blown by the wind. Large numbers of lightweight pollen grains are produced. Stigmas may be feathery to catch the pollen grains. They also project outside the flower. This type of pollination is found in *grass*.

Insect Flowers produce *nectar* to attract insects, e.g. bees and butterflies. Flowers also produce coloured petals and often a sweet scent, in order to attract insects.
As the insect enters the flower to collect nectar, pollen from the anthers is deposited on the insect's body. When the insect is leaving the flower, pollen may be deposited on to the stigma. When the insect visits another flower, pollen may be deposited on the stigma.
The pollen grains may be sticky, so fewer pollen grains are produced, compared to wind-pollinated plants, because with wind pollination there is a very high chance that the pollen will be lost before it comes into contact with the stigma of a plant.

Cross-Pollination Pollen from one plant is transferred to another plant. This allows variation in a population.

Self-Pollination Pollen from one plant is transferred to the stigma of the same plant, usually by the wind. Self-pollination does not allow genetic variation, so many plants are adapted to prevent this type of pollination from occurring. For example, the stigma and anthers may mature at different times.

Germination Germination is the development of a new plant from a seed. It requires certain conditions:

Water Seeds absorb water and swell up.

Temperature Seeds usually require a specific temperature for germination. Temperatures which are too high or too low prevent germination.

Oxygen Seeds are living things and so they require oxygen for respiration. This provides the energy for germination.

62

Seed Dispersal Seeds can be dispersed in several ways.

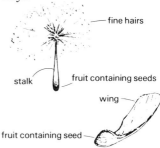

Wind Dispersal Seeds are very small and can easily be carried by the wind. Seeds may have a parachute, e.g. willow-herb. This allows the seed to be carried easily. Winged fruits, e.g. sycamore, carry the seeds. The wind may shake the fruit and dislodge the seeds, e.g. snapdragon and poppy.

Animal Dispersal The fleshy part of a fruit is eaten by animals and birds and the seeds or stones are discarded by, or pass through, the creature, e.g. strawberry, blackberry. Hooked fruits and seeds catch on the fur of animals and are carried away, e.g. burdock. Nuts are carried off and buried by squirrels and rodents.

Water Dispersal Coconut fruits contain trapped air to help them to float.

Propulsive Dispersal As fruits ripen, they dry. In some plants, e.g. pea and lupin, the seeds are flung out of the fruits as they dry.

Asexual Reproduction Asexual, or vegetative, reproduction does not involve the fusion of gametes. New plants are produced from one parent plant.

Advantages Fewer plants are lost. In sexual reproduction, many seeds are lost during dispersal. In asexual reproduction, the new plant grows on or close to the parent.
New plants always have the same characteristics as the parent. This is important when growing food, e.g. potatoes, and flowers, e.g. daffodils. New plants will always be identical to the parent.

Disadvantages Many plants may grow in the same area, which leads to overcrowding. As there is no variation between plants, they may all become susceptible to the same diseases.

Tuber (Swollen Stem) e.g. Potato

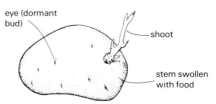

63

5 Inheritance and Genetics

Heredity Genetics is the study of inherited characteristics or *heredity*. In sexual reproduction, a new individual is formed by the fusion of gametes. The gametes are produced by two separate individuals. The zygote formed from the fusion of gametes inherits information from both parents. This genetic information is carried on structures called chromosomes in the nucleus of a cell.

Chromo- Chromosomes are long, thread-like structures found in the
somes nucleus of a cell. They are composed of protein and a nucleic acid called DNA (deoxyribonucleic acid). The DNA is arranged in units called genes.

Genes Genes appear as dark bands on each chromosome. They contain the genetic information which is inherited by an offspring from its parents. Each gene is responsible for a specific instruction in the body, e.g. ''Make a pigment to colour hair.''

Chromo- In humans, body cells, e.g. skin and muscle cells, contain a
some diploid number of chromosomes, i.e. 46. These chromosomes
Number are arranged into 23 pairs. Each chromosome in a pair is identical to its partner. The pairs of chromosomes are called homologous chromosomes. One set of 23 chromosomes is inherited from the mother and the other set is inherited from the father. Sex cells, e.g. eggs and sperm, contain only 23 chromosomes, or a haploid number of chromosomes. At fertilisation, fusion of gametes will result in a zygote containing 46 chromosomes.

Mitosis Mitosis is cell division which results in identical cells being produced. It occurs in organisms which reproduce asexually and in all body cells except for those which form gametes. The number of chromosomes in the nucleus of the new cell produced by mitosis is always the same as that of the parent cell.

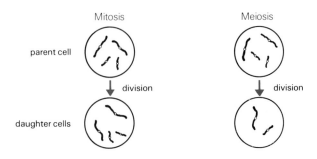

64

Meiosis Meiosis is cell division which produces eggs and sperm. Gametes produced by meiosis contain half the number of chromosomes as other cells in the body.

Sex Chromo- In the nucleus, one pair of homologous chromosomes carries
somes the genes which determine the sex of an individual. These are called the sex chromosomes and they appear as an X and Y shape under the electron microscope. The presence of two X chromosomes in a zygote produces a female child (XX). The presence of an X and a Y chromosome produces a male child (XY).

Genotype The genotype is the genetic make-up of an individual. It depends on the genes which are inherited from the parents.

Homozygous Homozygous genes are identical genes on a pair of homologous
Genes chromosomes. Each gene carries the same instruction, e.g. "Make a red pigment to colour hair."

Heterozygous Heterozygous genes are non-identical genes on a pair of
Genes homologous chromosomes. Each gene carries a different instruction. On one chromosome the instruction may be: "Make a red pigment to colour hair", but on the other chromosome the instruction might be: "Make a black pigment to colour hair."

Alleles Alleles are genes which determine the same characteristic, e.g. hair colour, but express it in different ways. One gene may carry instructions to make red hair, while the other may carry instructions to make black hair.

Phenotype The phenotype of an individual is the physical characteristics determined by the genes on the chromosomes in the nucleus. Hair colour is determined by the particular instructions carried on an individual's genes.

Dominant The dominant gene is the gene which is shown in an
Gene individual's phenotype. It will be the characteristic shown in both a homozygous and a heterozygous individual.

Recessive The recessive gene will be expressed or shown only in the
Gene phenotype of a homozygous individual. It can never be expressed if a dominant gene is present on the other homologous chromosome.

F_1 The F_1 generation, or *first filial generation*, is the name given to
Generation the offspring of a particular cross.

F_2 The F_2 generation, or *second filial generation*, is the name
Generation given to the offspring produced by a cross between individuals in the F_1 generation.

Examples of Genetic Crosses The gene which determines the ability to roll the tongue is *dominant*.
Let R be the gene for tongue-rolling (Dominant).
Let r be the gene for non-tongue-rolling (Recessive)

I Phenotype   Tongue-rolling female × Tongue-rolling male

Genotype

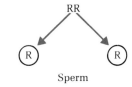

Gametes Formed by Meiosis

Possible Combinations of Gametes at Fertilisation

Male \ Female	R	R
R	RR	RR
R	RR	RR

(Sperm on the left; Eggs across the top)

Genotype of Offspring   All RR – Homozygous for the dominant gene.

Phenotype of Offspring   Tongue rollers.
This example shows the results of *possible combinations* of gametes at fertilisation.

II Phenotype   Tongue-rolling female × Non-tongue-rolling male

Genotype

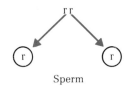

Gametes

Possible Combinations of Gametes

Male \ Female	R	R
r	Rr	Rr
r	Rr	Rr

Genotype of Offspring   Rr – Heterozygous.

Phenotype of Offspring   Tongue rollers.
All the offspring from this cross would be tongue rollers because they would inherit the dominant R gene from their mother.

III Phenotype   Tongue-rolling female × Tongue-rolling male

Genotype   Rr   Rr
                      Heterozygous   ×   Heterozygous

Gametes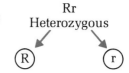

Possible
Combination
of Gametes

Male \ Female	R	r
R	RR	Rr
r	Rr	rr

Genotype of   RR – tongue roller (Homozygous)
Offspring   Rr – tongue roller (Heterozygous)
              rr – non-roller (Homozygous recessive)
              The results of this cross show that at fertilisation there is a 75%
              chance that the offspring will be a tongue roller (RR or Rr).
              There is a 25% chance that the offspring will be a non-roller
              (rr).

Incomplete Incomplete dominance is shown in human blood groups. The
Dominance   gene which determines blood group A is equally dominant to
                the gene which determines blood group B. Both of these genes
                are dominant over the gene which determines blood group O.

Variation   Sexual reproduction will always result in variation in a
                population. Variation may be of two types – continuous and
                discontinuous.

Continuous Continuous variation always produces a normal distribution
Variation   curve when measured in a population – e.g. height. There are
                very few extremely small individuals in a population. There
                are very few extremely tall individuals in a population. Most
                individuals have heights which fall in the mid-range of the
                distribution.

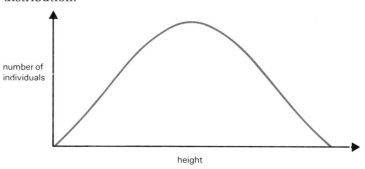

67

Discon- This type of variation arises as a result of a *mutation*, or
tinuous sudden change in an individual's genes or chromosomes.
Variation Nearly all mutations are harmful. Some mutations occur
naturally, at random, as in the case of Down's Syndrome
children.

Down's An individual with Down's Syndrome inherits one extra
Syndrome chromosome and so his or her body cells have a chromosome
number of 47, instead of 46.

Cancer Mutations may also be caused by exposure to harmful
radiation, e.g. ultra-violet radiation, X-rays and radioactive
radiation. These radiations may damage body cells and cause
them to grow abnormally. This is known as cancer. Abnormal
cells grow and divide and may spread to other parts of the
body and so spread the disease.

Inheritance Some diseases can be passed on to children from parents.
of Disease

Cystic This chronic complaint affects the lungs and pancreas. Thick
Fibrosis mucus is produced which blocks the air passage in the lungs
and leads to infections. It is caused by the inheritance of two
recessive genes: one from the mother and one from the father.
Neither parent has the disease. Research has identified the
gene responsible for cystic fibrosis and trials are being carried
out to treat the condition by injecting a normal gene into the
patient.

Huntington's This disease is passed on by one parent who has the disease.
Chorea Symptoms first appear between the ages of 20-40 years, by
which time the patient may have passed the condition on to
his or her children. The brain gradually loses its ability to
control movement and the patient loses mental ability.
Children have a 50:50 chance of inheriting the disease.

Haemophilia This disorder is passed on to male offspring from their mother.
She shows no symptoms of the disease. The haemophiliac
suffers from severe bleeding due to an inability of the blood to
clot if any damage to blood vessels occurs. The gene
responsible for the disease is carried on one of the X
chromosomes. If this is inherited by the son, he will suffer
from haemophilia as there is no corresponding dominant
(normal) gene on the Y-chromosome inherited from the father.

Evolution In animals and plants which reproduce sexually, each new
generation will contain individuals which are slightly
different from their parents and from each other. Some
individuals may inherit characteristics which enable them to
adapt to a particular change in the environment. These

individuals will survive and pass this characteristic on to their offspring.

Individuals which cannot adapt to environmental change will die, and so their genes will not be passed on to subsequent generations.

Natural Selection Charles Darwin tried to explain evolution in terms of natural selection. He suggested that new species arose from gradual changes which occurred in each new generation of individuals. Individuals which inherited genes that allowed them to adapt and survive environmental change, passed these genes on to their offspring. Individuals which could not adapt died out.

The peppered moth shows natural selection in action today. The moth occurs in two forms: a dark-coloured moth and a light-coloured moth. The normal moth is white and the dark moth has been produced as a result of mutation.

In very polluted areas, the bark of trees on which the moths live is black. Here, the mutant, or dark moth, is found in high numbers. It is well camouflaged on the bark and so cannot be seen easily by birds which prey on it. Many dark moths survive and reproduce. The gene determining the dark colour is passed on to the new individuals and so the population of dark moths will increase.

Any white moths living in a polluted area will tend to be seen and eaten by birds. They will not survive to reproduce and so the population of white moths will decrease.

In non-polluted areas the opposite effect will be seen, since the white moths are well camouflaged against the clean tree bark and so cannot be seen easily by birds. They will survive to produce offspring and so their population will increase. The population of the mutant moth, on the other hand, will decrease because they can be easily seen.

Artificial Selection We can select particular characteristics in plants and animals and, by selective breeding, can produce individuals which show these characteristics.

By this method, species of wheat have been produced which yield large amounts of grain and which can be harvested easily. Cattle which contain very little fat have been bred in order to supply lean meat. Cows have been bred to produce large quantities of milk.

6 Diversity and Variation

Physical Characteristics All living organisms have been placed into small groups according to their physical characteristics.

Kingdom The first division of living organisms is into two kingdoms: the animal kingdom and the plant kingdom.

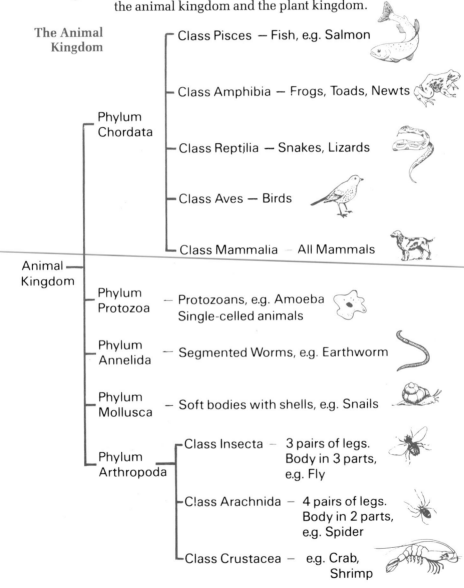

The Animal Kingdom

Phylum Chordata
- Class Pisces — Fish, e.g. Salmon
- Class Amphibia — Frogs, Toads, Newts
- Class Reptilia — Snakes, Lizards
- Class Aves — Birds
- Class Mammalia — All Mammals

Animal Kingdom

Phylum Protozoa — Protozoans, e.g. Amoeba Single-celled animals

Phylum Annelida — Segmented Worms, e.g. Earthworm

Phylum Mollusca — Soft bodies with shells, e.g. Snails

Phylum Arthropoda
- Class Insecta — 3 pairs of legs. Body in 3 parts, e.g. Fly
- Class Arachnida — 4 pairs of legs. Body in 2 parts, e.g. Spider
- Class Crustacea — e.g. Crab, Shrimp

Phylum Each kingdom is then divided into smaller groups called Phyla (singular: Phylum), e.g. Phylum Chordata – animals with a backbone. The diagram opposite shows only *some* of the Phyla in the animal kingdom.

The division continues into smaller and smaller groups until each species can be identified.

Class>Order>Family>Genus>Species

Classification of Humans Humans are classified as follows:

Species – Sapiens – Modern Man only.

Genus – Homo – Modern and Primitive Man.

Family – Hominidae – Modern Man and also Primitive and Ape-Men.

Order – Primate – grasping hands and feet.

Class – Mammalia – has hair; young fed on mother's milk.

Phylum – Chordata – has a backbone.

Kingdom – Animal

The Plant Kingdom

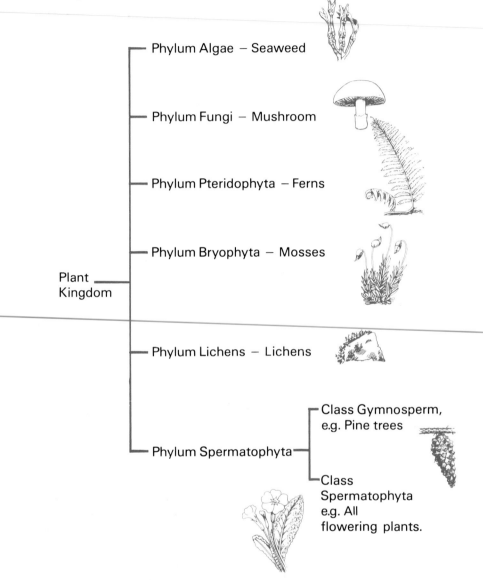

Plant Kingdom

- Phylum Algae – Seaweed
- Phylum Fungi – Mushroom
- Phylum Pteridophyta – Ferns
- Phylum Bryophyta – Mosses
- Phylum Lichens – Lichens
- Phylum Spermatophyta
  - Class Gymnosperm, e.g. Pine trees
  - Class Spermatophyta e.g. All flowering plants.

This diagram shows a greatly simplified classification of plants.

Many other living organisms, e.g. bacteria, viruses and some protozoa, can be classified into separate kingdoms.

Keys Keys are used to identify organisms. There are two types of key most commonly used: a branching key; a paired statement key.

Branching Key Fish, Crab, Bird, Butterfly, Worm, Centipede, Snake.

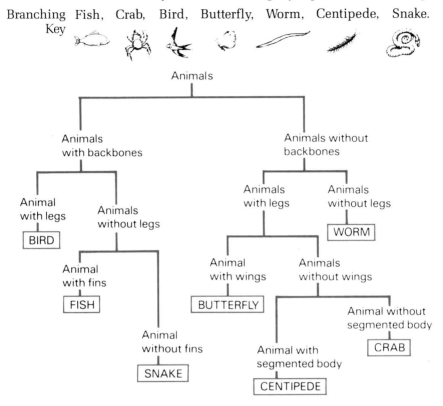

Paired Statement Key The same information can be obtained using a paired statement key.

1. Animals with backbones _____ 2.
   Animals without backbones _____ 4.

2. Animal with legs _____ Bird
   Animals without legs _____ 3.

3. Animal with fins _____ Fish
   Animal without fins _____ Snake

4. Animals with legs _____ 5.
   Animal without legs _____ Worm

5. Animal with wings _____ Butterfly
   Animals without wings _____ 6.

6. Animal with a segmented body _____ Centipede
   Animal without a segmented body _____ Crab

73

7 Ecology and the Environment

Ecology	Ecology is the study of an organism and its relationship to other organisms and to the environment.
Ecosystem	An ecosystem is made up from interacting groups of different organisms in a particular environment.
Habitat	A habitat is a particular place where a group or several groups of organisms live. Within a habitat may be found producers, consumers and decomposers.
Producers (Autotrophs)	Producers are organisms which make their own food, e.g. green plants manufacture carbohydrate during photosynthesis.
Consumers (Heterotrophs)	Consumers are organisms which cannot make their own food, but obtain it by feeding on other organisms, e.g. animals.
Decomposers (Saprophytes)	Decomposers are organisms which break down dead organisms, e.g. bacteria and fungi. They obtain energy from this decomposition and they also return valuable substances to the soil and the atmosphere.

Food-Chains Food-chains describe the flow of energy through a habitat. The energy available to organisms decreases as the levels in the food-chain increase.

Producer Grass – Grass plants use some of the sun's energy to manufacture food. They use this food to provide energy for metabolism. Of the total amount of energy absorbed by the grass, only a very small amount is stored in the plant to be used by the primary consumers.

Primary Consumer (Herbivore) Rabbit – A rabbit eats grass to obtain energy for metabolism. Some food is laid down as fat in the body and some is used to make tissues. Most of the energy absorbed by the rabbit is lost as heat energy from the body.

Secondary Consumer (Carnivore) Fox – A fox eats rabbits to obtain energy. Only a small fraction of this energy is stored in the fox. Most is lost from the body as heat.

Pyramid of Numbers As energy is lost in each step of the food-chain, fewer organisms can be supported on each level. The shorter the food-chain, the more energy is available to the organisms on the highest level.

FOX
RABBIT
GRASS

decrease in number of organisms

Food-Web A food-web is a series of interconnecting food-chains in an ecosystem.

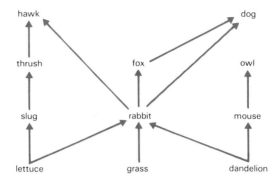

Predators Within the food-web are animals which kill other animals for their food. These animals are known as predators, e.g. fox kills a rabbit – fox is a predator.

Parasites Parasites are organisms which live on another organism called the host. They obtain food and shelter from the host. Only the parasite benefits from this relationship, e.g. flea on a dog – flea is a parasite; mistletoe on an apple tree – mistletoe is a parasite.

Population Growth Populations grow by doubling their numbers at certain intervals. This is called *exponential growth*.

Human Population Growth

Year	Human Population in Millions
1600	500
1800	1000
1900	1600
1950	2500
1975	4000
2000 (projected)	6000

This increase is due to several factors.

Decrease in Infant Mortality Fewer children die at or soon after birth. This is due to advances in medical treatment, improved living conditions and more nutritious food.

Family Size People in developed countries are educated and encouraged to have smaller families. This requires money to be spent on education and also on the different methods of birth control. The cost prevents some underdeveloped countries from having an efficient birth-control policy. Religious and ethical ideals also prevent some countries from developing a birth-control policy.

75

Increase in Life Expectancy
Improved food, living conditions and medical treatment ensure that many people have a long life. If more people live longer, more people can reproduce and so the population will increase. An increase in human population can lead to several problems.

Food Production
More food must be produced cheaply and efficiently to cater for a large population. This may lead to loss of forest and jungle when they are cleared to provide arable or grazing land for farmers.

The increased use of artificial fertilisers on the soil leads to the pollution of rivers and streams when the fertilisers are washed off the soil by rain.

Overcrowding
Large numbers of people may lead to overcrowding in cities and towns. This places additional strain on sewage treatment facilities.

Surrounding farmland may be used for building houses. Social and medical services may become overstretched, leading to an increase in disease and illness. Infections spread rapidly in large populations and may lead to an increase in epidemics.

Competition between individuals will develop for houses, work, etc., which in turn may lead to more stress in the population.

Animal Populations
The number of animals in a population is determined by several factors.

Competition
Individual members of the population have to compete with each other for food, water and space to live.

Predators
The level of predation will also affect the number of animals in a population. An increase in the number of predators in an area will lead to a decrease in the population of the prey.

Disease
Outbreaks of disease will reduce the numbers of animals in a population. Only those resistant to the disease will survive to reproduce.

Plant Populations
Plant populations are also limited by the factors which determine animal populations. Plants also have to compete for the available light to enable them to photosynthesise.

Natural Cycles
Natural cycles show how compounds are cycled through organisms and the environment.

The Nitrogen Cycle
Nitrogen is important for the synthesis of protein. It is absorbed by plants from the soil and is converted into protein. The plants can then be consumed by animals and used to make animal

protein. When plants and animals die, decomposers break down the protein and return nitrates to the soil. Animals return nitrates to the soil in the form of urea, which is excreted and forms ammonia.

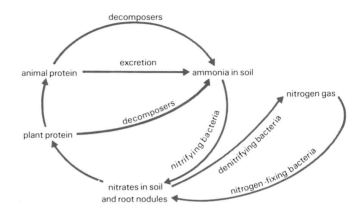

Sources of Nitrogen

Plants obtain nitrates from the soil from two types of bacteria.

1. Nitrogen-fixing Bacteria

Nitrogen-fixing bacteria absorb nitrogen gas from the air in the soil and convert it into nitrates which the plants can absorb through their roots. These bacteria can live either free in the soil or attached to plants, e.g. pea and bean, in the root nodules.

2. Nitrifying Bacteria

Nitrifying bacteria convert ammonia in the soil into nitrates if oxygen is present in the air in the soil. A rich source of ammonia is the excretory products of animals, i.e. manure and treated sewage.

Denitrifying Bacteria

Denitrifying bacteria break down nitrates into nitrogen gas which is returned to the atmosphere. This process does not require oxygen and so it will occur in waterlogged soil.

Fertilisers

Nitrates can be added to the soil in the form of inorganic fertilisers. Intensive farming methods result in high levels of nitrate being removed from the soil by the crops. This nitrate must be replaced in the soil in the form of fertiliser. Excessive use of nitrates leads to *leaching* (draining) of the chemicals from soil into rivers. This occurs particularly in sandy soils, since they do not retain fertilisers as well as clay soils. Rivers become polluted and the level of nitrates in drinking water can rise to a dangerous level.

The Water Cycle

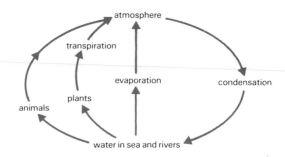

The water cycle describes how water circulates through animals, plants and the environment.

Water Balance If any part of the water cycle is altered even slightly, it can have a marked effect on the water balance.

Deforestation Destruction of large areas of forest can have serious effects on the water cycle and the environment.

Effects of Deforestation On Earth, vast areas of forest help to maintain the composition of air in the atmosphere. The trees absorb a large volume of carbon dioxide from the atmosphere during photosynthesis. They also release a large volume of oxygen and water vapour into the air. As the destruction of huge areas of forest continues, the composition of the atmosphere will change.

Increase in Carbon Dioxide The amount of carbon dioxide in the air will increase. Carbon dioxide is a gas which contributes to the condition called the greenhouse effect.

The Greenhouse Effect Heat energy from the sun passes easily through the gases in the atmosphere to the Earth. Some of it is reflected back into the atmosphere from the Earth's surface. Here, carbon dioxide traps the heat. The greater the amount of carbon dioxide in the atmosphere, the greater the amount of heat trapped. This raises the air temperature. Increasing the air temperature could result in the melting of the polar ice-caps. This would raise the level of the oceans and result in widespread flooding.

Methane, a waste gas produced by cattle in large amounts, also has the same effect as carbon dioxide increasing the greenhouse effect.

Soil Erosion Tree roots bind soil particles together, particularly on steep slopes. Removing trees causes the topsoil to be washed away by rainfall. This soil may block rivers and streams and cause widespread flooding of low-lying land.

Rainfall Trees return water to the atmosphere through transpiration. Fewer trees result in reduced transpiration and so rainfall decreases. This may lead to drought.

The Carbon Carbon is an element present in carbon dioxide gas in the
Cycle atmosphere.

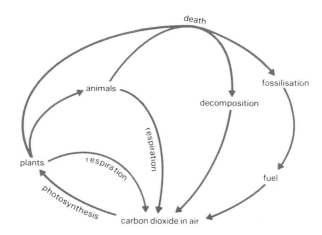

Photo- Carbon dioxide is absorbed by green plants during
synthesis photosynthesis and is used to make carbohydrates in the plant.
The carbohydrates stored in the plant can then be used by
animals as a source of energy.

Respiration Carbon dioxide is returned to the atmosphere by plants and
animals during respiration.

De- When plants and animals die, the decomposers break down the
composition stored carbohydrates in respiration and return carbon dioxide
to the atmosphere. Carbon dioxide is also produced from the
breakdown of organic waste, e.g. faeces from animals, by
bacteria and fungi.

Fossilisation Stored carbohydrates in dead plants and animals form fossil
fuels, e.g. wood, coal and oil. When these fuels are burned,
carbon dioxide is released into the atmosphere.

Pollution Scientists are becoming increasingly concerned over the
effects of pollution on water and land and in the air.

Water The removal of dissolved oxygen from rivers and streams
Pollution results in the death of the plants and animals which live in them
as they can no longer respire.

Anaerobic organisms, which respire without oxygen, break
down the dead organisms and produce methane gas as a waste
product.

79

Thermal Pollution of Water

Thermal pollution is caused by large volumes of warm water being discharged into a river. Less oxygen can dissolve in warm water than in cold water, and so less oxygen is available to the aquatic plants and animals for respiration when the water is warm.

Pollution by Sewage

Sewage contains large amounts of organic waste products from animals. It is rich in nitrates and phosphates which are essential nutrients for plants. When raw or untreated sewage is discharged into a river, the organic waste in the sewage stimulates the rapid growth of decomposers, e.g. bacteria and fungi.

The decomposers break down the organic material into carbon dioxide and water. Unfortunately, for this process they require oxygen which they absorb from the water. The level of dissolved oxygen decreases and so less oxygen is available to aquatic plants and animals for respiration and they die.

Treated sewage has had all the organic matter removed from it. However, the effluent which remains contains high concentrations of nitrates and phosphates. Together, these form a powerful nutrient which stimulates the rapid growth of microscopic plants called algae which live in water.

As they grow, the algae remove the oxygen from the water. Eventually, they form a green scum which covers the surface of the river or stream. This process, called *eutrophication*, prevents light from entering the water. Plants living on the river bed cannot photosynthesise and so they die. Animals in the river are deprived of food and oxygen when the plants die and so their numbers quickly decrease.

Land Pollution

Pollution of land is caused mainly by chemicals, including fertilisers, insecticides and herbicides, and by the disposal of rubbish.

The vast amounts of rubbish produced by humans are usually disposed of by burning or by being buried in landfill sites. Recently, however, old landfill sites which have now been built on have been found to be producing methane gas. This is a highly inflammable gas produced by the bacteria which break down the rubbish.

Air Pollution

The burning of fossil fuels, e.g. coal, gas and oil, is the most serious cause of air pollution. Burning coal releases large amounts of dust particles into the atmosphere. These blacken buildings and can damage the lungs. Carbon monoxide is produced from burning fossil fuels (page 27).

Most coal contains sulphur, which produces sulphur dioxide when the coal is burned.

Acid Rain Sulphur dioxide is a colourless, poisonous gas and it is oxidised by air to form sulphuric acid. When it rains, the sulphuric acid returns to Earth as a constituent of acid rain. The main damage caused by acid rain has been to rivers, trees and buildings. The acidic water in lakes kills the plants growing in the water. Fish and other animals soon die because of a shortage of food and oxygen. Acid rain dissolves minerals from the soil and this can have an adverse effect on the growth of trees. Metals, concrete and stone are broken down by the acid rain.

The amount of acid rain in Britain has been reduced due to the decrease in the amount of coal burned. Tall chimneys carry the gases from power-stations high into the atmosphere. The gases are then carried away from Britain, but are thought to have widespread effects in Scandinavia. In these countries, the gases leave the atmosphere as acid rain and have been responsible for the pollution and destruction of many lakes and forests.

Exhaust Nitrogen oxides are gases produced from car exhaust fumes. In Fumes the air, they are converted to nitrogen dioxide which is extremely toxic and irritating to the lungs. It can also be converted to nitric acid which is a constituent of acid rain.

Smog When nitrogen dioxide is produced in sunlight, it forms ozone. This is one of the gases present in smog. Smog, which is found in low-lying cities such as Los Angeles, is a very toxic and irritating mixture of gases.

Lead Lead is an air pollutant produced by cars. Petrol contains lead, Pollution which is then released into the atmosphere when the petrol is burned. Lead kills vegetation, and in young children it has been shown to cause brain damage. The amount of lead in the air can be reduced by the use of lead-free petrol.

Destruction The ozone layer is a layer of gases which surrounds the Earth. It of the Ozone protects the Earth from harmful radiation from the sun by Layer filtering out this radiation. Destruction of the ozone layer would increase the incidence of skin cancer caused by this harmful radiation. Recently, holes have been detected in the ozone layer above the North and South Poles.

The Sciences

MATERIALS AND THEIR PROPERTIES

8 What Materials Are Made Of

Chemistry Chemistry is the science concerned with the properties of different kinds of matter and the way in which one kind of matter reacts with another kind. Matter is composed of individual particles.

Evidence for Existence of Individual Particles

Diffusion Diffusion is the gradual mixing of one substance with another.

Examples of gas diffusion
1. The steam from a boiling kettle spreads throughout a room.
2. A gas jar of clear air on top of a gas jar of brown bromine (heavier than air) slowly mixes to form a lighter brown gas mixture.
3. A long tube with source of hydrogen chloride gas at one end and ammonia at the other slowly produces a white cloud at the end nearer the hydrogen chloride source. Why?

Because the ammonia is lighter (M_r = 17) than hydrogen chloride (M_r = 36.5) and so diffuses faster.

Examples of liquid diffusion
1. A dark crystal of potassium manganate (VII) added to a beaker of water slowly dissolves to give a purple solution.
2. The purple solution of potassium manganate (VII), when diluted with an equal amount of water, is still purple (but lighter); and with continued dilution, the purple colour (potassium manganate (VII) particles) can still be seen. The particles are spreading throughout the solution.

States of Matter There are three states of matter:

solid (s),

liquid (l),

gas (g).

The symbol in brackets is referred to as the state symbol.

The symbol (aq) is the symbol used to refer to *aqueous* (water) *solutions*.

Changes of State

$$\text{SOLID} \underset{\text{freezing}}{\overset{\text{melting}}{\rightleftharpoons}} \text{LIQUID} \underset{\text{condensation}}{\overset{\text{boiling or evaporation}}{\rightleftharpoons}} \text{GAS}$$

Melting point   Melting point (m.p.) is the temperature at which a solid melts to a liquid. A pure substance all melts at one constant temperature. Freezing point (f.p.) refers to the change from liquid to solid.

Boiling point   Boiling point (b.p.) is the constant temperature at which a pure liquid boils.

> Note: Boiling point is dependent on atmospheric pressure:
> lower pressure (e.g. up a mountain) → lower b.p.;
> higher pressure (e.g. pressure cooker) → higher b.p.

M.p. of impure solid   The m.p. of an impure solid is *lower* than that of pure substances (e.g. when salt is added to ice on roads).

B.p. of impure liquid   The b.p. of an impure liquid is *higher* than that of pure solvent.

Time-Temperature Graphs   If steady heat is applied to a solid and the temperature is recorded, a graph like this is obtained. Examine the graph and decide what is happening at each stage.

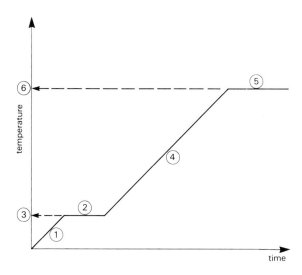

Stage 1   The solid absorbs heat on being warmed.

Stage 2   The solid uses absorbed heat to melt at a constant temperature.

Stage 3   Melting point.

Stage 4   The liquid absorbs heat as its temperature rises.

Stage 5   The liquid uses absorbed heat to boil at a constant temperature.

Stage 6   Boiling point.

Solutions and Solubility

Solute	The solute is the substance (solid, liquid or gas) dissolving in a solvent.
Solvent	The solvent is the liquid in which a solute dissolves to give a solution.
Solution	The solution is the mixture obtained.
Example	Salt (solute) in water (solvent) → salt solution.
Common solvents	Water, petrol, perchloroethene (used in dry-cleaning), alcohol, ether.
Saturated solution	A saturated solution is one in which as much solute is dissolved as possible at a particular temperature.
Solubility	Solubility is a measure of the amount of solute which can dissolve in a solvent. It is defined as: *the number of grams of solute which dissolve in 100 grams of the solvent at a particular temperature to give a saturated solution.*
Solubility of solids	Generally, the solubility of a solid increases as the temperature increases, but it is not linear (i.e. solubility does *not* double when temperature doubles).
Solubility of gases	Gases dissolve in liquids.
Example 1	Oxygen (in air) dissolves in water enabling plant and animal life in rivers and lakes to survive.
Example 2	Carbon dioxide dissolves in rain water giving an acidic solution, which may fall on limestone rocks, giving a type of hard water.
Effect of temperature	As the temperature increases, less gas dissolves.
Effect of pressure	If the pressure is increased, more gas will dissolve in a liquid, i.e. fizzy drinks.

Mixtures	Mixtures are made of more than one pure substance.
Pure Substances	Pure substances may be elements existing on their own or may be compounds.
Elements	Elements are pure substances that contain only one kind of atom.
Compounds	Compounds are pure substances containing more than one element. They have their own properties which are characteristic for the compound.

Differences between Mixtures and Compounds

	Mixture	Compound
Composition	Composition can be variable (i.e. any amount of each component).	Composition is fixed (i.e. the elements are present in a fixed ratio).
Properties	The properties are those possessed by each of the components.	The properties are characteristic for the particular compound.
Separation	Separation into the component pure substances can be achieved by physical means (i.e. not by a chemical reaction).	Separation into component elements can not be achieved by physical means.

Example	Mixture: iron powder and sulphur powder	Compound: iron (II) sulphide
Composition	—	Iron and sulphur atoms present in a constant ratio of 1:1. (Formula: FeS).
Properties	1. The mixture has appearance of grey with yellow specks (iron, powder-grey; sulphur, powder-yellow).	1. The compound is dark grey/black solid in appearance.
	2. The mixture reacts with dilute hydrochloric acid to evolve a gas which explodes when ignited in air,* i.e. iron + hydrochloric acid →hydrogen + iron (II) chloride or Fe(s) + 2HCl(aq) →H$_2$(g) + FeCl$_2$(aq)	2. The compound reacts with dilute hydrochloric acid to give off a gas with a smell of rotten eggs, i.e. iron (II) sulphide + hydrochloric acid →hydrogen sulphide + iron (II) chloride or FeS(s) + 2HCl(aq) →H$_2$S(g) + FeCl$_2$(aq)

*Pure iron powder has the same reaction.

87

Example *cont'd*	Mixture: iron powder and sulphur powder	Compound: iron (II) sulphide
	3. When ignited, burns with a blue flame giving off a gas with a choking smell,* i.e. sulphur + oxygen →sulphur dioxide or $S(s) + O_2(g) \to SO_2(g)$ *Pure sulphur burns in the same way.	3. Iron (II) sulphide does not burn.
Separation	A magnet will separate the iron from the mixture.	

Note: When the mixture of iron and sulphur powder is heated, a highly *exothermic* (see page 149) reaction occurs and iron (II) sulphide is formed.

iron + sulphur → iron (II) sulphide
$Fe(s) + S(s) \quad \to FeS(s)$

This is a chemical change.

Separation of Mixtures   In order to separate mixtures, we need to employ differences in the physical properties of the components.

Differences   These may be differences of, for instance, solubility or boiling point.

Experimental Techniques   We rely on various experimental techniques.

Dissolution   Dissolution is dissolving a substance, the *solute* (see page 86), in a solvent.

Filtration   Filtration is adding a mixture of a solid and liquid to a filter paper folded into a filter funnel. The solid remains in the paper as a residue while the liquid passes through as the filtrate.

Distillation   Distillation is the technique where a liquid mixture is boiled so that the components vaporise and condense in order of increasing boiling point (i.e. the liquid with the lowest boiling point boils first).

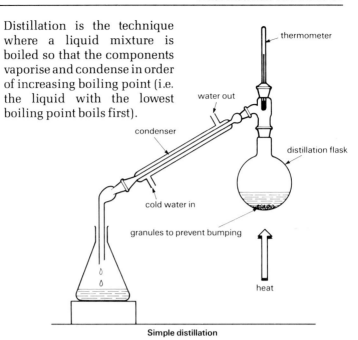

Simple distillation

Fractional distillation   This is as for distillation, but the apparatus includes a 'fractionating' column between the distillation flask and the condenser.

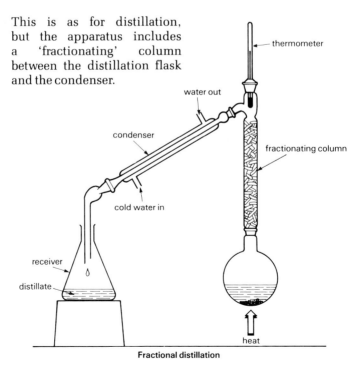

Fractional distillation

89

Evaporation   Evaporation is boiling a liquid mixture of a solid dissolved in a solvent to evaporate the unwanted solvent and leave the solid.

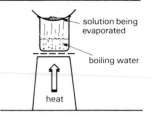

Chromato-   In chromatography, a spot of the liquid mixture is placed near
graphy   the bottom of paper, which is then dipped in a solvent below the spot. The components in the mixture rise up the paper at different rates and are separated as coloured spots.

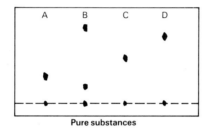 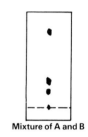

Pure substances   Mixture of A and B

**Types of
Separation**

Solid from a   Consider sand and water.
liquid in
which it is   The technique used is *filtration*. (The residue must be washed).
insoluble

Solid from its   Consider salt in water.
solution in an
unwanted   The technique used is *evaporation*. (Care must be taken not to
solvent   heat the remaining solid too much in case it decomposes.) This can safely be achieved using a water bath.

Two liquids   Consider water and alcohol.
which are
mixed   The technique used is *distillation*, based on the differing boiling points of the two liquids.
    When the boiling points are close together, or when the mixture is more complicated, then *fractional distillation* is used. The condensed liquids obtained at different stages are called *fractions*.

Coloured   Consider dyes; also, food colouring.
substances in
dyes   The technique used is *chromatography*.

Two solids   Consider potassium nitrate and potassium chloride in water.
dissolved in
the same   The technique used is *crystallisation*, based on the different
solvent   solubilities of the solids (see page 86).

Two solids, one of which sublimes on heating

Consider salt and iodine.

The technique is to *heat and allow the vapour of one of the solids to settle on a cool surface*. The iodine sublimes. (*Sublimation* is the process whereby, on heating, a solid is converted directly from solid to vapour, i.e. it does not melt to a liquid.)

Industrial Separation

Petroleum

The components of petroleum (crude oil) are treated in an oil refinery, initially by fractional distillation. The vapour separates into 'fractions' with different boiling ranges from low-boiling gas and petrol fractions to high boiling bitumen. (See page 140 for a table of the fractions).

Air

Air is first liquified by a series of cooling/compression steps. The liquid air formed is separated into its components by fractional distillation. Nitrogen boils first at −196°C before oxygen at −183°C. (Remember that −196°C is a lower temperature than −183°C.) Other useful products are noble gases like argon, neon and helium.

9 | How Materials Are Held Together

Pure Substances The materials obtained by separation (in Chapter 8) are those of pure substances. Pure substances can be broken down into even smaller particles called *atoms*. These atoms usually are quite different in properties from the original substance.

Atoms Atoms are the smallest particles of individual elements and have their own properties.

Elements Elements of about 100 different types of atom exist. Of these 100 types, about 90 occur naturally; the other 10 or so are made by scientists in a laboratory or reactor. Each element is given a name and a symbol.

Chemical Symbol A chemical symbol comprises one capital letter, or one capital followed by a small letter.

Examples

Name of element	Symbol for element
hydrogen	H
chlorine	Cl
iron	Fe
nitrogen	N
sodium	Na
zinc	Zn

> Note: You will probably have to be familiar with only about 30 elements and will have a data book to refer to. Check up on this.

Atoms and Molecules

Existence Atoms of many elements cannot exist on their own and have to combine with other atoms of either the same element or other elements to form molecules.

Molecules Molecules are defined as a group of atoms which are *bonded* (joined) together and which can exist as separate units.

Example Hydrogen (H) atoms cannot exist as single atoms but two hydrogen atoms bond to form the hydrogen molecule, H_2.

Hydrogen bonds with different atoms to form molecules such as water, H_2O.

Ions Ions are atoms or molecules which undergo a change and exist as charged particles.

Structure of the Atom

small heavy centre   surrounded by very light particles

Nucleus The nucleus is the small heavy centre of the atom, and consists of one or more protons and (except in the case of the smallest atom of hydrogen) one or more neutrons.

	Mass	Charge
proton	1	+ 1
neutron	1	0
electron	negligible	− 1
atom as a whole	sum of masses	0
ion (see below)	sum of masses	plus or minus

Atomic Number or Proton Number (Z) The atomic number (Z) is a number characteristic of a particular element, that represents the number of protons in the nucleus of an atom of that element.

Example 1 All hydrogen atoms contain 1 proton, so the atomic number of hydrogen is 1 (Z = 1).

Example 2 All chlorine atoms contain 17 protons, so the atomic number is 17 (Z = 17).

Mass Number or Nucleon Number (A) The mass number (A) is the sum of protons and neutrons in the nucleus of an atom. This can vary for an element.

Isotopes Isotopes are atoms of the same element (same atomic number and same number of protons) but with different numbers of neutrons (different mass number).

Example Chlorine (Z = 17) has two isotopes:
Cl (A = 35) – containing 17 protons and 18 neutrons, and
Cl (A = 37) – containing 17 protons and 20 neutrons.

Chemical similarity Because isotopes have the same number of protons and electrons, isotopes of an element are chemically similar.

Nuclides Nuclides are the nuclei of specified isotopes and are written as, for instance, $^{37}_{17}Cl$.

$$A \rightarrow 37$$
$$Z \rightarrow 17$$ Cl

Isotopes in everyday life Many isotopes occur naturally and are present in the normal chemicals we use frequently:

chlorine – $^{35}_{17}Cl$ and $^{37}_{17}Cl$
copper – $^{63}_{29}Cu$ and $^{65}_{29}Cu$
hydrogen – $^{1}_{1}H$ (hydrogen), $^{2}_{1}H$ (deuterium) and $^{3}_{1}H$ (tritium).

Radioactivity Some nuclei are unstable and spontaneously disintegrate. The protons and neutrons are not held together strongly enough. Atoms with such nuclei are described as being radioactive, emitting radiation which is able to ionise molecules it strikes.

Types of Ionising Radiation *Alpha (α) radiation* consists of heavy, positively-charged particles.

Alpha particles have low penetrating power. They travel about 3-4 cm in air and can be stopped by a sheet of paper. They have high speeds ~ 10^7 m/s.
- are deflected by a magnetic field.
- are capable of strong ionisation of gases.
- are very intense over short distances.
- do not penetrate skin.

Beta (β) radiation consists of light, negatively-charged particles.

Beta particles have intermediate penetrating power. They travel about 1 m in air and can be stopped by a thin sheet of aluminium or clothing.
They have high speeds – they can travel at speeds approaching that of light in air $(3 \times 10^8$ m/s).
- are deflected by a weak magnetic field.
- will be deflected in the opposite direction to that of an α particle.
- can penetrate skin to reach sensitive body tissues.

Gamma (γ) radiation is similar to X-rays. It consists of electromagnetic waves of very short wavelength (high energy).

Gamma rays are extremely penetrating. They can travel several hundred metres in air and can penetrate the whole body.
Lead reduces very effectively the propagation of γ rays but does not stop them completely.
They travel at the speed of light in a vacuum.
- are not deflected by a magnetic field.
- produce weak ionisation of gases.

Sources of Radiation

Natural radiation is found from some rocks, from air and from outer space. These give rise to ever-present 'background radiation'.
Man-made radiation is formed as a result of bombarding nuclei with radiation or with neutrons, etc.

Radioactive

Hazards Associated with Radioactive Emission

The effects of external β radiation are mainly confined to the body surface. Protective clothing can provide virtually complete shielding against β radiation. The greatest hazard with β emitting isotopes is when they are ingested in food or water or inhaled into the lungs. However, we all have measurable quantities of α emitters inside us. The source is radon emanating from the Earth, decaying into Po-210 which finishes up in our food and drinking water.

Neutrons are capable of being absorbed in another nucleus and β particles or γ rays (and to a lesser degree α particles) are emitted as by-products.

X-rays and γ rays are extremely penetrating and cause the least damage per unit of distance travelled, but they penetrate further into the body. β radiation, X-rays and γ rays can cause radiation burns.

Safety Precautions When Using Radioactive Materials

For industrial sources:
1. Surround strong sources with a material such as lead or concrete.
2. Work behind shielding or at a distance from the radiation source.
3. Use remote handling techniques.
4. Monitor working area with, for example, a Geiger counter.
5. Monitor air content.
6. Wear protective clothing.
7. Limit time spent with source.
8. Have washing facilities available.
9. Wear a film badge – part of the film is covered by a cadmium shield which only γ rays can penetrate. The unshielded area will blacken more readily, being accessible to both γ rays and β particles. It is thus possible to distinguish between the dose of each of these radiations received by an individual. By including two films of different sensitivities one can check the dosage received weekly and over a longer period.
10. Maintain high standards of cleanliness.

Detection of Radiation	*Photographic film* is exposed in the presence of radiation (intensity of blackness of developed film indicates degree of exposure). *Geiger-Müller (G.M.) detectors* produce impulses when exposed to ionising radiation.
Half-Life $(t_{\frac{1}{2}})$	Half-life is the time taken for the activity of a radioisotope to decay to half of its original value. Symbol $t_{\frac{1}{2}}$. Half-lives of different substances vary over a very wide range from less than a millionth of a second to more than a million years, e.g. polonium-212 has a half-life of 3×10^{-7} s whilst uranium-235 has a half-life of 7×10^8 years.
Uses of Radioisotopes:	
γ Rays	γ rays can kill bacteria in food. They can kill cancer cells in a patient. They can also sterilise medical instruments even after these have been sealed in a plastic container.
Carbon Dating	Carbon-14 has a half-life of 5600 years. Living things including plants take in and give out C-14 whilst alive. When dead, they no longer take in C-14; and by measuring the activity present in, for example, a sample of wood or linen, it is possible to estimate the age of it. Using a new method of carbon dating, laboratories in Arizona, Oxford and Zürich have shown that linen from the Turin Shroud dates from the period 1260-1390 and *not* from the time of Jesus Christ.
Thickness Gauge	The thickness of metal, paper and plastic sheets can be controlled automatically. If a G.M. tube is placed on one side of a moving sheet of material in line with a suitable radioisotope placed on the other side, then as the count rate increases the thickness decreases and vice versa. Use of appropriate instrumentation ensures the count rate is constant, i.e. the sheet thickness is constant.
Tracers	The progress of a radioisotope injected into a *system* (including the human body) can be followed using, for example, a G.M. tube. Tumours in a person take up more radioisotope than other parts of the body and so can be located.
	Injection of a radioisotope into an oil or a gas pipeline enables leaks to be located.
Relative Atomic Mass (A_r)	Relative atomic mass (A_r) is a measure of the mass of the 'average' atom of an element (taking into account the masses of the various isotopes present) on a scale which uses the carbon-12 isotope as its base.

Example   Chlorine-35, present as 75% of Cl atoms.
Chlorine-37, present as 25% of Cl atoms.

Average mass (A_r) = (75% of 35) + (25% of 37) = 35.5
(Most values of A_r are approximated to whole numbers for GCSE use).

Relative Formula Mass (M_r)   Relative formula mass (M_r) is a measure of the mass of the average 'molecule' of a compound on the same scale as A_r. It is obtained by adding up the values of A_r for the different elements, taking into account the numbers of atoms of each element in the formula.

Example 1 H_2O

$A_r(H)$ = 1, $A_r(O)$ = 16

$M_r(H_2O)$ = $\underset{H}{1}$ + $\underset{H}{1}$ + $\underset{O}{16}$

= 18

Example 2 $(NH_4)_2CO_3$

$A_r(N)$ = 14, $A_r(H)$ = 1, $A_r(C)$ = 12, $A_r(O)$ = 16

$M_r[(NH_4)_2CO_3]$ = $2 \times (\underset{N}{14} + \underset{H}{1} + \underset{H}{1} + \underset{H}{1} + \underset{H}{1}) + \underset{C}{12} + \underset{O}{16} + \underset{O}{16} + \underset{O}{16}$

= 96

Example 3 $CuSO_4.5H_2O$

(In examples where there is water of crystallisation the M_r for $5H_2O$ must be added to M_r for $CuSO_4$.)

$A_r(Cu)$ = 64, $A_r(S)$ = 32, $A_r(O)$ = 16, $M_r(H_2O)$ = 18

$M_r(CuSO_4.5H_2O)$ = $\underset{Cu}{64} + \underset{S}{32} + \underset{O}{16} + \underset{O}{16} + \underset{O}{16} + \underset{O}{16} + (5 \times \underset{H_2O}{18})$

= 250

Arrangement of Electrons

Energy Levels   Electrons exist at a distance from the nucleus, dependent on the amount of energy they possess (the more energy, the further away). Electrons can possess only certain amounts of energy, so that energy levels exist at which electrons can be found. At each level there is a maximum possible number of electrons.

Maximum Number of Electrons

	K shell	L shell	M shell	N shell
nucleus $\oplus$	(1st energy level)	(2nd energy level)	(3rd energy level)	(4th energy level)
	2 electrons MAXIMUM	8 electrons MAXIMUM	8 electrons MAXIMUM*	

increasing energy →

*This maximum is revised in more advanced courses.

| Filling Energy Levels | Electrons will always be at the lowest level possible until the maximum number of electrons is present. |

Example 1   *Oxygen* (Z = 8).
Since the atom is neutral, there will be 8 electrons as well as 8 protons.

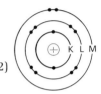

level	K	L
electrons	2 (full)	6

$$(2 + 6 = 8)$$

Example 2   *Magnesium* (Z = 12).

level	K	L	M
electrons	2 (full)	8 (full)	2

$$(2 + 8 + 2 = 12)$$

Example 3   *Neon* (Z = 10).

level	K	L
electrons	2 (full)	8 (full)

$$(2 + 8 = 10)$$

Bonding of Atoms

Noble gases   Electron arrangements for some of these unreactive elements are as follows.

	K	L	M	N	
He	2				⎫
Ne	2	8			⎬ all full levels
Ar	2	8	8		⎭

Reactive metals		K	L	M	N	
	Na	2	8	1		⎫ 1 electron in
	K	2	8	8	1	⎬ outermost level

Reactive non-metals		K	L	M	
	F	2	7		⎫ 1 electron less
	Cl	2	8	7	⎬ than full in outermost level

Reason for bonding   Atoms bond with each other to form compounds in order to become more stable (less reactive). They do this by getting an electron arrangement like that of a noble gas (above), by gaining, losing or sharing electrons (e^-).

Electron Transfer   Na atom 2, 8, 1 (1 e^- too many)
Cl atom 2, 8, 7 (1 e^- too few)

Sodium gives its outer electron to chlorine:

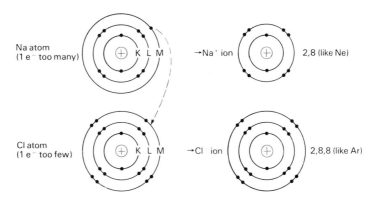

Ions The Na$^+$ ion now has 11 protons ($+$)
 but 10 electrons ($-$),

i.e. 1 more proton than electrons (hence $+$ve charge on ion).

The Cl$^-$ ion now has 17 protons ($+$)
 but 18 electrons ($-$),

i.e. 1 more electron than protons (hence $-$ve charge on ion).

Ionic bonding The Na$^+$ and the Cl$^-$ ion are then attracted (opposite charges attract) to form sodium chloride:

Na$^+$ + Cl$^-$ → NaCl
 sodium chloride

in which the ions are held together by an ionic bond.

Note: The new compound formed by ionic bonding has quite different properties from the component elements.

Magnesium Chloride If magnesium reacts with chlorine:

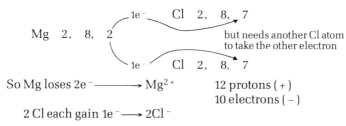

So Mg loses 2e$^-$ ⟶ Mg^{2+} 12 protons ($+$)
 10 electrons ($-$)

2 Cl each gain 1e$^-$ ⟶ 2Cl$^-$

The compound formed is written as MgCl$_2$.

Electron Sharing When electrons are *shared* between two atoms, a covalent bond is formed.

Example 1 Hydrogen.
2 hydrogen atoms share 2 electrons to form H_2.

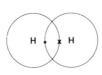

Each atom "thinks" it has $2e^-$ and so has the e^- arrangement of He.
The bond is represented thus:
H — H

Example 2 Chlorine.
2 chlorine atoms share 2 electrons (1 from each) to form Cl_2.

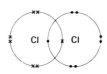

Each atom now has 8 electrons in outer level 7 of its own and 1 belonging to other atom).
The bond is represented thus:
Cl — Cl

Note: In 'dot-cross' diagrams like these, only the outermost energy levels are drawn.

Example 3 Hydrogen chloride.

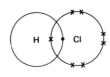

. . . forming HCl, hydrogen chloride
The bond is represented thus:
H — Cl

Example 4 Water.

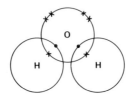

. . . forming H_2O, water
The bonding is represented:
H — O — H

Example 5   Ammonia.

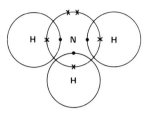

... forming NH_3, ammonia
The bonding is represented:

Example 6   Methane.

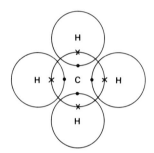

... forming CH_4, methane
The bonding is represented:

Bonding in Metals   Metals are composed of atoms with a small number of electrons in the outer energy level (e.g. sodium, magnesium). In the solid state these electrons are released to move throughout the metal structure, rather like a cloud or sea of electrons. These electrons form a kind of 'glue' holding the atoms together.

This is called metallic bonding.

Bond Type and Properties   The properties of a compound depend on the bonds between atoms and the bonds holding molecules to each other.
Monatomic gases like helium and neon exist as single atoms, with only very weak bonds between them.

Simple molecules   *Hydrogen.*
H — H; strong covalent bonds between atoms. Weak bonds between H_2 molecules. Hydrogen is therefore a gas at room temperature.

Water.
H_2O; strong covalent bonds between H and O. Fairly strong bonds between water molecules, so they are more difficult to separate – water is a liquid at room temperature.

101

Paraffin Wax.
Strong covalent bonds between atoms. Bonds between the molecules are strong enough to make paraffin wax a solid at room temperature.

Giant molecular (or macro- molecular solids)

Some solids occur with covalent bonds which are not restricted to a few atoms in a molecule but are spread throughout a large structure. These are called giant molecular (or macro- molecular) solids.

Diamond.
A very hard substance with a high melting point. *Each* carbon atom is at the centre of a tetrahedron surrounded by four other carbon atoms.

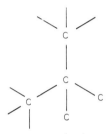

All covalent bonds are the same strength. The hardness of diamond makes it useful to tip drill bits. It is a non-conductor of electricity.

Graphite.
Carbon atoms arranged in layers. The bonds in the layers are strong, but those holding the layers together are weak, so the layers can slide over one another.

Graphite conducts electricity (due to free electrons moving between layers). Its softness makes it useful in pencil 'leads'.

Poly(ethene).
A very large molecule made up of carbon and hydrogen.

Ionic solids

Ionic solids are arranged regularly in a pattern or lattice so that the maximum attraction of opposite ions is obtained, as for instance with sodium chloride.

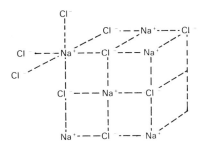

Each Na$^+$ is surrounded by 6 Cl$^-$ and each Cl$^-$ is surrounded by 6 Na$^+$.

Ionic solids have fairly high melting points (sodium chloride melts at 801°C) since the strong attractive forces between the ions have to be overcome in order to separate them to form a liquid.

Differences in Property between Ionic and Covalent Compounds

	Ionic compounds	Covalent compounds
Melting point	fairly high	generally low (except for giant covalent compounds)
Boiling point	fairly high	—
Solubility in water	generally soluble	generally insoluble
Solubility in organic solvents	insoluble	generally soluble
Electrical conductivity	solid state – no conductivity; molten state – good conductor; aqueous soln – good conductors	do not conduct (the exception is graphite)

10 Writing and Counting Chemicals

Ionic Compounds The formulae for ions you have met up to now (e.g. Na^+, Mg^{2+}, Cl^-) are for simple ions composed of one element only. Other simple ions are:

Positive Ions				Negative ions	
hydrogen	H^+	iron (II)	Fe^{2+}	bromide	Br^-
lithium	Li^+	lead	Pb^{2+}	fluoride	F^-
potassium	K^+	zinc	Zn^{2+}	iodide	I^-
silver	Ag^+				
calcium	Ca^{2+}	aluminium	Al^{3+}	oxide	O^{2-}
copper (II)	Cu^{2+}	iron (III)	Fe^{3+}	sulphide	S^{2-}
barium	Ba^{2+}				

More complex ions are also common. These consist of atoms of more than one element bonded together, but with a charge on the whole ion.

Positive ion		Negative ions		
ammonium	NH_4^+	hydroxide	OH^-	carbonate CO_3^{2-}
		nitrate	NO_3^-	sulphate SO_4^{2-}
		hydrogen-carbonate	HCO_3^-	phosphate PO_4^{3-}

Writing Ionic Formulae A correct ionic formula shows the number of positive and negative ions necessary to 'balance' the electrons donated by the positive ion and accepted by the negative ion, i.e. balance the charges.

Example 1 Sodium oxide (Na^+ with O^{2-}).
Two Na^+ needed (total 2^+) to balance one O^{2-} (total 2^-).

∴ formula = Na_2O

The balancing 2 needs to be written as a subscript after the Na.

Example 2 Aluminium sulphide (Al^{3+} with S^{2-}).
Two Al^{3+} needed (total 6^+) to balance three S^{2-} (total 6^-).

∴ formula = Al_2S_3

Note: When complex ions are involved, you must remember to put the whole ion in brackets *if more than one of it is needed*, with the subscript outside the bracket.

Example 3 *Calcium nitrate* (Ca^{2+} with NO_3^-).

One Ca^{2+} needed (total $2+$) to balance two NO_3^- (total $2-$).

$\therefore$ formula = $Ca(NO_3)_2$

Example 4 *Ammonium sulphate* (NH_4^+ with SO_4^{2-}).

Two NH_4^+ needed (total $2+$) to balance one SO_4^{2-} (total $2-$).

$\therefore$ formula = $(NH_4)_2SO_4$

Example 5 *Potassium hydroxide* (K^+ with OH^-).

One K^+ needed (total $1+$) to balance one OH^- (total $1-$).

$\therefore$ formula = KOH (no brackets needed)

Note:
1. The positive ion is always written first.
2. Never write the balancing numbers anywhere other than to the lower right of the ion.

Covalent Compounds The number of electrons to be shared by an atom is often called its valency. In a similar way to ionic compounds, the total number of electrons shared by each atom must balance.

Example 1 *Water* [H(valency = 1) with O(valency = 2)].

$\therefore$ formula = H_2O

Example 2 *Ammonia* [N(valency = 3) with H(valency = 1)].

$\therefore$ formula = NH_3

Chemical Equations

What is a chemical equation? A chemical equation is a shorthand representation of what happens in a chemical change. It shows which chemicals are involved and, in a symbol equation, the ratio of the numbers of molecules of reactants to products.

Reactants Reactants are the chemicals started with.

Products Products are the chemicals formed.

REACTANTS $\longrightarrow$ PRODUCTS
give on reaction

Word equation e.g. iron + sulphur → iron (II) sulphide

Symbol Equation Fe(s) + S(s) → FeS(s)

Law of conservation of mass The law of conservation of mass is a basic law of nature which means that you finish a chemical reaction with the same amount of each element as you started with.

105

Balancing an equation	We have to make sure that the same number of atoms of each element appear on both sides of the equation without changing any correct formulae.

Example 1   iron   + hydrochloric acid → iron (II) chloride + hydrogen.

Correct formulae $Fe(s)$ + $HCl(aq)$ ⟶ $FeCl_2(aq)$ + $H_2(g)$
(unbalanced)

LHS   Fe   1   RHS   Fe   1

H   1   H   2

Cl   1   Cl   2

Balancing the equation	To balance you need to adjust the number of molecules of a substance by putting a new number *in front*. Note that the number 1 is understood.

If a 2 is put in front of HCl you get:

$Fe(S)$ + $2HCl(aq)$ ⟶ $FeCl_2(aq)$ + $H_2(g)$
(balanced)

Example 2   iron (III) oxide + hydrogen → iron   + steam.

Correct formulae $Fe_2O_3(s)$ + $H_2(g)$ ⟶ $Fe(s)$ + $H_2O(g)$

Balance O $Fe_2O_3(s)$ + $H_2(g)$ ⟶ $Fe(s)$ + $3H_2O(g)$

Balance H $Fe_2O_3(s)$ + $3H_2(g)$ ⟶ $Fe(s)$ + $3H_2O(g)$

Balance Fe $Fe_2O_3(s)$ + $3H_2(g)$ ⟶ 2 $Fe(s)$ + $3H_2O(g)$
(balanced equation)

Example 3   sodium hydroxide   + copper (II) nitrate ⟶ copper (II) hydroxide + sodium nitrate.

Correct formulae $NaOH(aq)$ + $Cu(NO_3)_2(aq)$ → $Cu(OH)_2(s)$ + $NaNO_3(aq)$

Balance NO_3 group $NaOH(aq)$ + $Cu(NO_3)_2(aq)$ → $Cu(OH)_2(s)$ + $2NaNO_3(aq)$

Balance Na $2NaOH(aq)$ + $Cu(NO_3)_2(aq)$ → $Cu(OH)_2(s)$ + $2NaNO_3(aq)$

Check OH group and Cu   Both balanced – so equation is balanced.

The Mole (abbreviation = mol)	The mole is the unit of quantity of atoms, molecules, ions, etc. It represents a very large number (6×10^{23}) and is:

the number of atoms in 1 g of hydrogen [$A_r(H) = 1$]

in 12 g of carbon [$A_r(C) = 12$]

or in the relative atomic mass in grams of any element;

or the number of molecules in 2 g of hydrogen, $H_2[M_r(H_2) = 2]$

in 18 g of water, $H_2O[M_r(H_2O) = 18]$

in 250 g of $CuSO_4$, $5H_2O$ ($M_r = 250$)

or in the relative formula mass in grams of any molecule.

We don't have to talk about exactly 1 mole of particles but can talk about any number of moles (small or large).

Example 1 0.2 mol of water molecules have a mass of (0.2×18) g $= 3.6$ g.

4 mol of $CuSO_4$.$5H_2O$ molecules have a mass of (4×250) g $= 1000$ g.

3.5 mol of H_2 molecules have a mass of (3.5×2) g $= 7.0$ g.

Example 2 1.8 g of water contain $\frac{1.8}{18}$ mol ($= 0.1$ mol) of water molecules.

10.0 g of hydrogen contain $\frac{10.0}{1}$ mol ($= 10.0$ mol) of hydrogen *atoms.*

$\frac{10.0}{2}$ mol ($= 5.0$ mol) of hydrogen *molecules.*

Problems using Moles

Example 1 What is the mass of 1.5 mol of NaOH molecules?

$M_r(NaOH) = 23 + 16 + 1 = 40$

1 mol of NaOH molecules has a mass of 40 g ←————Always start with a statement of what you know.

∴1.5 mol have a mass of $(1.5 \times 40) = 60$ g

Example 2 What is the mass of 0.25 mol of H_2SO_4 molecules?

$M_r (H_2SO_4) = 2 + 32 + 64 = 98$

1 mol of H_2SO_4 molecules has a mass of 98 g

∴0.25 mol has a mass of $(0.25 \times 98) = 24.5$ g

Example 3 How many moles of FeS molecules are contained in 4.4 g FeS?

$M_r(FeS) = 56 + 32 = 88$

88 g of FeS is the mass of 1 mol

∴4.4 g of FeS is the mass of $\frac{4.4}{88} = 0.05$ mol

Molar Volume Molar volume is the volume occupied at a particular temperature and pressure by 1 mol of *any* gas particles. At room temperature and pressure (r.t.p.), the molar volume is 24 litres.

Examples 1 mol of H_2 gas occupies a volume of 24 l at r.t.p.

0.5 mol of CO_2 gas occupies a volume of 12 l at r.t.p.

Formula from Mass Composition

Given the mass of each element present in a compound, the formula may be found.

Example

An oxide of copper is found to contain 8 g of copper combined with 1 g of oxygen [$A_r(Cu) = 64$, $A_r(O) = 16$]. What is the formula?

	Cu	O
Mass	8 g	1 g
No. mol	$\dfrac{8}{64}(=0.125)$	$\dfrac{1}{16}(=0.0625)$

Simplest ratio

Divide by the lowest number of moles:

$$\frac{0.125}{0.0625} = 2 \qquad \frac{0.0625}{0.0625} = 1$$

Mole ratio

$Cu:O = 2:1$

$\therefore$ Formula $= Cu_2O$

Note: This is the simplest formula (called the empirical formula). We would need to know the relative formula mass to determine the actual (molecular) formula.

Calculations Based on Equations

Earlier in the Chapter we said that a chemical equation could be considered in terms of numbers of atoms, molecules, etc. Since a mole represents a very large fixed number of particles, we can also consider an equation in terms of moles.

Example

$2Mg(s)$	+	$O_2(g)$	$\rightarrow$	$2MgO(s)$
2 mol Mg atoms	react with	1 mol O_2 molecules	to give	2 mol MgO molecules
$[A_r(Mg) = 24]$		$[M_r(O_2) = 32]$		$[M_r(MgO) = 24 + 16$ $= 40]$

$\therefore (2 \times 24)$ g Mg $+$ 32 g O_2 $\rightarrow$ (2×40) g MgO

Note: The total mass of Mg and O_2 ($48 + 32 = 80$ g) is the same as the mass of MgO(80 g).

Calculations Based on Mass

Example 1

What mass of magnesium oxide will be formed when 6 g of magnesium ribbon is burned completely in oxygen?

Balanced equation

$2Mg(s) + O_2(g) \longrightarrow 2MgO(s)$

What we know and need from equation in moles	2 mol Mg $\longrightarrow$ 2 mol MgO	We don't need to consider the amount of oxygen since it is in excess, i.e. more than enough.
Convert to masses	48 g Mg $\longrightarrow$ 80 g MgO	
What are we asked?	$\therefore$ 6 g Mg $\longrightarrow$ $(80 \times \frac{6}{48})$ g MgO $\longrightarrow$ 10 g MgO	The fraction of Mg we take compared with our known $48\,g\,(\frac{6}{48})$ must be the same as the fraction of MgO we form.

Example 2 What mass of hydrogen will be formed when 0.092 g sodium reacts with excess water?

Balanced equation	$2Na(s) + 2H_2O(l) \longrightarrow 2NaOH(aq) + H_2(g)$	
Equation moles	2 mol Na $\longrightarrow$ 1 mol H_2	H_2O is in excess and we're not asked about NaOH.
Convert to masses	46 g Na $\longrightarrow$ 2 g H_2 $\therefore$ 0.092 g Na $\longrightarrow$ $(2 \times \frac{0.092}{46})$ g H_2 $\longrightarrow$ 0.004 g H_2	

Calculations Based on Volume Since we know the volume occupied by 1 mole of any gas at r.t.p. is 24 l, we can involve volumes in calculations.

Example What volume of hydrogen will be formed at room temperature and pressure, if 3 g magnesium reacts with hydrochloric acid?

Balanced equation	$Mg(s) + 2HCl(aq) \longrightarrow MgCl_2(aq) + H_2(g)$
Equation in moles	1 mol Mg $\longrightarrow$ 1 mol H_2
Convert to mass or vol as needed	24 g Mg $\longrightarrow$ 24 l H_2 $\therefore$ 3 g Mg $\longrightarrow$ $(24 \times \frac{3}{24})$ l H_2 $\longrightarrow$ 3 l H_2 at r.t.p.

Concentration of Solutions The concentration of a solution is expressed as:

grams in 1 l of solution (g/l),

or moles in 1 l of solution (mol/l).

It doesn't matter how much solution we have since, to write the concentration, we scale up (or down) to a volume of 1 l, i.e. we write down how many grams or moles would be contained in 1 litre of solution of the same concentration.

Example 1 g of NaOH in 100 cm^3 solution is equivalent to:

$(1 \times \dfrac{1000}{100})$ g NaOH in 100 $\times \dfrac{1000}{100}$($= 1000$ cm^3) solution (or 1 l)

that is to say, 10 g NaOH in 1 l

$\therefore$ concentration of NaOH $= 10$ g/l

Converting g/l to mol/l Since the relative formula mass in grams is the mass of 1 mole, g/l can be converted to mol/l by dividing by M_r. Thus, from the above example:

Concentration of NaOH $= 10$ g/l

$= \dfrac{10}{40}$ mol/l [M_r(NaOH) $= 40$]

$= 0.25$ mol/l

Example 25 g H_2SO_4 is contained in 5 l of solution. What is the concentration in (a) g/l, (b) mol/l?

25 g H_2SO_4 in 5 l is equivalent to $\dfrac{25}{5}$ g H_2SO_4 in 1 l

$\therefore$ concentration of $H_2SO_4 = 5$ g/l

or $\dfrac{5}{98}$ mol/l [M_r(H_2SO_4) $= 98$]

$= 0.051$ mol/l

The Effect of Electricity on Chemicals

Electrolyte   An electrolyte is a liquid which conducts electricity and contains positively and negatively charged ions, which move independently inside the liquid.

Electric Current   An electric current is a flow of electrons in a metal or a movement of ions towards a charged rod in an electrolyte.

Conductors (1)   Solid metals
Liquid metals   } conducting, due to free moving electrons.
Graphite

Examples   Cu, Fe, mercury.

Conductors (2)   Molten ionic substances
Ionic substances in aqueous solution   } conducting, due to free moving ions.

Examples   NaCl(l), NaCl(aq).

Non-conductors   Gaseous metals   – not conducting, due to no free moving electrons.

Solid ionic compounds   – ions fixed in lattice, so not free to move.

Covalent compounds   – no ions.

Electrolysis   Electrolysis is a process where electrical energy is used to decompose an electrolyte.

Electrodes   Electrodes are conducting rods or plates dipping into electrolyte.

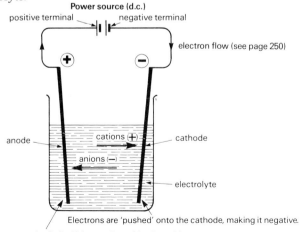

Power source (d.c.)
positive terminal   negative terminal
electron flow (see page 250)
anode   cations (+)   cathode
anions (–)
electrolyte
Electrons are 'pushed' onto the cathode, making it negative.
Electrons are 'pulled' off the anode, making it positive.

111

Anode	The electrode on the positive side of battery supply is called the anode.
Cathode	The electrode on the negative side of battery supply is called the cathode.
Anions	Anions are negative ($-$) ions attracted towards the positive anode ($+$).
Cations	Cations are positive ($+$) ions attracted towards the negative cathode ($-$).

Electrolysis of Molten Sodium Chloride

Ions present	Na^+ and Cl^-.
Cathode reaction	The Na^+ ions are attracted to the cathode ($-$) where they gain electrons.
	$$Na^+(l) + e^- \rightarrow Na(l)$$
	Sodium metal is discharged at the cathode.
Anode reaction	The Cl^- ions are attracted to the anode ($+$) where they lose electrons.
	$$Cl^-(l) - e^- \rightarrow Cl(g) \text{ but Cl atoms cannot exist on their own.}$$
	$$Cl(g) + Cl(g) \rightarrow Cl_2(g)$$
	Chlorine gas is discharged at the anode.
Overall change	$2NaCl(l) \rightarrow 2Na(l) + Cl_2(g)$

Electrolysis of Aluminium Oxide (Al_2O_3)

Industrial importance	Aluminium metal, used a lot in industry, is obtained by electrolysis.
Source of Al_2O_3	The ore bauxite is mined and purified before use.
Electrodes	Carbon electrodes are used.
Electrolyte	The purified bauxite is dissolved in the molten liquid of another aluminium ore, cryolite, at 900°C.
Ions present	Al^{3+} and O^{2-}.
Cathode reaction	Al^{3+} ions are attracted to the cathode ($-$) where they gain electrons.
	$$Al^{3+}(l) + 3e^- \rightarrow Al(l)$$
Anode reaction	O^{2-} ions are attracted to the anode ($+$) where they lose electrons.
	$$O^{2-}(l) - 2e^- \rightarrow O(g) \text{ but O atoms cannot exist on their own.}$$
	$$O(g) + O(g) \rightarrow O_2(g)$$

Overall change	$2Al_2O_3(l) \rightarrow 4Al(l) + 3O_2(g)$
Source of power	Since large amounts of electricity are needed for this industrial process, the manufacturing plant is sited near a power station or hydro-electric generator.

Electrolysis of Brine NaCl(aq)

Brine	Brine is a concentrated solution of sodium chloride in water.
Ions present	Na^+ (aq) (from brine) and H^+ (aq) (from water) Cl^- (aq) (from brine) and OH^- (aq) (from water)
Competition between ions	When more than one ion of a particular charge is present, both may be attracted to an electrode, but only one gains or loses electrons and is discharged.
Cathode reaction	H^+ (aq) ions gain electrons. (Na^+ ions need much more energy. They are more stable than Na atoms.) $H^+(aq) + e^- \rightarrow H(g)$ $H(g) + H(g) \rightarrow H_2(g)$
Anode reaction	Cl^- (aq) ions lose electrons. $Cl^-(aq) - e^- \rightarrow Cl(g)$ $Cl(g) + Cl(g) \rightarrow Cl_2(g)$
Useful products	H_2 can be used in the food industry. Cl_2 is used for several purposes (see page 134).

Electrolysis of Acidified Water (or Dilute Sulphuric Acid)

Pure water does not produce enough ions for it to conduct, so some dilute sulphuric acid is added.

Ions present from water	H^+ and OH^-.
Anode reaction	$OH^-(aq) - e^- \longrightarrow OH$ $OH + OH \longrightarrow H_2O + O$ $O + O \longrightarrow O_2(g)$ (overall) $4OH^-(aq) - 4e^- \rightarrow O_2(g) + 2H_2O$
Cathode reaction	$H^+(aq) + e^- \longrightarrow H$ $H + H \longrightarrow H_2(g)$ or $4H^+(aq) + 4e^- \longrightarrow 2H_2(g)$ (So same number of e^- are gained by H^+ as lost by OH^-)

113

Volume ratio $O_2:H_2$	$mol\ O_2 : mol\ H_2 = 1 : 2$
	$\therefore vol.\ O_2 : vol.\ H_2 = 1 : 2$

In practice, the volume of oxygen formed is *less* than half that of hydrogen, since oxygen is slightly soluble in water.

Electrolysis of Copper Sulphate Solution

Cathode reaction — Copper as a red brown solid (often shiny) is deposited with either inert or copper electrodes.

Anode reaction — *Inert electrode* – oxygen gas discharged as with the electrolysis of acidified water.

Copper electrode – slowly gets thinner as copper is converted into copper ions which go into the solution.

Refining of Impure Copper

Cathode — The cathode is a rod of pure copper.

Anode — The anode is the impure copper.

Electrolyte — The electrolyte is copper sulphate solution.

Cathode reaction — Cu^{2+} ions are converted to Cu metal, deposited on the pure copper rod.

Anode reaction — The copper from the impure copper is converted to Cu^{2+} ions at the same rate as the pure copper is deposited at the cathode.

Anode sludge — The impurities which collect below the anode are called anode sludge.

Amounts of Product — Since the number of electrons gained at the cathode must equal the number lost at the anode, the amount of product at one electrode can be found if one knows the amount formed at the other.

Example — In the electrolysis of acidified water, 0.016 g of oxygen is released at the anode. What mass of hydrogen is formed at the cathode?

Anode reaction: $4OH^-(aq) - 4e^- \rightarrow O_2(g) + 2H_2O(l)$

Cathode reaction: $4H^+(aq) + 4e^- \rightarrow 2H_2(g)$

(Note: same number of e^- lost and gained)

1 mol of oxygen (O_2) formed at anode

$$\equiv 2 \text{ mol of hydrogen } (H_2) \text{ at cathode}$$

($\equiv$ means 'corresponds to')

0.016g O_2 contains $\dfrac{0.016}{32}$ (= 0.0005) mol O_2

(1 mol of O_2 molecules has a mass of 32 g ($M_r(O_2) = 32$))

$\therefore$ Mol H_2 gas formed = $0.0005 \times 2 = 0.001$ mol

(since mol H_2 = twice mol O_2 – from equation)

$\therefore$ Mass H_2 formed = 0.001 mol $\times$ 2 g/mol = 0.002g

Dependence on Current and Time

The amount of product will depend on:

(a) the size of the current (I) passed, which is proportional to the number of electrons involved.

(b) the time for which the current is passed.

Amount of electrical charge in coulombs (C)
= size of current in amperes (A) $\times$ time in seconds (t)

Example

A trophy is plated with silver using a current of 2A for 1 hour (3600 s), and 8.1 g of silver is deposited.

Calculate (a) the amount of electrical charge;
(b) the number of moles of silver deposited;
(c) the mass of copper which would be deposited if the same current was passed for the same time through copper sulphate solution.

(a) Electrical charge = 2 amps $\times$ 3600 seconds
= 7200 C

(b) Moles of silver = $\dfrac{8.1 \text{ g}}{108 \text{ g/mol}}$ = 0.075 mol

(108g is mass of 1 mole of silver)

(c) $2 Ag^+ (aq) + 2e^- \rightarrow 2Ag (s)$ } same number of
$Cu^{2+} (aq) + 2e^- \rightarrow Cu (s)$ } electrons gained

$\therefore$ For same quantity of electricity,

2 mol Ag will be deposited, but only 1 mol of Cu

$\therefore$ moles of copper = $\frac{1}{2} \times$ moles of Ag

$= \frac{1}{2} \times 0.075$

$\therefore$ mass of copper = $\frac{1}{2} \times 0.075$ mol $\times$ 64 g/mol

= 24 g

Electroplating	Metal objects can be plated with a thin layer of another metal by applying the principles of electrolysis.
Metal object	The metal object is connected as the cathode of the cell.
Electrolyte	The electrolyte must contain the metal ions of the metal to be coated.
Examples	Chromium plating, nickel plating, silver plating

General Rules on Electrolysis

Metal ions, Hydrogen ions	The metal ions (and the hydrogen ions) are attracted to the cathode and discharged there as the metal (or H_2).
Non-metal ions (except H^+ ions)	Non-metal ions are attracted to the anode and discharged as a gas at the anode.
Choice of products	At a particular electrode, the ion which gains or loses electrons is the one which requires the least amount of energy.

Types of Chemical Reaction

Simple reactions can be classified into two main types:

1. Where ions are exchanged between substances.
2. Where oxygen is added to or removed from a substance.

Acid and Alkali Reactions

Acids Acids are generally soluble in water to produce H^+ ions.

Examples hydrochloric acid, HCl
nitric acid, HNO_3
sulphuric acid, H_2SO_4
citric acid
ethanoic (acetic) acid, CH_3COOH

Alkalis Alkalis are substances which are soluble in water to produce OH^- ions.

Examples sodium hydroxide, NaOH
potassium hydroxide, KOH
ammonium hydroxide, NH_4OH
calcium hydroxide, $Ca(OH)_2$

pH Scale The pH scale measures the strength of acids and alkalis. It is based on the amount of H^+ ions in an acid solution and amount of OH^- ions in an alkaline solution.

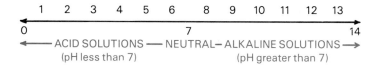

Since the value of pH depends on the number of H^+ ions and OH^- ions in solution, it depends on the extent of ionisation of the acid or alkali, in other words the proportion of the molecules in solution which separate into ions.

Measuring pH The pH of a solution can be measured using pH paper or a pH meter. When using pH paper, a small sample of the liquid (often on a glass rod) is placed on the indicator paper. After leaving for 30 seconds, the colour of the paper is compared with a colour chart to give the pH. Modern pH meters provide a read-out of the pH when an electrode is dipped in the solution.

117

Neutralisation Neutralisation is a reaction where an acid reacts completely with an alkali to form a salt and water:

$$\text{nitric acid} + \text{potassium hydroxide} \rightarrow \text{potassium nitrate} + \text{water}$$

$$HNO_3(aq) + KOH(aq) \rightarrow KNO_3(aq) + H_2O(l)$$

In the solution each of the chemicals except water ionises completely. We can write:

$$H^+(aq) + NO_3^-(aq) + K^+(aq) + OH(aq)$$
$$\rightarrow K^+(aq) + NO_3^-(aq) + H_2O(l)$$

In a reaction we are really interested in those parts which undergo a change.

Spectator ions Spectator ions are ions, like K^+ and NO_3^- in the above reaction, which are present in solution *both* at the start *and* at the end of the reaction.

Ionic equation The ionic equation of the reaction is the equation showing the ions undergoing a change in the reaction, and the products – but omitting the spectator ions.

Ionic equation for any neutralisation reaction $H^+(aq) + OH^-(aq) \rightarrow H_2O(l)$
(from acid)   (from alkali)
This equation applies to *any* neutralisation reaction.

Indicators Indicators are substances which are a different colour in acid and alkaline solutions. They are used to enable us to detect when an alkali is exactly neutralised by an acid (or vice versa):

Examples

	Colour in acidic solution	Colour in alkaline solution
universal indicator	red	purple
litmus	red	blue
methyl orange	red	yellow

> Further examples of indicators may be given in your data book.

Reactions of Acids

Alkalis Alkalis neutralise acids.

Metals Metals generally react with acids to give off hydrogen gas. (The metals have to be fairly reactive.)

Examples	iron + $\dfrac{\text{hydrochloric}}{\text{acid}}$ → $\dfrac{\text{iron (II)}}{\text{chloride}}$ + hydrogen

$$\text{Fe(s)} + 2\text{HCl(aq)} \longrightarrow \text{FeCl}_2\text{(aq)} + \text{H}_2\text{(g)}$$

Other metals reacting like this include magnesium, zinc and aluminium.

> Note: Copper does *not* react with acids to release hydrogen.

Insoluble Metal Oxides and Metal Hydroxides

These are bases and so react with acids to form a salt and water.

Examples

$$\dfrac{\text{copper}}{\text{oxide}} + \dfrac{\text{sulphuric}}{\text{acid}} → \dfrac{\text{copper}}{\text{sulphate}} + \text{water}$$

$$\text{CuO(s)} + \text{H}_2\text{SO}_4\text{(aq)} → \text{CuSO}_4\text{(aq)} + \text{H}_2\text{O(l)}$$

Metal Carbonates and Hydrogen Carbonates

These react with acids to form carbon dioxide, water and a metal salt.

Examples

$$\dfrac{\text{sodium}}{\text{carbonate}} + \dfrac{\text{nitric}}{\text{acid}} \longrightarrow \dfrac{\text{sodium}}{\text{nitrate}} + \dfrac{\text{carbon}}{\text{dioxide}} + \text{water}$$

$$\text{Na}_2\text{CO}_3\text{(l)} + 2\text{HNO}_3\text{(aq)} → 2\text{NaNO}_3\text{(aq)} + \text{CO}_2\text{(g)} + \text{H}_2\text{O(l)}$$

Reaction of Alkalis

Acids

Acids react with alkalis to form a salt and water.

Metal salt solutions

Metal salt solutions often react with the OH$^-$ ions from an alkali to form an insoluble metal hydroxide, as a precipitate (ppt), which is a solid formed in a reaction on mixing together two solutions.

Example

$$\text{FeSO}_4\text{(aq)} + 2\text{NaOH(aq)} → \text{Fe(OH)}_2\text{ (s)} + \text{Na}_2\text{SO}_4\text{(aq)}$$
$$\text{green ppt}$$

Ionic equation

$$\text{Fe}^{2+}\text{(aq)} + 2\text{OH}^-\text{(aq)} → \text{Fe(OH)}_2\text{(s)}$$

Further examples

$$\text{Al}^{3+}\text{(aq)} + 3\text{OH}^-\text{(aq)} → \text{Al(OH)}_3\text{(s)} \qquad \text{white ppt}$$

$$\text{Cu}^{2+}\text{(aq)} + 2\text{OH}^-\text{(aq)} → \text{Cu(OH)}_2\text{(s)} \qquad \text{pale-blue ppt}$$

$$\text{Fe}^{3+}\text{(aq)} + 3\text{OH}^-\text{(aq)} → \text{Fe(OH)}_3\text{(s)} \qquad \text{red-brown ppt}$$
from iron (III) salts

Everyday Substances

Acidic substances

Acidic substances include vinegar (containing ethanoic acid), soda water (carbon dioxide in water), fruit juices (containing citric acid), acid rain.

Alkaline substances
Alkaline substances include domestic ammonia solution and milk of magnesia (for neutralising the excess stomach acid in indigestion).

Salts
Salts are composed of two ions.

Examples

Salt	Positive ion	from	Negative ion	from
$NaNO_3$	Na^+	$NaOH$	NO_3^-	HNO_3
$CuSO_4$	Cu^{2+}	CuO or $Cu(OH)_2$	SO_4^{2-}	H_2SO_4
NH_4Cl	NH_4^+	NH_4OH	Cl^-	HCl
$Fe_2(SO_4)_3$	Fe^{3+}	Fe_2O_3 or $Fe(OH)_3$	SO_4^{2-}	H_2SO_4

Precipitation
All the reactions above involve ions which can be seen to be exchanged in a reaction like

$$A^+X^- + B^+Y^- \rightarrow A^+Y^- + B^+X^-$$

but where A^+ is the H^+ ion from an acid, or Y^- is the OH^- from an alkali.
Another example of this type of reaction is where AY or BX is insoluble in water, so a precipitate is formed.
A precipitate, remember, is a solid formed as a result of mixing two solutions.

Example
To make insoluble barium sulphate (containing Ba^{2+} ions and SO_4^{2-} ions), mix:

Ba^{2+} *ions* from $BaCl_2$ solution or $Ba(NO_3)_2$ solution

with

SO_4^{2-} *ions* from H_2SO_4 solution or Na_2SO_4 solution.

The equation is:

$BaCl_2(aq) + H_2SO_4(aq) \rightarrow BaSO_4(s) + 2HCl(aq)$
$Ba^{2+}(aq) + SO_4^{2-}(aq) \rightarrow BaSO_4(s)$ (ionic equation)

Reactions Involving Oxygen and Hydrogen

Oxidation and Reduction
These are processes in which any combination of the following changes takes place.

Oxidation	Reduction
oxygen is gained; and/or hydrogen is lost	oxygen is lost; and/or hydrogen is gained

Oxidation and reduction must take place *simultaneously* into a reaction, i.e. if one chemical loses oxygen atoms, another chemical must gain them (Law of Conservation of Mass).

Example 1 $2Mg(s) + O_2(g) \longrightarrow 2MgO(s)$

Summary   The magnesium is oxidised by the oxygen.

Example 2 $CuO(s) + H_2(g) \rightarrow Cu(s) + H_2O(l)$

Copper oxide loses oxygen to form copper   *reduction*

and hydrogen gains oxygen to form water   *oxidation*.

Summary   The copper in copper oxide is reduced to copper metal and the hydrogen is oxidised to water.

> Note: The oxygen is present in combined form in both CuO and H_2O, and so is basically unchanged in the reaction.

Example 3   When iron objects rust, the metal is oxidised to Fe^{3+} in the air (in the presence of moisture).

$4Fe(s) + 3O_2(aq) \rightarrow 2Fe_2O_3(s)$
(simplified equation)

Example 4   When metal ores (often metal oxides) are roasted with coke (carbon) or carbon monoxide, the oxygen is removed so the oxide is reduced to the metal.

Blast furnace.
Iron ore (Fe_2O_3) is converted to Fe metal in the reaction with carbon monoxide (see page 131).

$Fe_2O_3(s) + 3CO(g) \rightarrow 2Fe(l) + 3CO_2(g)$

reduced ——— oxidised

Example 5   *Combustion reactions*.
In any reaction where a fuel is burned in oxygen, the fuel is oxidised.

Burning of $CH_4(g) + 2O_2(g) \rightarrow CO_2(g) + 2H_2O(l)$
Methane

Fire Triangle   All three are needed for combustion. This would apply to any combustion reaction.

13 Air and Water

Gases in Air   The gases which exist in air are nitrogen, oxygen, and small amounts of carbon dioxide, neon, argon and water vapour. (See page 26 for percentage composition.)

Carbon dioxide in air   Carbon dioxide in air can be shown by blowing air from a syringe or bicycle pump through lime-water, to see if it turns cloudy.

Water in air   Water in air can be shown by leaving out in the air some white copper (II) sulphate to see if it turns blue. (Blue cobalt chloride could be used and would turn pink.)

Combustion   Combustion occurs when substances burn in air.

Magnesium $2Mg(s) + O_2(g) \rightarrow 2MgO(s)$

Carbon $C(s) \quad + O_2(g) \rightarrow CO_2(g)$ (complete combustion)

Sulphur $S(s) \quad + O_2(g) \rightarrow SO_2(g)$

Fossil fuels   coal $\rightarrow CO_2(g)$ (complete combustion)

others $\rightarrow CO_2(g) + H_2O(g)$

Air Pollution

Common pollutants   The most common air pollutants are carbon monoxide, sulphur dioxide, oxides of nitrogen, lead compounds, dust particles, unburnt hydrocarbons.

Carbon monoxide   Carbon monoxide results from the incomplete combustion of fuels such as petrol.

When fuels burn there is rarely enough oxygen for complete combustion. The following equations show what happens.

Incomplete combustion: $C(s) + \frac{1}{2}O_2(g) \rightarrow CO(g)$

Complete combustion: $C(s) + O_2(g) \rightarrow CO_2(g)$

That is to say, twice as much oxygen is needed for complete combustion.

Carbon monoxide is highly toxic, and is absorbed by haemoglobin in blood. To prevent pollution, smoke-free zones, catalytic oxidisers, more effective burners, engines, etc. are needed.

Sulphur dioxide   Sulphur dioxide pollution comes from sulphur contained in fossil fuels.

$S(s) + O_2(g) \rightarrow SO_2(g)$

It is a lung irritant. It dissolves in water vapour to form acid rain. Sulphur dioxide pollution can be prevented by careful removal of sulphur from fuels at refineries.

Oxides of nitrogen

Oxides of nitrogen are released by burning fossil fuels. These fuels were once living plants, which contained proteins containing nitrogen.

The oxides are respiratory irritants; they also dissolve in water vapour to form acid rain. Pollution can be prevented by removal of the nitrogen at oil refineries.

Hard Water

Hard water contains considerable amounts of Ca^{2+} and Mg^{2+} ions.

Advantages

It is good for bones, teeth and for reducing heart disease.

Disadvantages

1. It requires a lot of soap to form a lather.

2. It leaves a scum after washing.

3. It causes kettles to scale.

4. It 'furs' pipes, by forming a deposit on the inside, reducing the bore.

Composition

$Ca(HCO_3)_2$ and other salts.

Characteristics

$Ca(HCO_3)_2$ decomposes on heating:

$$Ca(HCO_3)_2(aq) \to CaCO_3(s) + CO_2(g) + H_2O(l).$$

It is the insoluble $CaCO_3$ which forms the 'fur' on pipes and kettles.

Hard water is caused by rainwater (containing carbon dioxide) passing over and reacting with limestone rocks and dissolving small amounts of other rocks.

Soft Water

Soft water is water containing only small amounts of Ca^{2+} or Mg^{2+} ions which does not have the advantages or disadvantages of hard water.

Aerated Water

Aerated water is water containing dissolved oxygen from air. It is essential to life in water (i.e. plant and fish life).

Water Softening

Water softening involves the removal of the Ca^{2+} ions from the water.
It is achieved by the following means.

1. Distillation – leaves dissolved solids in the flask.

2. Using extra soap.

123

3. Adding a chemical softener, such as washing soda $Na_2CO_3.10H_2O$.

The Na_2CO_3 reacts with Ca^{2+} to form insoluble $CaCO_3$.

$$Na_2CO_3(aq) + Ca^{2+}(aq) \rightarrow CaCO_3(s) + 2Na^+(aq)$$

4. Using ion exchange.

Uses of Water
1. Water is essential for life.
2. It is a solvent.
3. Water is a raw material for many chemical processes, e.g. manufacture of ammonia and ethanol.
4. Water is used as a coolant in some power stations and other industrial processes.

Drinking Water
Water treatment plants remove solids by filtration and then use chlorine to kill bacteria so that the water is safe to drink. In some areas, fluoride ions are added to domestic water to prevent tooth decay.

Properties of Water

Melting point The melting point of pure water is 0°C ⎫ at atmospheric

Boiling point The boiling point of pure water is 100°C ⎬ pressure.

Identification The identification of pure water is by boiling.

Check the boiling point of an aqueous solution and, if 100°C, the water is pure.

Pure water and aqueous solutions will turn

cobalt chloride blue → pink,

anhydrous copper (II) sulphate white → blue.

Oxygen and Hydrogen

Occurrence of Oxygen
Oxygen is the most abundant element – occurring as compounds in most rocks.

Properties
1. Oxygen is a colourless, odourless gas.
2. Density – similar to that of air.
3. Solubility in water – slightly soluble.

Test for Oxygen
A glowing splint (*heat, fuel*) is reignited in *oxygen* (see Fire Triangle, page 121).

Uses of Oxygen
1. Supports life (respiration) and combustion.
2. Rocket fuel mixtures.

3. Manufacture of steel.

4. Welding (in oxy-acetylene torches).

5. Medicine – oxygen-enriched air.

Oxides   Oxides are compounds made of an element and oxygen only. They are often made by heating the element in oxygen.

Examples $2Mg(s) + O_2(g) \rightarrow 2MgO(s)$

$S(s) \quad + O_2(g) \rightarrow SO_2(g)$

Metal Oxides   Some metal oxides like Na_2O are soluble in water, giving alkaline solutions.

Example $Na_2O(s) + H_2O(l) \rightarrow 2NaOH(aq)$

Others may be insoluble in water, like CuO, Fe_2O_3, Al_2O_3.

Non-metal Oxides   Some non-metal oxides like CO_2 and SO_2 are soluble in water, giving acidic solutions.

Example $SO_2(g) + H_2O(l) \rightarrow H_2SO_3(aq)$ (sulphurous acid)

Others may be insoluble in water, like SiO_2.

Properties of Hydrogen   Hydrogen is a colourless, odourless gas.

Density   It is very light (M_r of $H_2 = 2$, compared with 28 for N_2 in air).

Solubility   Hydrogen is insoluble in water.

Burning of Hydrogen   If ignited, hydrogen burns to form water.

Safety Precautions   Safe storage, no naked flames. Avoid contamination with air.

Uses of Hydrogen   1. Manufacture of ammonia.

2. Hydrogen as a fuel. The advantages are that hydrogen burns to form water only (no pollution); and, in space travel, recycling is possible. The disadvantages include difficulty of storage and the risk of explosion.

14 Metals/Non-Metals and the Periodic Table

The Periodic Table

This is an arrangement of the chemical elements in order of increasing atomic numbers.

METALS | NON-METALS | Gp 0

Gp I	Gp II									$_1$H	Gp III	Gp IV	Gp V	Gp VI	Gp VII	Gp 0 $_2$He
$_3$Li	$_4$Be				Period						$_5$B	$_6$C	$_7$N	$_8$O	$_9$F	$_{10}$Ne
$_{11}$Na	$_{12}$Mg										$_{13}$Al	$_{14}$Si	$_{15}$P	$_{16}$S	$_{17}$Cl	$_{18}$Ar
$_{19}$K	$_{20}$Ca						$_{26}$Fe			$_{29}$Cu	$_{30}$Zn					$_{35}$Br
				transition metals												$_{53}$I
											$_{82}$Pb					

Group ↑ Gr o u p ↓

Period A period is a horizontal row where elements with similar properties occur periodically. Each period starts with a reactive metal [sodium (Na), potassium (K), etc.] and ends with a very unreactive element, a noble gas [neon (Ne), argon (Ar), etc.].

Group A Group is a vertical column containing elements with similar properties.

Examples Group I (Li, Na, K, etc., called alkali metals)

Group II (Be, Mg, Ca, etc., called alkaline earth metals)

Group VII (F, Cl, Br, I, called halogens)

Group 0 (He, Ne, Ar, etc., called noble gases)

Group Number and Electrons The number of electrons in the outer energy level of all elements in a group is generally the same (see Group 0 below for exception).

Examples

Group I	Li $(Z = 3)$	2,1
	Na $(Z = 11)$	2, 8, 1
	K $(Z = 19)$	2, 8, 8, 1
Group VII	F $(Z = 9)$	2, 7
	Cl $(Z = 17)$	2, 8, 7
Group 0	He $(Z = 2)$	2
	Ne $(Z = 8)$	2, 8
	Ar $(Z = 18)$	2, 8, 8

In the case of the noble gases, the number in the outer energy level is the maximum for that level.

Group and Type of Element	Elements lose, gain or share electrons when forming compounds in order to get an electron structure like that of the nearest noble gas.
Group I	Group I elements lose $1e^- \rightarrow M^+$ ion.
Group II	Group II elements lose $2e^- \rightarrow M^{2+}$ ion. Elements forming positive ions are generally *metals*.
Group VII	Group VII elements may gain $1e^- \rightarrow X^-$ ion. Elements forming negative ions are generally *non-metals*.

Look carefully at the table on page 126 and note how it divides into metals and non-metals.

Order of Reactivity	
Group I	Li in water – metal does not melt, but reacts steadily. Na in water – melts and reacts vigorously. K in water – melts and reacts violently so that H_2 gas formed catches fire. So K is more reactive than Na (reactivity increases down the group).
Group VII	The most reactive element is fluorine (F) at the top. These elements react by gaining electrons. The closer the incoming electron is to the nucleus the more strongly it will be held.

Differences in Properties between Metals and Non-metals

	Metals	Non-Metals
Physical state at 20°C	Generally solids (exception mercury).	Can be solid, liquid (bromine only), or gas.
Melting point	Generally high (sodium and potassium are quite low).	Generally low (exceptions: diamond, graphite and silicon).
Shininess	Generally shiny, mostly silvery appearance.	Solid may be shiny but rarely silvery.
Malleability	Malleable (i.e. able to be beaten into sheets).	Brittle when solid.
Ductility	Ductile (can be drawn into wire).	—
Thermal conductivity	Good conductors.	Non-conductors (insulators).

	Metals	Non-Metals
Electrical conductivity	Good electrical conductors.	Generally non-conductors (exception: graphite).
Formation of oxides	Form basic oxides (exceptions: Al_2O_3 and ZnO which are amphoteric).	Form acidic oxides.

Tests to Identify an Element as Metallic or Non-metallic

	Metallic	Non-metallic
Burn in oxygen	Oxide formed is a solid.	Oxide formed is often a gas.
Solubility of oxide	If soluble, will give an alkaline solution. If insoluble, will react with an acid to form a salt.	Non-metal oxides are mostly soluble in water to give an acid solution.
Electrical conductivity	If element conducts it is most likely to be a metal.	

Metals

Activity Series   Metals are placed in order of their reactivity (with the most reactive at the top).

Most reactive

Potassium	(K)
Sodium	(Na)
Calcium	(Ca)
Magnesium	(Mg)
Aluminium	(Al)
(Carbon)	
Zinc	(Zn)
Iron	(Fe)
Nickel	(Ni)
Tin	(Sn)
Lead	(Pb)
(Hydrogen)	
Copper	(Cu)
Silver	(Ag)
Gold	(Au)
Platinum	(Pt)

Least reactive

The more reactive the metal, the greater is the likelihood that it is to form ions. (Hydrogen is included in the series, since like metals, it forms positive ions (H^+). Carbon is included since it can displace metals below it.)

Displacement

When a solid metal X is placed in a solution containing ions of a less reactive metal Y, the less reactive metal is displaced as the solid metal:

$$X(s) \quad + \quad Y^{2+}(aq) \rightarrow Y(s) + X^{2+}(aq)$$

more reactive $\qquad$ less reactive

Example 1

Iron (Fe) metal in copper (Cu^{2+}) solution.
Fe is above Cu, so Fe will finish as Fe^{2+} ions.
For this to happen copper metal will be displaced from its ions:

$$Fe(s) + Cu^{2+}(aq) \rightarrow Cu(s) + Fe^{2+}(aq)$$

Example 2

Zinc (Zn) metal in magnesium (Mg^{2+}) solution.
Mg is above Zn, so Mg will finish as Mg^{2+} ions. Mg^{2+} ions are already present, so no reaction needs to occur.

Example 3

Hydrogen (H_2) gas and copper oxide (CuO).
H is above Cu, so H will finish as a compound.
H_2 will displace Cu from Cu^{2+} (in CuO):

$$H_2(g) + CuO(s) \rightarrow Cu(s) + H_2O(l)$$

Example 4

Magnesium (Mg) metal in dilute hydrochloric acid (HCl).
Mg is above H, so Mg will finish as Mg^{2+} ions.
To achieve this H_2 gas will be displaced from H^+ ions (in the acid):

$$Mg(s) + 2HCl(aq) \rightarrow MgCl_2(aq) + H_2(g)$$

Example 5

Copper (Cu) metal in dilute hydrochloric acid (HCl).
H is above Cu, so H will finish as a compound.
H is already present as HCl(aq), so no reaction will occur.

Position of an Unknown Metal

The position of an unknown metal can be determined by placing the metal in a series of solutions of known metal ions (and H^+ ions) and seeing which metals are displaced. A check of position can be made by adding different known metals to solutions of the unknown metal ion.

Reactions with Air

Potassium
Sodium
Calcium
Magnesium
} All burn in air to form oxides.

Example

$$2Mg(s) + O_2(g) \rightarrow 2MgO(s)$$
(Burns with a bright flame).

Aluminium	Aluminium reacts slowly with air to form a protective aluminium oxide (Al_2O_3) coating; but when heated, burns to form the oxide.
Zinc	Zinc burns in air to form zinc oxide.
Iron	Iron rusts in the cold in the presence of moisture. Iron also burns in air to form Fe_2O_3. Note that iron (III) oxide forms since O_2 in air is an oxidising agent.
Copper	When strongly heated in air, black copper oxide (CuO) is formed.

Reactions with Water (or Steam)

In general	Metal + $H_2O \rightarrow$ metal oxide or hydroxide + $H_2(g)$
Trend	Reactions become more difficult as one moves down from potassium to copper.
Potassium	Potassium reacts violently in *cold* water → alkaline solution. (The hydrogen released catches fire).

$$2K(s) + H_2O(l) \rightarrow 2KOH(aq) + H_2(g)$$

Sodium	Sodium reacts vigorously in *cold* water → alkaline solution. (The hydrogen released only occasionally catches fire.)
Calcium	Calcium reacts steadily in *cold* water → alkaline solution (milky due to partially dissolved calcium hydroxide) and hydrogen.

$$Ca(s) + 2H_2O(l) \rightarrow Ca(OH)_2(s) + H_2(g)$$

Magnesium	Magnesium reacts slowly in *cold* water (equation similar to that with calcium), but reacts readily in *steam* → magnesium oxide and hydrogen.
Aluminium	Aluminium does not react if the oxide coating is left on.
	If the oxide layer is removed, aluminium reacts vigorously to form aluminium hydroxide $Al(OH)_3$ and hydrogen H_2.
Zinc	Zinc reacts with *steam* → zinc oxide ZnO(s) and hydrogen H_2.
Iron	Iron reacts with steam → $Fe_3O_4(s)$ and hydrogen H_2.
Copper	Copper does *not* react with water or steam.

Reactions with Dilute Acids

In general	Metal + dilute acid → salt + hydrogen, except that dilute nitric acid behaves differently.
Trend	The trend from potassium to copper is from very reactive to unreactive.

Magnesium	Magnesium + hydrochloric acid:
	$Mg(s) + 2HCl(aq) \rightarrow MgCl_2(aq) + H_2(g)$
Iron	Iron + sulphuric acid:
	$Fe(s) + H_2SO_4(aq) \rightarrow FeSO_4(aq) + H_2(g)$
Copper	Copper does not react with dilute hydrochloric or sulphuric acids (and *never* releases hydrogen from an acid).

Storage of Alkali Metals

Potassium ⎫
Sodium ⎬ These metals are so reactive with water that they have to be stored under oil.
Lithium ⎭

Occurrences of Metal Ores

Compounds	Most metals occur in the earth's crust as compounds.
Chlorides	These include NaCl (rocksalt), $MgCl_2$ – containing the more reactive metals.
Oxides	These include Al_2O_3 (bauxite), ZnO, and Fe_2O_3 (haematite).
Free metal	A few metals (the least reactive ones) occur naturally as the element: copper, gold, silver.

Extraction of Metal Ores

Electrolysis	The more reactive metals need to be extracted from their ore by electrolysis. It can provide the large amounts of energy needed to force the metal ion to take back the electrons.
Examples	Na from NaCl (molten), and Al from Al_2O_3.
Reduction with carbon	The reducing agent, carbon, is used as coke to convert several metal oxides to the metal.
Examples	Fe from Fe_2O_3 in the blast furnace (see below). Zn from ZnO, and Cu from CuO.

Blast Furnace

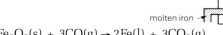

iron ore + limestone + coke

Reactions	Coke + air → carbon dioxide
	$C(s) + O_2(g) \rightarrow CO_2(g)$
Formation of CO	CO_2 is reduced by coke to CO:
	$CO_2(g) + C(s) \rightarrow 2CO(g)$

hot air

hot air

molten iron

molten slag

| Reduction of Fe_2O_3 | $Fe_2O_3(s) + 3CO(g) \rightarrow 2Fe(l) + 3CO_2(g)$ |

Limestone	The limestone is decomposed by the heat to form CaO and CO_2: $$CaCO_3(s) \rightarrow CaO(s) + CO_2(g)$$
Slag	CaO is a basic oxide and reacts with acidic impurities (mainly SiO_2) from the ore to form a slag, which is less dense than molten iron – so floats on it.
Iron metal	The iron metal formed in the blast furnace is not very pure, the main impurity being carbon. This crude iron is called *pig iron*.
Environmental problems	Air pollution arises from impurities in the metal ores. Surface pollution is mainly holes and scars from mining, together with spoil tips and slag heaps.
Recycling of Metals	The earth contains a limited supply of all metals. Collecting, treating and re-using (i.e. re-cycling) is essential to help maintain the supply.

Rusting of Iron

Reaction	$$4Fe(s) + 3O_2(aq) \rightarrow 2Fe_2O_3(s)$$ rust
	This will only take place in the presence of water, but is faster in salt solutions.
Proof of conditions	Four experiments can be carried out:

1. Iron nails in tap water (containing dissolved O_2).

Nails *rust.*

2. Iron nails in ordinary air (containing water vapour).

Nails *rust.*

3. Iron nails in dry air – in sealed tube containing a drying agent (e.g. anhydrous calcium chloride). Nails *do not rust.*

4. Iron nails in boiled water (boiled to remove dissolved O_2) and with oil or wax on top of water (to prevent fresh O_2 dissolving). Nails *do not rust.*

Protection of Iron and Steel	To keep oxygen and water from the surface of the iron or steel, one can use a number of methods.
Greasing	Greasing is used for moving parts, but has to be renewed.
Painting	Painting is used for large objects (e.g. bridges), but needs to be re-applied if the surface is broken.
Galvanising	The steel is galvanised by being coated with a layer of zinc metal. If the surface is scratched, the oxygen reacts with the zinc rather than the iron. (Zinc is more reactive than iron.)
Tin-plating	Steel cans are coated with tin, but tin is less reactive than iron, so if the surface is scratched, the iron reacts.
Chromium-plating	The steel is plated (by electrolysis) with chromium. This offers some protection, but it is mainly for decoration.

Sacrificial metals	On the hull of a ship, bars of a metal, such as zinc or magnesium, are attached. These metals are more reactive than iron and so react, and are 'sacrificed'.
Properties of Iron	Iron is a typical metal – but is magnetic. Iron reacts with non-metals.
Examples	$Fe(s) + S(s) \rightarrow FeS(s)$
	$2Fe(s) + 3Cl_2(g) \rightarrow 2FeCl_3 (s)$
	Iron also reacts with acids.
Example	*Dilute sulphuric acid.*
	$Fe(s) + H_2SO_4(aq) \rightarrow FeSO_4(aq) + H_2(g)$
Aluminium	
Abundance	Aluminium (Al) is the most abundant metal in the earth's crust (7.5% of all elements).
Occurrence	It occurs in most rocks and clays.
	It is obtained commercially from bauxite (Al_2O_3).
Extraction	Pure aluminium is obtained by electrolysis as described on page 112.

Uses of Metals	Use	Reason
Magnesium	Alarm flares, flash bulbs	Reactive metal
Aluminium	Domestic: Kitchen foil, pans, window frames. Industrial: Car engines, power cables, aeroplanes.	Light and strong
Zinc	Galvanising steel	More reactive than iron
Iron	Construction, transport	Strong metal
Copper	Electrical wiring Water pipes	Good conductor of electricity Low reactivity

Alloys	Alloys are specific mixtures of metals and other elements.
Examples	Bronze is a mixture of copper and tin.
	Solder is made of tin and lead (and other mixtures).
	Steel is made up of iron and other elements.
Use of Alloys	An alloy is usually designed for a particular purpose, making use of the properties of the individual components.
Example	Titanium is used in alloys for hip-joints and rockets, due to its low density and high melting point.

15 Some Raw Materials for Industry

Salt

Occurrence of Salt

Salt is sodium chloride. It is found in sea water and rock salt.

Uses of Salt

Health

It is essential for maintaining body metabolism. Too much salt may lead to high blood pressure. Too little salt may lead to high heat exhaustion.

De-icing Roads

Salt is added to roads so that a solution of salt is formed, which freezes at a temperature lower than 0°C, *but* salt on roads speeds up the rate of rusting of cars.

Industry

Important sodium compounds like sodium hydroxide are made from salt, as is chlorine, used to make compounds containing chlorine like PVC.

Chlorine

Chlorine (Cl_2) is a greenish gas, denser than air, fairly soluble in water. It is a choking, toxic, oxidising agent and a bleaching agent (e.g. moist litmus turned to white).

Uses of Chlorine

1. In making bleach.

> Note: Never mix bleach with other domestic cleaning agents.

2. Water treatment – chlorine is added to mains water at treatment plants to kill bacteria so it is safe to drink.

3. Manufacture of other products, such as PVC and chlorinated solvents.

Displacement

A more reactive halogen displaces a less reactive halogen from its ions:

Cl_2 displaces Br_2 (or I_2) from a solution containing Br^- (or I^-),

Br_2 displaces I_2 from a solution containing I^-,

but I_2 will not displace Cl_2 or Br_2

> Note: The more reactive halogen always finishes as its ion if it can.

Example $Cl_2(g) + 2I^-(aq) \rightarrow I_2(aq) + 2Cl^-(aq)$

Test for Halides   Halide in solution, plus dilute nitric acid and silver nitrate solution.

If the precipitate is white then a chloride is present;
    creamish then a bromide is present;
    pale yellow then an iodide is present.

In each case the insoluble silver halide is formed.

Example $Br^-(aq) + AgNO_3(aq) \rightarrow AgBr(s) + NO_3^-(aq)$

Limestone

Occurence of Limestone   Limestone occurs naturally as calcium carbonate ($CaCO_3$) in limestone rocks, also in chalk and marble.

Extraction   It is extracted by quarrying, though this leaves holes and scars on the surface of the earth.

Thermal decomposition $CaCO_3(s) \xrightarrow[\text{heat}]{\text{strong}} CaO(s) + CO_2(g)$
      limestone   quicklime

Uses of Calcium Compounds   Common calcium compounds are:

calcium carbonate ($CaCO_3$), calcium oxide or quicklime (CaO), and calcium hydroxide or slaked lime [$Ca(OH)_2$].

Agriculture   All three are used to control soil acidity.

Cement   Clay and gypsum ($CaSO_4$) as well as limestone are required in the manufacture of cement.

Blast furnace   Limestone enables acid impurities to be removed as slag.

Glass   Glass is made by melting together limestone, sand and sodium carbonate.

Carbon Dioxide

Preparation   Marble chips are reacted with dilute hydrochloric acid in apparatus where carbon dioxide is collected over water.

Equation $CaCO_3(s) + 2HCl(aq) \rightarrow CaCl_2(aq) + CO_2(g) + H_2O(l)$

Burning of fossil fuels   When fossil fuels are burned *completely* (i.e. in plenty of air) carbon dioxide is produced.

Example $CH_4(g) + 2O_2(g) \rightarrow CO_2(g) + 2H_2O(g)$
methane

135

Properties of
Carbon
Dioxide

Physical   1. Colourless, odourless gas.

2. Fairly easily solidified → 'dry ice'.

3. Density – heavier than air (M_r = 44).

4. Slightly soluble in water → weakly acidic solution.

Test for Carbon   1. Carbon dioxide bubbled into lime-water → cloudy solution.
Dioxide

$$CO_2(g) + Ca(OH)_2(aq) → CaCO_3(s) + H_2O(l)$$
insoluble

2. More carbon dioxide bubbled into cloudy solution
→ clear solution.

$$CaCO_3(s) + CO_2(g) + H_2O(l) → Ca(HCO_3)_2(aq)$$
soluble

Uses of Carbon
Dioxide

Fire   An atmosphere of carbon dioxide will not allow fuels to burn,
extinguishers   due to the exclusion of oxygen (see Fire Triangle).

Fire extinguishers involving carbon dioxide can be of two main
types.

Type A: *Compressed carbon dioxide* in a cylinder.

Type B: *Acid/Carbonate*. Some extinguishers contain a small
bottle of acid above a solution of sodium hydrogen carbonate
($NaHCO_3$). When activated the acid reacts with the sodium
hydrogen carbonate to form carbon dioxide and a water
solution, which is sprayed on the fire.

Note: Type B must *not* be used on electrical fires.

Carbonated   These include beer, lemonade, soda water, etc.
Drinks

Sulphur

Occurrence of   Sulphur occurs naturally as the element in 'sulphur beds', in
Sulphur in   volcanic regions. It sometimes occurs as sulphide ores: for
Nature   instance, copper sulphide (CuS) and iron (II) sulphide (FeS).
Sulphur also occurs in crude oil, natural gas and coal. (The
sulphur needs to be removed during refining to prevent
pollution later.)

Uses of Sulphur	1. Making sulphuric acid (see below).
	2. Hardening of rubber (vulcanisation).

Properties of Sulphur Dioxide

Solubility Sulphur dioxide is very soluble in water forming an acidic solution:

$$SO_2(g) + H_2O(l) \rightarrow H_2SO_3(aq) \quad \text{sulphurous acid}$$

Acid Rain Sulphur dioxide, released into the air as a pollutant, dissolves in water vapour, and is oxidised to form sulphuric acid. This is a component of acid rain.

Smell Sulphur dioxide has a choking smell and is an irritant poison.

Uses of Sulphur Dioxide 1. Sulphur dioxide is used as a sterilising agent and food preservative.

2. It is also a bleaching agent.

Sulphuric Acid Sulphuric acid (H_2SO_4) is used extensively in many processes in the chemical industry. It is made by passing sulphur dioxide and air at atmospheric pressure, over a catalyst of vanadium (V) oxide at 450°C.

$$2SO_2(g) + O_2(g) \rightarrow 2SO_3(g)$$

The sulphur dioxide is passed into concentrated sulphuric acid to form oleum (fuming sulphuric acid).

Uses of Sulphuric Acid 1. To make fertilisers.

2. To make detergents.

3. As battery acid (contains 30% H_2SO_4).

Test for Sulphate Ion Solution of possible sulphate + dil HCl + $BaCl_2$ solution

$\rightarrow$ a white precipitate if SO_4^{2-} ion is present.

Ionic equation $Ba^{2+}(aq) + SO_4^{2-}(aq) \rightarrow BaSO_4(s)$

Nitrogen

Occurrence of Nitrogen Nitrogen (N_2) is a fairly unreactive gas, making up about 78% of air, by volume.

Uses of nitrogen 1. Nitrogen is used in the manufacture of ammonia (see below).

2. Its inertness means it can safely be used to flush out oil tanks and pipelines. It is used in tungsten filament light bulbs, and in the storage of apples.

3. Liquid nitrogen is utilised in preserving foods by freeze drying.

Manufacture of Ammonia

Ammonia (NH_3) is manufactured by the Haber Process.

Raw materials

$$N_2(g) + 3H_2(g) \rightleftharpoons 2NH_3(g)$$

from air
by fractional
distillation of
liquid air

from methane
by its reaction with steam,

i.e. $CH_4(g) + H_2O(g) \rightarrow 3H_2(g) + CO(g)$

and

$CO(g) + H_2O(g) \rightarrow H_2(g) + CO_2(g)$

Conditions

1. Nitrogen and hydrogen gas mixed in the mole ratio 1:3.
2. Pressure – high.
3. Temperature – about 450°C.
4. Catalyst – mainly iron and aluminium oxide.

Recycling of N_2 and H_2

The gaseous mixture formed contains N_2, H_2 and NH_3. When ammonia has been removed, the remaining N_2 and H_2 (still in ratio 1:3) is recycled.

Properties of Ammonia

Chemical properties

1. Ammonia turns moist red litmus blue.
2. Ammonia is a base. It accepts a proton from an acid.
3. Alkali – since it is a base soluble in water,

$NH_3(g) + H_2O(l) \rightleftharpoons NH_4OH(aq)$,

(ionises partially into NH_4^+ and OH^- ions).

4. Forms ammonium salts.

Uses of ammonia

1. Ammonia is used in the manufacture of fertilisers and itself is used as a direct fertiliser.
2. Household ammonia solution is used for degreasing.
3. Ammonia is oxidised to nitric acid which is an important material for making explosives and fertilisers.
4. Ammonium nitrate is made by reacting ammonia with nitric acid.

$NH_3(g) + HNO_3(aq) \rightarrow NH_4NO_3(aq)$

The ammonium nitrate is separated and crystallised to be used as a fertiliser.

Fertilisers	Fertilisers are used to supplement natural sources of nitrogen, phosphorus and potassium.
Examples	N-nitrogen: ammonium sulphate, $(NH_4)_2SO_4$
	ammonium nitrate, NH_4NO_3
	P-phosphorus: calcium phosphate, $Ca_3(PO_4)_2$
	K-potassium: potassium chloride, KCl.

Plants need these elements for healthy growth, but different plants need different amounts of each. Leafy plants (lettuce, for instance) need a high proportion of nitrogen.

Fertilisers are sold with different NPK values written on the sack to indicate the proportions of the three elements.

Water Pollution Fertilisers, being washed into streams and rivers cause aquatic plant life to flourish too much – and this results in water pollution.

Fossil Fuels

Occurrence of Carbon Carbon occurs as the element in the ground as coal, diamond, graphite; and in compounds such as carbon dioxide, carbonates, sugars and hydrocarbons.

Chemical Properties of Carbon

Combustion Incomplete: $2C(s) + O_2(g) \rightarrow 2CO(g)$

Complete: $C(s) \;\; + \; O_2(g) \rightarrow CO_2(g)$

Reducing Agent Fe_2O_3 in blast furnace: $Fe_2O_3(s) + 3CO(g) \rightarrow 2Fe(l) + 3CO_2(g)$

Copper oxide: $CuO(s) \;\; + \; C(s) \;\;\;\; \rightarrow Cu(s) \; + \; CO(g)$

Fossil Fuels Fossil fuels are those derived from dead plants etc. and subsequently extracted from under the earth or sea. They are:

coal (mostly carbon)

natural gas (mostly methane, CH_4)

petroleum (mostly hydrocarbons).

Combustion All fossil fuels burn:

$\dfrac{\text{in plenty of air}}{}\longrightarrow CO_2(g) + H_2O(g)$
$+\ heat\ energy$

$\dfrac{\text{in limited supply}}{\text{of air}}\longrightarrow CO(g) \;\; + \; H_2O(g)$
toxic, so
ventilation needed
$+\ heat\ energy$

Toxic

139

Petroleum and Natural Gas

Origin The formation of petroleum and natural gas is similar to that of coal but with marine animals and plants being decayed. Gas occurs above the oil.

Location Gulf States, Nigeria, Venezuela, Russia & Republics, North Sea and other places.

Separation Separation is by fractional distillation in a refinery into components based on their differing boiling points. The components are mostly hydrocarbons (compounds containing carbon and hydrogen only). The larger the number of carbon atoms, the higher the boiling point.

Fractions

Name of fraction	No. of C atoms per molecule	Boiling range	Use(s)
gas	1 – 4	below 25°C	domestic gas (CH_4); bottled gas (C_3H_8, C_4H_{10}); lighter fuel (C_4H_{10})
petrol	4 – 12	40° – 100°C	making petrol itself after further treatment
naphtha	7 – 14	90° – 150°C	making medicines, plastics, fibres, etc.
kerosene	9 – 16	150° – 240°C	making aviation fuel
diesel oil	15 – 25	220° – 250°C	making diesel fuel
lubricating oil	20 – 70	250° – 350°C	lubrication of moving parts
bitumen	over 70	above 350°C	waterproofing roofs; roads

In an industrial fractional distillation, the vertical column has a series of 'trays' where vapour condenses. (It doesn't have a condenser section like that in the laboratory version on page 89). The liquid formed can be removed as a fraction, or the lower boiling components can revaporise and condense in a higher 'tray'.

The lower the boiling point of a component (i.e. the more volatile it is) the higher up the column will be the fraction containing it. Each fraction contains hydrocarbons covering a range of molecular size.

Cracking and Reforming   All the fractions are composed of mixtures of hydrocarbons, most of which either need to be separated further, or treated to make them more useful. The higher fractions may be refined by 'cracking' to make smaller hydrocarbons (2, 3 or 4 carbons).

Examples   hydrocarbons with 14 carbon atoms $\xrightarrow[\text{catalyst}]{\text{heat}}$ hydrocarbons (often mixtures of alkanes and alkenes) with 7 carbon atoms

hydrocarbon with 13 carbon atoms $\xrightarrow[\text{steam}]{\text{heat}}$ alkenes with 2 or 3 carbon atoms, and other hydrocarbons

Reforming   The smaller hydrocarbons obtained by cracking can be treated to form useful hydrocarbons.

Hydrocarbons   Hydrocarbons all contain the elements carbon and hydrogen only.

Bonding   Bonding is covalent (electron-sharing) between atoms. Carbon has the special property of being able to bond to other carbon atoms, i.e. to form chains. Each carbon atom needs to share 4 pairs of e$^-$ (valency of 4) while hydrogen atoms share 1 pair of e$^-$ (valency of 1).

Saturated hydrocarbons   Saturated hydrocarbons are those in which each carbon atom is bonded to a total of four other atoms (either carbon or hydrogen).

Example   *Alkanes.*

Unsaturated hydrocarbons   Unsaturated hydrocarbons are those in which each carbon atom is bonded to *less than* four other atoms. It can do this by sharing two or three pairs of electrons with another carbon atom.

Example   *Ethene* C_2H_4.

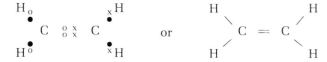

Where 2 pairs of electrons are shared, a double covalent bond ($C=C$) is formed. Where 3 pairs of electrons are shared a triple covalent bond ($C\equiv C$) is formed.

141

Alkanes Alkanes are a group of saturated hydrocarbons which have a general formula of C_nH_{2n+2} (where n = the number of carbon atoms). The group all have similar chemical properties and their physical properties change gradually as the number of carbon atoms increases. A group such as the alkanes is called a *homologous series*.

Methane to Propane

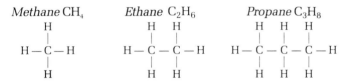

Methane CH_4

$$H-\underset{\displaystyle H}{\overset{\displaystyle H}{C}}-H$$

Ethane C_2H_6

$$H-\underset{\displaystyle H}{\overset{\displaystyle H}{C}}-\underset{\displaystyle H}{\overset{\displaystyle H}{C}}-H$$

Propane C_3H_8

$$H-\underset{\displaystyle H}{\overset{\displaystyle H}{C}}-\underset{\displaystyle H}{\overset{\displaystyle H}{C}}-\underset{\displaystyle H}{\overset{\displaystyle H}{C}}-H$$

Alkenes Alkenes form a homologous series of hydrocarbons with one double bond $(C=C)$ per molecule.

Examples

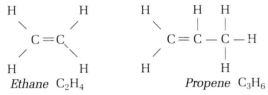

Ethane C_2H_4

Propene C_3H_6

Alkenes are *unsaturated* with a double bond.

Addition Addition is possible. The double bond breaks, leaving a spare bond (or electron) on each of the two carbon atoms. New atoms can share one of their electrons to form a new bond.

The X_2 has *added* across the double bond.

Reactions of Alkenes

Bromine with water If ethene gas is bubbled into bromine water, the red-brown colour disappears showing that the bromine has reacted.

1,2-dibromoethane

> Note: This reaction can be used as a test to distinguish between alkanes and alkenes.

Potassium Manganate VII solution

$KMnO_4$ is a substance which oxidizes an alkene, breaking the double bond to a single bond and adding OH groups.

Example

$$
\begin{array}{ccc}
\text{H} \quad\quad \text{H} & & \text{H} \quad\quad \text{H}\\
\diagdown \quad\; \diagup & \xrightarrow[\text{in NaOH(aq)}]{KMnO_4\text{(aq)}} & | \quad\quad |\\
\text{C} = \text{C} & & \text{H} - \text{C} - \text{C} - \text{H}\\
\diagup \quad\; \diagdown & & | \quad\quad |\\
\text{H} \quad\quad \text{H} & & \text{OH} \quad \text{OH}
\end{array}
$$

glycol (used in antifreeze)

Polymerisation

Alkenes can add to themselves to form a long chain called a polymer. This is done in industry using special conditions.

Example

$CH_2 = CH_2 + CH_2 = CH_2 \rightarrow -CH_2 - CH_2 - CH_2 - CH_2 -$
ethene
written as $+CH_2 - CH_2+_n$
polyethene (or polythene)

and $n\, CH_2 = CHCl \longrightarrow \quad +CH_2 - CHCl+_n$
chloroethene
(or vinyl chloride)
polychloroethene
(or polyvinyl chloride, PVC)

In general, polymers form when small molecules (called *monomers*) join together into massive chains.
(*mono* = one, *poly* = many)

Condensation Polymers

Polymers can also be formed by joining pairs of molecules into a chain with the elimination of a small molecule like water. These are called condensation polymers.

$$\text{H} \dashv \text{A} \dashv \text{H} \; + \; \text{HO} \dashv \text{B} \dashv \text{OH} \; + \; \text{H} \dashv \text{A} \dashv \text{H}$$

$\rightarrow -\text{A} - \text{B} - \text{A} - +$ water

(written as $+$A$-$B$+_n$

Polymers like polyesters and nylon form in this way.

Cross-linking

When monomers are linked such that branched chains (instead of straight chains) result from polymerisation, cross-linking occurs. This gives rise to a stronger polymer.

143

Plastics	Plastics are polymers which can soften on heating and harden on cooling.
Thermo-softening plastics	These can be softened by heating and cooled *many times*.
Examples	Polythene, PVC, polystyrene, nylon.
Thermosetting plastics	These can be softened by heating and cooled *once only*.
Examples	Melamine, bakelite.
Formation	The principal raw material is petroleum:

$$n \text{ (monomer)} \longrightarrow \text{polymer}$$

Danger	Many plastics burn very readily, giving off toxic fumes.
Environmental hazards	Most plastics do not decay naturally (i.e. they are not biodegradable). When they are discarded, they become pollutants and a waste of our natural resources.
Fermentation	Sugar solution is mixed with yeast and left at 25°C for several days:

$$\text{sugar} \xrightarrow[\text{in the warm}]{\text{enzymes in yeast}} \text{ethanol} + CO_2(g)$$

The carbon dioxide can be shown to be released by testing the gas evolved with limewater, which will turn cloudy (or milky). The solution formed after fermentation is distilled to give almost pure ethanol (alcohol).

Yeast is used in bread-making. The carbon dioxide causes the bread to rise, while the ethanol evaporates during baking.

6 Tests for Common Substances and Ions

This chapter contains a summary of the tests for different substances and ions which appear elsewhere in the text in the appropriate topic chapters.

> Note: Care should always be taken when carrying out tests where gases might be evolved. Only attempt to smell gases when under the supervision of a teacher.

Tests for Common Substances

Hydrogen

Hydrogen gas is colourless, odourless (no smell) and lighter than air. It has no effect on moist red or blue litmus paper.

To test for the gas a lighted splint is carefully held near the mouth of the inverted tube. If hydrogen is present, the gas will either burn quietly or explode ('pop') and condensation may be seen on the inside of the tube.

Oxygen

Oxygen is colourless and odourless, and has no effect on moist red or blue litmus paper.

To test the gas, a glowing splint is placed in the tube. It bursts into flame if the gas is fairly pure oxygen.

Carbon dioxide

Carbon dioxide is colourless and odourless, and turns moist blue litmus paper to red. It is heavier than air.

When bubbled through lime-water it turns cloudy (or milky).

If more carbon dioxide is bubbled through the solution, it turns clear.

Ammonia

Ammonia is a colourless gas with a characteristic pungent smell (CARE). It is very soluble in water and lighter than air.

The gas will turn moist red litmus paper to blue.

Chlorine

Chlorine has a slight greenish colour and a choking smell (CARE). It is slightly soluble in water and heavier than air.

It will turn moist blue litmus paper to red and then quickly bleach it.

When bubbled into a solution of potassium iodide, a yellow-brown colouration appears.

Tests for Ions Present in Compounds

The tests for each of the following ions may give conclusive evidence for its presence or it may only give a strong indication.

145

(a) Cation Tests

> Remember: Cations are positive ions which, in electrolysis, are attracted to the cathode (–).

Addition of NH₄OH(aq)

Several cation solutions will form a precipitate when ammonium hydroxide solution is added.

iron (II)	green, which turns yellowish on walls of tube, on standing
iron (III)	red-brown
copper (II)	pale-blue

Flame tests

Metals in Groups I and II of the Periodic Table often give a colour to a non-luminous bunsen flame when their salts are put into the flame. The salt is applied either as a solid or as a solution on a clean flame test wire. Two examples are given below.

Sodium ion

Persistent bright orange-yellow flame (like the common street light) appears.

Potassium ion

A pinky (lilac) colour appears in a small part of the flame, which can only be seen for a few seconds.

(b) Anion Tests

> Remember: Anions are negative ions which, in electrolysis, are attracted to the anode (+).

If trying to identify an unknown anion, it is important to perform these tests in the order given. Otherwise, erroneous results may be obtained.

Carbonate ion

Addition of dilute hydrochloric acid to the sample will give effervescence of carbon dioxide.

Sulphate ion

The sample is dissolved in deionised (or distilled) water. Dilute hydrochloric acid is added, followed by barium chloride solution. A white precipitate is formed if a sulphate ion is present.

Halide ion

(That is: a chloride, bromide or iodide ion.)

The sample is dissolved in deionised water and dilute nitric acid is added. When silver nitrate solution is added, a curdy precipitate may be formed as follows:

chloride ion – a white ppt. which turns greyish or purple on exposure to light. The ppt. dissolves in aqueous ammonia.

bromide ion – a creamy-coloured ppt.

iodide ion – a pale yellow ppt.

Types of Materials

How useful a material is depends on its properties and on the use to which it is to be put.

Properties

Density	The amount of material per unit volume.
Melting Point	The temperature at which the material changes from solid to liquid.
Electrical Conductivity	The extent to which the material conducts electricity. Good conductivity would be necessary in uses such as power cables and electrodes. Poor conductivity would be essential in electrical insulators.
Thermal Conductivity	The extent to which the material conducts heat.
Elasticity	How well a material returns to its original shape when it is stretched or hit is important in uses of many metals or plastics.
Strength	The degree to which a material will withstand external forces.
Chemical Reactivity	The chemical properties of a material are often critical in deciding its use. Sodium, for instance, could not be used in any situation where it would come in contact with water (page 130).

Materials

Metals (See Chapter 14).

Density – generally high (but not alkali metals).

Melting Point – generally high.

Electrical and thermal conductivity – very high.

Elasticity – metals can be pulled into wire (ductile) and can be beaten into shapes (malleable).

Strength – generally hard and tough.

Chemical reactivity – a few metals react with water and most react with acids.

Plastics *Density* – depends on the type of plastic considered.

Conductivity – plastics are insulators, of both electricity and heat.

147

Elasticity and strength – although flexible, plastics do not return to their original shape when stretched, but they can be strong. Man-made fibres are made by drawing out plastics into long threads which are very strong along their length.

Reactivity – plastics are fairly inert, but usually burn, often forming poisonous fumes.

Ceramics and Glasses

Density – ceramics and glasses are usually quite dense.

Melting point – for ceramics they are very high, but for glasses are much lower.

Elasticity and strength – very brittle but hard (with ceramics harder than glasses).

Composite Materials

Often a material is made which combines two or more substances, employing the properties of each for particular purposes.

Examples

1. Concrete – very strong to withstand force but cannot be stretched.

2. Rocks – similar to concrete.

3. Reinforced concrete – uses the properties of concrete and those of the reinforcing rods of steel.

How Energetically, How Fast?

Energy and Chemical Change

Energy Changes	In most chemical reactions, energy is either *given out to* the surroundings (e.g. tube gets hotter) or *taken in from* the surroundings (e.g. tube gets colder).
	Heat is the most usual form of energy associated with chemical reactions, but light and electrical energy are also met.
Exothermic	Exothermic reactions are those where *heat is given out* (Ex = out, as in exit).
Endothermic	Endothermic reactions are those where *heat is taken in*.
Units of heat change	The units of heat change are joules or kilojoules per mole of a specified chemical.
Symbol	The symbol for heat change is ΔH.

For *exothermic* reactions, ΔH is *negative*, i.e. heat is given out, so products have less stored energy than the reactants.

For *endothermic* reactions, ΔH is *positive*, i.e. heat is absorbed, so products have more stored energy than the reactants.

Exothermic Changes

Example 1   *Combustion* (a) $C(s) + O_2(g) \rightarrow CO_2(g)$ $\Delta H = -394$ kJ/mol

(b) $CH_4(g) + 2O_2(g) \rightarrow CO_2(g) + 2H_2O(g)$

$\Delta H = -882$ kJ/mol

(c) *Respiration*
Sugar + $O_2 \rightarrow CO_2 + H_2O$ + energy

Example 2   Water added to anhydrous $CuSO_4$. ΔH negative

Example 3   Conc. H_2SO_4 added to water. ΔH negative

Example 4   *Neutralisation reactions*. For instance:

$HCl(aq) + NaOH(aq) \rightarrow NaCl(aq) + H_2O(l)$ $\Delta H = -57$ kJ/mol

Endothermic Changes

Example 1   *Photosynthesis*.

$CO_2 + H_2O$ + energy $\rightarrow$ sugar + O_2

Example 2   *Dissolution of certain salts*. For instance:

$KNO_3(s) \rightarrow KNO_3(aq)$ $\Delta H = +35$ kJ/mol

Example 3   *Electrolysis reactions* (see pages 111-114).

Energy Involved in Starting a Reaction

Do exothermic reactions always start spontaneously?

No. When methane is mixed with air it does not burn until a flame is applied.

Energy has to be supplied to start off the reaction. Once started, it can continue on its own. This energy is called the *activation energy*.

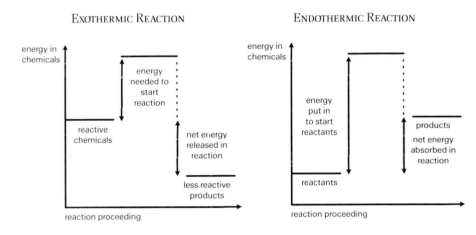

EXOTHERMIC REACTION

ENDOTHERMIC REACTION

Bond-breaking/ -forming

~~Generally, when bonds are broken, heat needs to be put in~~ (endothermic); but when bonds are formed, heat is released (exothermic).

Chemical Cells

In a chemical cell a chemical reaction is used to make electrical energy. If the apparatus below is set up, electrons flow from the zinc rod, through the external wire, to the copper rod, giving a voltmeter reading, i.e. an electric current flows.

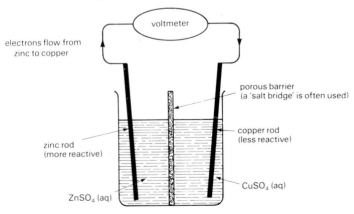

Applications of chemical cells	1. Dry cell batteries are used in radios, clocks, etc.
	2. Lead-acid accumulators are used in car batteries.
	3. Fuel cells are used in space vehicles.

Rates of Reaction

Rate in terms of Product Rate in terms of product is the rate at which a product is formed.

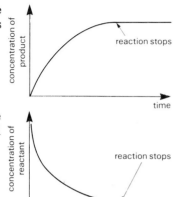

Rate in terms of Reactant Rate in terms of reactant is the rate at which a reactant is used up.

Steepness of curve The steeper the curve the faster the reaction (i.e. the higher the rate). As the curve becomes more shallow (i.e. less steep), the reaction slows down.

Factors Affecting Rate

(a) Concentration of Reactant The more reactant there is present, the faster the rate. Look at the second graph. When the concentration of reactant is higher, the curve is steeper. When the concentration is lower, the curve is more shallow.

Why? When the concentration is higher, there are more reactant molecules around, and so the chance of molecules colliding (and reacting) is greater.

Example $Mg(s) + 2HCl(aq) \rightarrow MgCl_2(aq) + H_2(g)$

The higher the concentration of HCl (in mol/l), the higher the rate.

Gas pressure The pressure of a gas is equivalent to the concentration of a solution. The more gas particles, the higher the pressure. So an increase in gas pressure will increase the rate of reaction.

(b) Particle Size The smaller the size of solid reactant particles, the faster the reaction.

Example   Large lumps of marble with HCl produce a slower reaction, whereas powdered marble with HCl produces a faster reaction:

$$CaCO_3(s) + 2HCl(aq) \rightarrow CO_2(g) + H_2O(g) + CaCl_2(aq).$$

Why?   For the same mass of reactant, there is a much greater surface area with small pieces than with one large lump. Compare the surface area of 1 cube 10 mm each side (= 600 mm^2) with 1000 cubes each 1 mm side (= 6000 mm^2): they both occupy the same total volume, 1000 mm^3. The greater the surface area, the more molecules that will be exposed to the acid.

(c)
Temperature   The higher the temperature, the faster the reaction.

Example   If hot hydrochloric acid of the same concentration is used in the reaction with magnesium above, the metal will be completely reacted much more quickly than with acid at room temperature.

Why?   The higher the temperature, the more kinetic energy the molecules possess; and so the reactants will collide with greater force and with a greater chance of a reaction occurring.

(d)
Catalyst   A catalyst is a chemical which speeds up a chemical reaction, but which is chemically unchanged at the end.

Example   In industry, catalysts are used to speed up reactions so that useful products are manufactured at a lower cost. In the production of ammonia from nitrogen and hydrogen, a mixture of iron and aluminium oxide is used as a catalyst.

Enzymes   Enzymes are natural catalysts, produced in living matter. Their chemical nature is that of proteins (see page 12).

Human enzymes work best at body temperature. In fermentation, the yeast enzymes have an optimum temperature of 25°C.

What the Earth Is Made Of

Types of Rocks

Sedimentary Rocks These are the weathering products of earlier rocks or organic remains of living things which over millions of years have been compressed with the removal of water. Younger sedimentary rocks will always be found on top of older rocks, unless disturbed by earth movements.

Fossils Sedimentary rocks often contain the remains of organisms deposited before the rock was formed. These are known as fossils. The trilobites (example pictured on right) were marine animals living in shallow water.

Main types of sedimentary rock

Fine-grained e.g. shale – layered
e.g. mudstone – unlayered.

Medium-grained e.g. sandstone.

Coarse-grained conglomerate – consists of rounded pebbles cemented together.

Chemically formed rocks Material dissolved in sea-water is precipitated to form a deposit, e.g. rock salt.

Organically deposited rocks Skeletal remains of sea creatures accumulate to form a limestone.

Igneous Rocks Material which forms the upper mantle of the earth is much hotter than the crust. Sometimes it melts to form *magma*. When magma is forced upward into the crust and crystallises below the surface in the upper layers of the crust, *intrusive* igneous rocks are formed. When magma erupts through the surface (from a volcano), *extrusive* igneous rocks are formed. Igneous rocks are composed of randomly arranged minerals.

Some types of igneous rocks *Granite* is an example of *intrusive* igneous rocks. It consists of the minerals quartz, feldspar and mica and is coarse-grained because it crystallises slowly underground.

Basalt is an example of *extrusive* igneous rocks. It consists of feldspar and ferro-magnesium minerals and is fine-grained because it cools rapidly on the Earth's surface (on land or under water).

153

Metamorphic Rocks	When both sedimentary and igneous rocks become subjected to high pressures and temperatures, changes take place to the texture and mineral composition of the rock, although the original nature can sometimes still be identified.

Some types of metamorphic rock

Original Rock	Metamorphic Rock
limestone	marble
sandstone	metaquartzite
mudstone and shale	slate → schist→ gneiss (increasing pressure)

Fossil Fuels	Coal and oil have formed as a result of heat and pressure on sedimentary deposits of organic materials. Coal is derived from land plants and oil from marine animals on the sea bed.
Minerals	Minerals are naturally occurring inorganic solids with a definite chemical composition and structure.
Examples	quartz (silicon dioxide, SiO_2) haematite (iron (III) oxide, Fe_2O_3) halite (sodium chloride, $NaCl$)
Hardness	Minerals are graded according to hardness on Mohs scale, on which diamond (very hard) is 10 and talc (very soft) is 1.

Structure of the Earth

Composition of the Earth	The Earth is composed of a central core (diameter about 7000 km of which the centre is solid and outer part liquid, surrounded by the mantle (thickness about 2800 km). The crust forms the outer layer, the thickness of which varies between 8 km (over oceans) and 90 km (over continents).

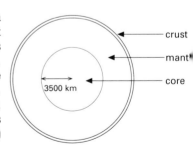

Density	Earth density varies – crust about 2.8 g/cm^3
	mantle from 3.3-5.6 g/cm^3
	core from 10-16 g/cm^3

It can be concluded that the core material must be different from that on the surface.

Seismology   Much of our knowledge of the Earth's structure has been obtained by the study of the passage through the Earth of shockwaves caused by earthquakes and artificial explosions. This study is known as seismology, and the waves are detected by seismographs.

P and S Waves   These are the two types of shock waves passing through the Earth.

P waves (Primary or Pressure waves) vibrate along the direction of propagation of the wave. These are faster than S waves and can pass through both solids and liquids.

S waves (Secondary or Shear waves) vibrate at right-angles to the direction of propagation. They are slower than P waves and can only pass through solids.

Refraction of Waves   Since the Earth's density varies from crust to core, waves are refracted just as light waves are refracted as they pass through materials of different density (page 229). In addition to their speed changing, their path is curved. The deeper into the Earth the waves pass, the faster they travel. They slow down again as they approach the surface on the other side.

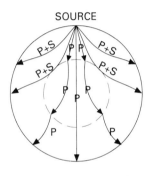

Earth's Magnetic Field   The Earth as a whole behaves as if it had in its centre a giant bar magnet with a North and South pole. This magnetism may originate from electron movements and hence electric currents within the liquid part of the core. Rocks containing iron are themselves magnetic and form in line with the Earth's magnetic field. The direction of the field in rocks varies with its location and age. Study of the magnetism of old rocks can tell us how continents have moved with time.

Age of Rocks   The age of rock can be estimated by two methods:

1. from its geological position in the strata and its fossil content, and

2. by examining the remaining radioactive emission from certain isotopes – potassium, rubidium and uranium. By comparing the emission now with that of a known new sample, the age can be calculated using the half-life (page 96).

Earth Movements

Folds   Forces within the Earth have, over the millions of years of its existence, caused the layers of rock to become folded.

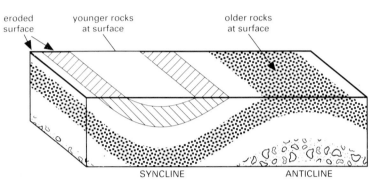

eroded surface   younger rocks at surface   older rocks at surface

SYNCLINE   ANTICLINE

The two simplest types of fold are the *syncline* (concave, looking at the folds from the surface) and *anticline* (convex, looking from the surface). The syncline leaves younger rocks at the eroded surface compared to the anticline.

Sea floor sediments have been folded up to form mountain ranges at various times in the Earth's history. The highest mountains today are the ones most recently formed in this way (e.g. Alps, Himalayas).

Faults   Stresses within the Earth sometimes cause fractures to form. If movement occurs along these fractures, they are called faults.

They can be recognised by the displacement of rocks against each other.

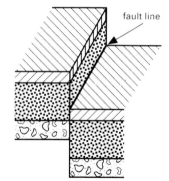

fault line

Earthquakes   What we know as earthquakes are movements along these faults. The point of origin of the earthquake is referred to as its *focus*, and the point on the surface vertically above the focus is called its *epicentre*.

156

Tectonic Plates Both earthquakes and igneous activity (like volcanoes) can be explained in terms of tectonic plates. It is now thought that the Earth's crust exists as a series of very large plates. These plates are moving very slowly but steadily, as a result of convection currents within the mantle which is hotter than the crust itself. Natural radioactivity generates heat which drives these tectonic processes.

Crustal Rocks Rocks forming the Earth's crust are of two types. Those forming the continents are largely granitic and those forming the ocean beds are largely basaltic in composition. Granitic rocks are slightly lower in density than basaltic rocks and so rise high above the mantle. (Remember: less dense objects like cork float higher in water than a fairly dense wood.)

Behaviour of Tectonic Plates

1. In some places the plates may move away from each other and magma will rise to fill the space, forming new basalt. This is occurring in ocean ridges, e.g. in the Atlantic. Basalt contains ferro-magnesium minerals which crystallise in line with the Earth's magnetic field. The polarity of this field reverses every few million years. Successive eruptions of basalt along the ridge show roughly symmetrical distribution of rock either side of the ridge but with the magnetic field of each being reversed. This proves that rocks move apart at ridges all the time.

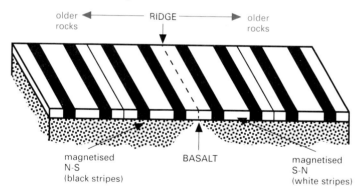

older rocks ◄—— RIDGE ——► older rocks

magnetised N-S (black stripes)   BASALT   magnetised S-N (white stripes)

2. In other places, the plates may move towards each other. As a result the denser oceanic crust will be forced down and remelted to form magma beneath the continental crust, which is forced upwards. This movement can cause folding and earthquakes. Volcanoes may result if the magma can find a way through the crust.

3. The plates may slide side to side, giving rise to earthquakes only.

Surface Processes

Effect of Weathering

As rocks are exposed to weather, the surface breaks into fragments. For example, where water soaks into cracks in a rock, it freezes and expands. This process eventually splits the rock. Small fragments mix with decayed plants and animals to form soil.

Effect of Moving Water

Rock fragments may be carried along by water in oceans, rivers and streams. As they move along they are bounced into one another, breaking into smaller pieces and being rounded into smooth pebbles.

Water Cycle

Most of the water associated with the Earth has been here as long as the Earth has. The water molecules are continually being recycled, forming a process called the water cycle (see also page 78 and 163).

Water on the surface of the Earth evaporates, forms clouds, condenses and falls as rain and snow. This water flows as streams and rivers into lakes and man-made reservoirs before finally returning to the sea, less pure than it was. Water is purified at a treatment plant for domestic use.

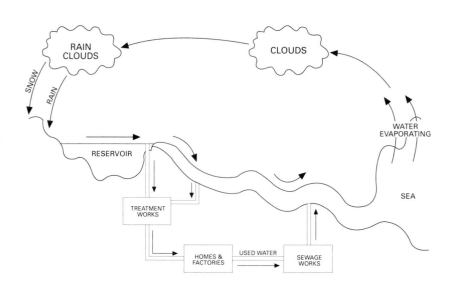

Effect of Atmospheric Gases	The normal atmosphere (page 26) contains gases which will attack certain rocks. Carbon dioxide dissolves slightly in water to form a weakly acidic solution (carbonic acid) which will attack limestone rocks, containing calcium carbonate. The product is calcium hydrogencarbonate which forms hard water (page 123). The effect on rock itself is the formation of caves as the acidic water passes through.

Industrial air pollution causes more acidic gases (page 81) to be present which, with water, form acid rain. This will attack limestone rocks more quickly than carbonic acid.

Rock Cycle

The processes described in this chapter refer to rock movements both on a large and on a small scale. They can be combined in a rock cycle, similar in principle to the carbon cycle (page 79) and nitrogen cycle (page 77).

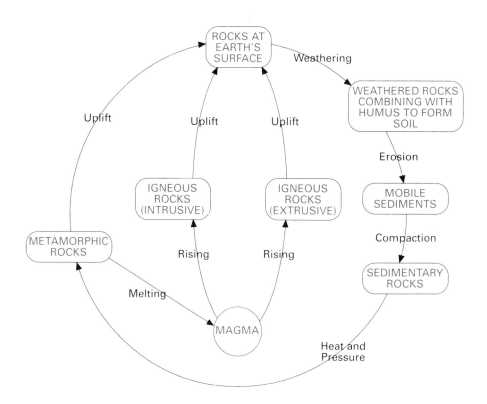

Geological Time-Scale

The events described above have been taking place over millions of years from the formation of the earth. The periods of time from then until the ice-age are shown in a table (see your data book).

These periods include:

Holocene – about 10 000 years ago – end of ice age

Jurassic – about 150 million years ago – dinosaurs present

Carboniferous – about 300 million years ago – fossil fuels formed

Precambrian – about 4500 million years ago – formation of earth

(Note: The geological time scale is always written with the oldest period of time at the bottom.)

How We Get Our Weather

The Weather The weather at any place is the sum total of its atmospheric conditions (temperature, pressure, winds, moisture and precipitation) for a *short* time period.

Climate Climate is a generalisation of the diversity of day-to-day weather conditions.

The Atmosphere The atmosphere is the gaseous envelope surrounding the Earth. It is retained in place by gravity. It separates us from the vacuum of space, shields us from harmful radiation and maintains a stable range of global temperatures.

Vertical Structure of the lower atmosphere

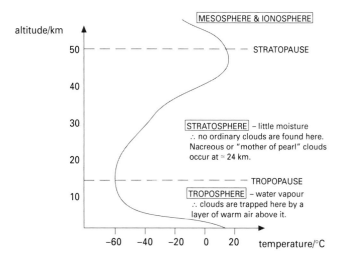

NB. The Ozone layer is found in the stratosphere. A 'sphere' denotes a deep layer, and a 'pause' a boundary. The height of the tropopause varies with latitude. It is found at altitudes of about 20-30km over equatorial regions and 8km over the poles.

Without the atmosphere, temperatures on Earth could rise to 82°C during the day and drop to −140°C at night. 98% of the Earth's atmosphere can be found below an altitude of 30 km, with another 1.999% to 80 km. The tenuous outer shell extends hundreds of kilometres into space. The most changeable layer is the bottom 11 kilometres or so. This is called the troposphere and is where weather mostly happens. There is little water vapour above the troposphere. The troposphere is characterised by a fall of temperature with height.

161

Composition of the Atmosphere

The atmosphere is composed of a mixture of gases, mainly nitrogen and oxygen. Argon is the main trace gas with carbon dioxide and other greenhouse gases contributing only a tiny fraction of 1%. The composition of the atmosphere is maintained by living organisms, especially green plants and micro-organisms.

Condensation Nuclei

Airborne particles including salt, desert sand and man-made pollutants act as condensation nuclei for water vapour. Without these particles, clouds would only form when the air became supersaturated with water vapour.

Water Vapour

Water vapour is a minor gas in terms of atmospheric volume but is the most important one in terms of weather and climate. It is the source of all forms of condensation and precipitation (clouds, dew, frost, sleet, hail, rain and snow).

Atmospheric Heating

The source of the Earth's heat is the Sun which emits short-wave radiation. Tropospheric gases do not absorb this short wave radiation. The Earth's surface reflects some of this solar radiation back into space. The rest is partially absorbed and converted into heat. Surface temperature at any place depends on

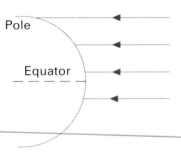

1. latitude – as we move from the equator to the poles the Sun's heat becomes increasingly more spread-out over a larger area
2. season
3. time of day, and
4. nature of surface – dark surfaces (e.g. soil) absorb more radiation than bright surfaces (e.g. snow) or 'polished' surfaces.

A *shallow* layer of air (air is a poor conductor) immediately above the ground is heated by the process of *conduction*. This warm air expands, becomes less dense and rises. Cold air sinks to take its place to be warmed in turn. This process is known as *convection*. The Earth constantly emits long wavelength radiation. Water vapour and CO_2 readily absorb it converting it into heat. Atmospheric gases act something like a greenhouse allowing short-wave radiation to pass through but absorbing and converting into heat outgoing long-wave radiation. The atmosphere is thus heated from *below*.

Temperature Differences between Land and Sea

The temperature variation between day and night over open sea is small (≈ 0.5°C) whilst over land it is large (≈ 15°C). This is because:

1. the specific heat capacity of water is about three times bigger than 'land';
2. convective mixing in water (a fluid) results in heat energy being spread through some depth;
3. water absorbs less solar radiation at low angles of Sun elevation;
4. solar radiation can penetrate to greater depths in water, resulting in smaller surface temperature changes.

Cloud Cover

During the day, clouds reflect solar radiation back into space. Temperatures rise little. At night the long-wave radiation emitted by the Earth is absorbed by clouds, converted into heat and re-radiated back to the Earth's surface as long-wave radiation. It is absorbed and converted into heat. The process repeats.

Effect on temperatures

High temperatures occur on cloud-free summer days, and low temperatures on cloud-free winter nights. The Earth loses about the same amount of heat energy as it gains so its overall temperature is fairly constant.

Oktas

Cloud cover is measured in oktas (eighths). The symbols used are shown below.

Clear Sky

Completely cloud-covered sky

| Oktas | 1 Okta | 2 Oktas | 3 Oktas | 4 Oktas | 5 Oktas | 6 Oktas | 7 Oktas | 8 Oktas |

The Water Cycle

Water covers 70% of the Earth's surface. It evaporates (changes into water vapour) from the surface of seas, oceans, lakes, rivers, soil and from plants, especially trees. Air containing water vapour in contact with a warm patch of the Earth's surface is less dense than surrounding cooler air. It rises through it and cools. The water vapour condenses out onto floating airborne particles.

Dew Point

The *dew point* of air is the temperature at which condensation occurs. Clouds (and fog), are made up of millions of droplets of water (or ice particles). Atmospheric upcurrents under most clouds are initially balanced by the pull of gravity. It is only

163

when cloud droplets coalesce* (and become heavier) that they fall as precipitation. (The mass of a raindrop is ~10^6 times the mass of a cloud droplet.) The rain and melted snow collect in streams, which flow into rivers which in turn flow back to the seas, lakes and oceans. The cycle repeats. The total cycle can be fulfilled in as little as an hour in tropical coastal areas yet take tens of thousands of years in the Arctic.

*Coalescence
Mechanisms

(i) Different size cloud droplets move at different speeds. On collision the large drops absorb the small ones, finally becoming big enough to fall as rain.
(ii) Droplets in the same part of a cloud as ice crystals evaporate and freeze on to the ice crystals until they are heavy enough to fall as snow or sleet. On falling through the warmer air closer to the Earth they may melt becoming raindrops.
(iii) Air currents can mix differently charged parts of a thundercloud. Positively-charged droplets are attracted to negatively-charged droplets eventually growing big enough to fall as rain.

Cloud Types

All cloud types are variations on the three basic types.

Cumulus

Cumulus means a heap. The formation of cumulus cloud is associated with thermals, i.e. bubbles of warm air (produced by unequal heating of the surface air layer) rising through low temperature air masses until they reach saturation point. The cumulus cloud is born and continues upwards. Cumulus clouds only produce rain if they grow at a rapid pace becoming progressively darker.

Symbol for Cumulus

Abbreviation: Cu

Stratus

Stratus means layer. Stratus clouds form a continuous sheet or layer. Layer cloud is formed when a mass of the Earth's atmosphere is elevated to condensation point. When stratus is more than 2 km above the Earth's surface it is known as altostratus. Nimbostratus refers to the typical sheet of rain clouds with a base between about 70 and 700 metres. Provided the air mass has a high moisture content, rain is a certainty.

Symbol for Stratus

Abbreviation: St

Scud clouds are ragged quickly moving clouds. They form underneath cumulus and stratus soon *after* rain has begun to fall. They are associated with prolonged rain.

Cirrus

Cirrus means a hair. Cirrus cloud is thin, streaky, very high cloud (occurring at heights between 6 and 13 km). If it appears in increasing amounts after a fine spell with a falling barometer, change is indicated. If the barometer is steady and the cloud shows no sign of thickening, it has no special significance. Usually the sun can be seen through cirrus. If it thickens to such an extent that it spreads over most of the sky, rain is likely within 24 hours. The individual hairs of the cirrus join giving rise to an unbroken sheet known as *cirrostratus*. Soon after, other types of cloud form below it. Multi-layer cloud systems are associated with bad weather.

Symbol
for
Cirrus

Abbreviation:
Ci

Fog, Mist and Smog

If air (containing water vapour) in contact with the ground is cooled below its dew point as on a clear, cloudless night, it is cooler than the 'lid' of warmer air above. It cannot rise up through this temperature inversion and spreads out underneath it making layers of cloud. This fog or mist is thus trapped. Fogs containing smoke particles are called smogs – vapour condenses on particles of smoke or chemical wastes. Los Angeles in the USA is famous for its smogs.

Atmospheric Pressure

Atmospheric pressure in the UK measured at sea level varies between 975 mbar (low pressure) and 1030 mbar (high pressure). There is high pressure (more air) whenever air sinks and low pressure (less air) whenever air rises.

The Millibar

The millibar (mbar) is the unit of atmospheric pressure. 100 000 Pa = 1000 mbar (Pa = pascal).

Isobars

Isobars are lines on weather charts joining points with equal pressure. They are usually spaced at 4 mbar intervals. Closely spaced isobars indicate strong winds. Widely spaced isobars indicate light winds.

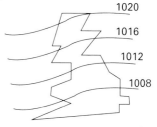

1020

1016

1012

1008

Barometer Barometers measure atmospheric pressure. A rapidly falling barometer coupled with a strengthening southerly or south-westerly wind in the UK is an indication of rain within the next few hours. After rain has cleared and the weather has been dry for 24 hours, a slowly rising barometer indicates that a short spell of settled weather will follow.

Anticyclones ('Highs') *Anticyclones* are high-pressure areas. In the northern hemisphere, winds around a 'high' blow in a clockwise direction parallel to the isobars. The weather around anticylones tends to be clear, calm and generally settled. They are more stable than depressions and may persist for a considerable time.

Cyclones ('Lows' or 'Depressions') *Cyclones* are low pressure areas. In the northern hemisphere, winds around a 'low' blow in an anticlockwise direction parallel to the isobars. The weather around cyclones tends to be wet, windy and generally unsettled, though a few do not have a clearly defined rain belt and rainfall associated with others is slight. In young vigorous depressions discontinuities between warm and cold air bring heavy rainfall. They occur at what are called the warm front and the cold front. If you stand with your back to the wind (in the northern hemisphere), the depression is always on your left.

Tropical Cyclone, Hurricane and Typhoon The term 'cyclone' also refers to violent tropical storms in the Indian Ocean. If the same type of storm develops in the Atlantic Ocean or the Caribbean Sea they are called *hurricanes* and in the Pacific Ocean they are called *typhoons*. They are intense depressions with pressures at the centre far lower than anything recorded in Britain or British waters.

Coastal Breezes Sand absorbs heat more readily than the sea. During the day the warmed air above the sand rises and cooler heavier air over the sea flows inshore to take its place. This is a *sea breeze*. The smaller specific heat capacity of sand means that it cools down very quickly at night. At night cool air over the sand replaces rising warmer air over the sea. This is a *land breeze*.

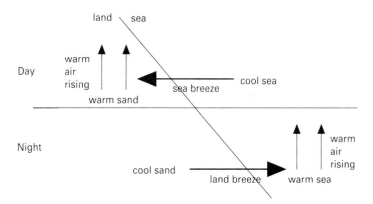

The Monsoon   The monsoon is an extremely powerful sea and land breeze that brings torrential rain and flooding to the tropics. The continents of India and Asia heat up in summer more than the surrounding ocean. Convection currents rise above the land. Air laden with moisture flows in from the ocean resulting in the rain-bearing summer monsoon. In winter, the sea is warmer than the land and the process reverses.

Mountain Ranges   Mountain ranges force moisture-laden winds upwards. The water vapour is prematurely released as rain. The ensuing hot dry air causes drier warmer weather on the sheltered leeward side of mountains. Mountain ranges thus act as a barrier for storms. Indian winters are comparatively mild because of the Himalayas.

Wind   Wind is moving air. The wind direction is always given as the place the wind is blowing from. Winds are caused by differences in temperature and pressure. Air flows from areas where the pressure is high to areas where the pressure is low.

Differences in pressure   Differences in pressure are caused by unequal heating of the Earth's surface by the Sun. Low latitudes receive a lot of the Sun's energy and are very hot while high latitudes receive little of the Sun's energy and are very cold. This temperature difference causes convection currents to be set up.

Effect of Earth's rotation   Warm air rising near the equator blows as wind towards the poles. At about 30° north and south air piles up, making belts of high pressure. Some of this air cools, sinks and blows as wind to the equator. Because the Earth rotates eastwards, these winds are turned towards the west (the northeasterly and southeasterly trade winds). Other winds blow away from the high pressure belts and carry on towards the poles. The Earth's rotation turns these into westerly winds.

General Circulation of the Earth's Winds

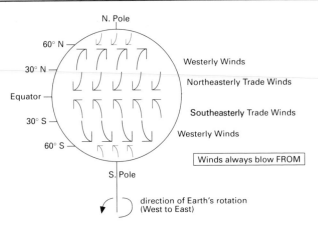

N. Pole

60° N — Westerly Winds

30° N — Northeasterly Trade Winds

Equator — Southeasterly Trade Winds

30° S — Westerly Winds

60° S —

S. Pole

Winds always blow FROM

direction of Earth's rotation (West to East)

Cup Anemometer

A cup anemometer measures wind speed. Wind blows the cups around. Arms connect the cups to a central vertical shaft which rotates. A counter or dial converts the number of rotations per minute into wind speed.

Wind Vane

Wind vanes consist of a horizontal arm with an arrow at one end and a fin at the other. Wind blows the fin round. The arrow points in the direction the wind is coming from.

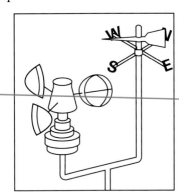

Knot

A *knot* is a nautical mile per hour (1.85 km/h). Meteorologists report wind speeds in knots.

Beaufort Scale

Beaufort numbers are associated with wind speed in knots.

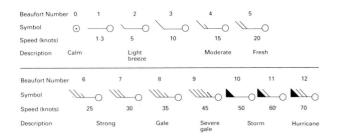

Beaufort Number	0	1	2	3	4	5
Symbol	⊙					
Speed (knots)		1·3	5	10	15	20
Description	Calm		Light breeze		Moderate	Fresh

Beaufort Number	6	7	8	9	10	11	12
Symbol							
Speed (knots)	25	30	35	45	50	60	70
Description		Strong	Gale	Severe gale	Storm		Hurricane

168

Airstreams The map shows those responsible for the weather in the British Isles.

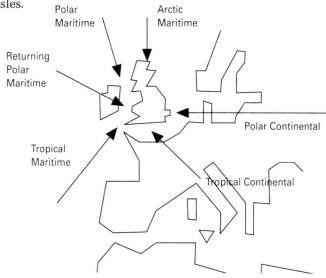

Airstream	Source	Source Characteristics	Associated Weather
1. Tropical Continental	Sahara desert	very hot and dry	fine/steady wind
2. Tropical Maritime	Azores anticyclone	warm and moist	cloud/drizzle/ steady winds
3. Polar Continental	Europe/Asia	*Winter:* cold and dry *Summer:* hot and dry	gusty winds/ cloudy/wintry showers steady winds/ cloud/drizzle/sea fog on east coast/ fine elsewhere
4. Polar Maritime	Arctic Ocean	cold and relatively dry	gusty winds/ cloudy/showers
5. Returning Polar Maritime	Arctic Ocean	cold and relatively dry	cloudy/light precipitation/ steady winds
6. Arctic Maritime	North Pole	very cold and dry	gusty winds/ cloudy/wintry showers

Initially the air mass will be cold or warm, moist or dry. These properties will be modified as the air mass moves away from its source region.

Air Masses   Air masses (large volumes of air) containing water vapour may rise and cool if

1. they move over land and are forced to rise over mountains;
2. they are heated preferentially to adjacent air masses (see 'coastal breezes' on page 166);
3. cool air masses and warm air masses meet.

Front   If a cool air mass and a warm air mass meet, it takes time for them to mix. The warmer, less dense air is forced to rise as a result of colder denser air undercutting it. The boundary between the two air masses is called a *frontal surface*. Where the frontal surface meets the Earth's surface is called a *front*.

Warm Front

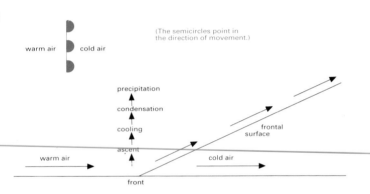

A *warm front* is one where warm air rides up and over cold air, slowly pushing it back. When warm air from nearer the equator pushes away colder air, clouds gradually build up and the spell of warmer weather often begins with a period of rain, especially if the air has passed over a large area of water.

Cold Front

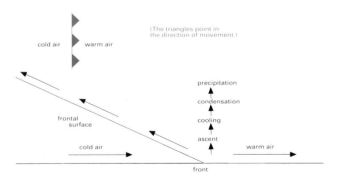

A *cold front* is one where advancing cold air pushes like a wedge against a mass of warmer air. The warm air is rapidly forced up on top of the colder air mass. When cold air, usually from polar regions, pushes away warmer air, a period of colder, clearer weather often begins with heavy squally showers accompanied by thunderstorm activity. Rain is more likely if the air has recently passed over a large area of water and less likely if it has passed over a large land mass.

Occluded Front

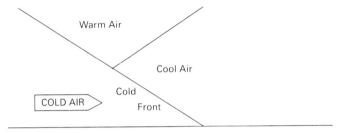

An *occluded front* is one where a cold front overtakes a warm front (undercuts it) squeezing the warm air aloft. A wide band of rain and cloud accompanies an occluded front.

Synoptic Chart (Weather Map)

A synoptic chart displays:

1. a pressure distribution pattern (isobars).
2. anticyclones (with attendant ridges of high pressure).
3. cyclones (with associated troughs of low pressure).
4. warm fronts, cold fronts, occlusions.
5. barometric tendency (pressure trend), i.e. is the barometer rising or falling, and the rate of rise or fall.
6. temperature.
7. cloud type, cloud cover (in oktas) and height of low cloud base.
8. wind direction and strength.
9. degree of visibility.
10. dew point

The Terrestrial Planets

Mercury, Venus, Earth and Mars are called terrestrial because of their similar characteristics, e.g. size and density.

Atmospheres of the Terrestrial Planets

Planets have atmospheres because of the gravitational pull they exert on gas molecules. Fast moving ('hot') gas molecules escape into space.

171

Mercury Mercury has a low escape velocity. Any atmosphere it had, has dispersed into space. Mercury is comparatively close to the Sun and its 'sunny side' gets very hot, but its dark side is relatively cold.

Venus and Mars On both planets, CO_2 is the dominant gas (95%). Nitrogen is the next abundant gas. Atmospheric pressure on Venus is 90 times that on the Earth and 30 000 times that of Mars. Clouds on Venus are composed of sulphuric acid droplets. Its surface temperature can rise as high as 480°C. An unprotected person standing on the surface of Venus would be suffocated, crushed, corroded and fried. The Martian day is almost identical to the Earth's day but a Martian year is twice as long. Its angle of tilt is similar to Earth's and thus it has seasons rather like ours (but twice as long). Mars is approximately half the size of the Earth having a mass of one tenth of the Earth's. It has two moons, Phobos and Deimos (Fear and Terror!). There is evidence to suggest that both Venus and Mars have lost water they once had. What little water remains on Mars is largely trapped as ice in the north polar cap. It would appear that the original atmospheres of the terrestrial planets were made from gases released from the hot rocks that made them up – water vapour, carbon monoxide, carbon dioxide, hydrogen, nitrogen and small amounts of methane and ammonia. Hydrogen (the lightest gas) escaped into space.

Earth The evolution of the Earth's atmosphere appears to have been determined by:
1. the presence of liquid water followed by
2. the emergence of life.

All the free oxygen present has been released by living organisms. Photosynthesis, the process by which green plants manufacture their carbohydrates from atmospheric CO_2 and water in the presence of solar energy, releases oxygen. The formation of oxygen in the atmosphere resulted in the development of an ozone layer which filters out harmful UV from the Sun allowing the evolution of new living organisms. Most of the carbon from the CO_2 in the air gradually became locked up in sedimentary rocks as carbonates (e.g. limestone) and fossil fuels. Nitrogen gas was released into the air, partly from the reaction between oxygen and ammonia but mainly from living organisms including soil bacteria. In the absence of oxygen, these break down nitrates and nitrites and evolve free oxygen.

Terraforming Mars Some scientists believe that Mars can be transformed into a second Earth. How?

1. Introduce gases into the Martian atmosphere that trap the Sun's heat. More CO_2 is released as surface rocks warm. The greenhouse effect is enhanced. We have to be careful to ensure we do not finish up with the 'runaway greenhouse effect' that prevails on Venus! Ice trapped in the soil melts. Rivers, lakes and seas form.
2. Introduce bacteria to turn the CO_2 into oxygen.

The Sciences

Physical Processes

21 Forces and their Effects

Scalar Quantity	A scalar quantity has only size associated with it.
Scalar Addition	Scalar addition is straightforward. Thus 3 + 4 *always* equals 7.
Examples of Scalar Quantities	Scalar quantities include mass, length, volume, density, pressure, speed, temperature and energy.
Vector Quantity	A vector quantity has both size and direction associated with it.
Examples of Vector Quantities	Vector quantities include displacement, velocity, acceleration and force.
Force	A force is that which is capable of altering the state of rest or uniform motion of a body or changing the shape of a body.
Units of Force	The unit of force is the newton (N).

Vector Addition of Forces Acting in the Same Direction

Resultant force, R = 7N (to the right).

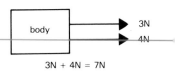

$$3N + 4N = 7N$$

Vector Addition of Forces Acting in Opposite Directions

Resultant force, R = 1N (to the right).

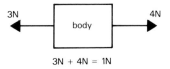

$$3N + 4N = 1N$$

Vector Addition of Forces Acting at Right Angles

Resultant force, R = 5N (in the direction shown).

Here, the resultant is found by letting, say, 1N be represented by 1 cm. A rectangle is drawn and the length of the diagonal of the rectangle in cm gives the size of the resultant in newtons. It turns out to be 5. Alternatively, we could use Pythagoras's theorem:

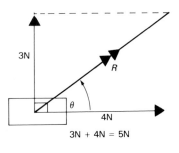

$$3N + 4N = 5N$$

$$R^2 = 3^2 + 4^2 = 9 + 16 = 25, \quad \text{so } R = 5N.$$

Direction of the Resultant	The direction of the resultant with say the horizontal, angle θ, could be measured with a protractor.

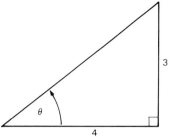

Alternatively, we know $\tan \theta = \dfrac{3}{4} = 0.75$. So $\theta = 36.87°$, i.e. the resultant force has a size of 5N and acts at 36.87° to the horizontal.

Resolving a Single Force into Two Forces at Right Angles to Each Other	Given: $R = 5N$ and $\theta = 36.87°$ then $\cos \theta = \dfrac{X}{R}$, so $\quad X = R \cos \theta = 4N$ and $\sin \theta = \dfrac{Y}{R}$, so $\quad Y = R \sin \theta = 3N$

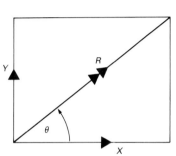

Body A body is a general term that covers whatever we want it to cover – a car, a truck, a bus, chairs, and so on.

Units of Mass The unit of mass is the kilogram (kg).

Gravitational Field A gravitational field is produced by any concentration of mass, e.g. a planet or star. The field will exert an attractive force on any other mass nearby, e.g. a spacecraft.

Strength of a Gravitational Field The strength is defined as the gravitational force acting on a body in the field per kilogram of its mass.

Acceleration due to Gravity Acceleration due to gravity is the downward acceleration (g) of a body attracted by the Earth's field.

Weight of a Mass Weight is the downward gravitational force (W) acting on the mass (m) during its descent. It still acts when the mass reaches the Earth's surface. From the definition of gravitational field strength:

$$g = \frac{W}{m} \quad \text{so,} \quad \boxed{W = m \times g}$$

Since W is a force, its unit is the newton. One newton is the weight of an average sized apple.

177

Strength of Earth's Gravitational Field

The strength of the Earth's gravitational field is about ten newtons for every kilogram ($\simeq$ 10 N/kg).

In fact, a more accurate approximation is 9.8 newtons per kg (N/kg).

Over the Earth	
Mass (kg)	Weight (N)
1	10
2	20
5	50
100	1000

Inertia

Suppose your Rolls-Royce and my Mini have both broken down on a stretch of level road. You would find it much more difficult to push your Rolls-Royce into a safe area than I would my Mini, and you would also find it more difficult to stop it after you had initiated movement. All matter has a built-in resistance to being moved if it is at rest or to having its motion changed if it is moving. This property of matter is called *inertia*, and the larger the mass of a body the greater is its inertia.

Mass of a Body

The mass of a body measures its inertia.

Mass and Weight

To convert masses on the Earth into weights, we multiply by ten (or, more correctly, 9.8). Since we would need to multiply the mass of *every* object in kilograms by ten to convert to newtons, it is simpler not to bother in everyday life.

However, in science:

1. we do not confine ourselves to the Earth; and
2. the gravitational field strength (denoted by the symbol g) *does* vary slightly over the surface of the Earth – for example, an object is pulled more by the Earth at sea-level than at the top of a high mountain, therefore its weight is greater at sea-level.

Surface Gravitational Field Strength

Planet	Surface gravitational field strength (N/kg)
Mercury	3.7
Venus	8.8
Earth	9.8
Jupiter	25.8

Average Speed

$$\text{Average speed} = \frac{\text{total distance travelled}}{\text{total time taken}}$$

Example Problem

Suppose a 360-kilometre road journey takes 5 hours. Our speed is continually changing depending on road conditions. What is our average speed?

Solution

$$\text{Average speed} = \frac{360 \text{ km}}{5 \text{ h}} = \frac{72 \text{ km}}{1 \text{ h}} = 72 \text{ km/h}$$

In the answer, the divider has gone and kilometres and hours have been brought together on one line.

Speed Conversions

Often it is convenient to quote speeds (and velocities) in metres per second as opposed to kilometres per hour.

$$72 \text{ km/h} = \frac{72 \text{ km}}{1 \text{ h}} = \frac{72\,000 \text{ m}}{60 \times 60 \text{ s}} = \frac{20 \text{ m}}{1 \text{ s}} = 20 \text{ m/s}$$

Average Velocity

$$\text{Average velocity} = \frac{\text{distance travelled in a given direction}}{\text{time taken}}$$

Displacement

Displacement is denoted by s and is the distance travelled in a given direction.

Acceleration

When the velocity of a body changes we say it accelerates. An acceleration is *positive* if the velocity increases and negative if it decreases. A *negative* acceleration is often called a deceleration or retardation.

Definition of Acceleration

$$\text{Acceleration} = \frac{\text{change in velocity}}{\text{time taken}}$$

Units of Acceleration

The unit of acceleration is the $\frac{(\text{m/s})}{(\text{s})}$, i.e. the m/s^2.

Formula

$$a = \frac{v - u}{t}$$

where u = initial velocity,
v = final velocity, and
t = time period over which the change in velocity takes place.

Stopping Distance and the Highway Code

Pressing the accelerator pedal enables a car to accelerate. Pressing the brake pedal decelerates it. The faster a car is moving, the greater the force needed to stop it in a certain time. The highway code relates overall stopping distance to speed for a good car with good brakes and tyres (and an alert driver) on a dry road.

Shortest stopping distance – in metres			
mph	Thinking distance (m)	Braking distance (m)	Overall stopping distance (m)*
20	6	6	12
30	9	14	23
40	12	24	36
50	15	38	53
60	18	55	73
70	21	75	96

*Stopping distances increase greatly with wet and slippery roads, poor brakes and tyres and tired drivers.

Newton's 1st Law of Motion (NI)

Newton's First Law of Motion states that a body will stay at rest or continue moving with constant velocity in a straight line unless external forces make it behave differently.

The Acceleration a Body Experiences

The acceleration a body experiences is:
1. directly proportional to the net force F, acting (*for a fixed mass*); and
2. inversely proportional to the mass m (*for a fixed force*).

Mathematically:
$$a \propto F \quad (m \text{ constant}) \quad \text{and} \quad a \propto \frac{1}{m} \quad (F \text{ constant})$$

$$\therefore a \propto \frac{F}{m}$$

Thus: $\boxed{a = \frac{kF}{m}}$ where k is a constant of proportionality.

The Newton

The newton is defined in such a way that the value of the constant of proportionality k is 1. The newton is that force which will give a mass of 1 kg an acceleration of 1 m/s^2; so, $a = \dfrac{F}{m}$.

Newton's 2nd Law of Motion (NII)

Newton's Second Law of Motion is thus:

$$\boxed{F = m \times a}$$

Use of NII

Suppose that the force on an aircraft of mass 725 kg due to the engine is 15 000 N and suppose the size of the frictional drag forces operating is 9925 N.

frictional drag forces
9925 N

engine force
15 000 N

The net or *resultant* force is 5075 N.

Knowing $F = m \times a$: $\quad a = \dfrac{F}{m} = \dfrac{5075}{725} = 7 \text{ m/s}^2$

If the force due to the engine counteracted exactly the opposing frictional force, there would be no resultant or net force acting, so no acceleration would be produced. Therefore, the aircraft would travel at a constant velocity.

If the aircraft were capable of travel in outer space, then on turning the engines off, it would continue to move in a straight line (with whatever velocity it had achieved immediately prior to switching off the engines) for ever – provided there are no planets, asteroid belts or other heavenly bodies exerting a gravitational pull. Force is thus not required to keep a body moving with constant velocity so long as no opposing forces are operating.

Newton's 3rd Law of Motion (NIII)

Newton's Third Law of Motion states that if a body X exerts a force on body Y, then body Y exerts an equal and opposite force on body X.

Consider an object resting on the ground. The downward force W (the weight), called the action force, produces an equal and opposite upward force called the reaction R. An alternative way of expressing Newton's 3rd Law is to say, 'Action and reaction are equal and opposite.'

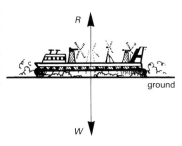

The weight of a hovercraft at rest on the shore is exactly balanced by the upward normal reaction of the ground. When the craft is in motion across the sea the same force balance exists but this time via the air-cushion sandwiched between the hovercraft and the sea. The air-cushion provided by the hovercraft considerably reduces friction between the craft and the sea, allowing it to travel faster than ordinary boats.

Horizontal and Vertical Velocities

Consider two balls dropped from a particular height. One X is dropped vertically; the other Y is thrown sideways. Both have a vertical acceleration of 9.8 m/s^2. Y also has a constant horizontal velocity. The horizontal motion of Y is independent of its vertical motion.

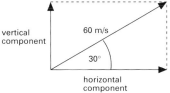

Example Problem

A ball is thrown at 30° above the horizontal with a velocity of 60 m/s.

a) What are the initial horizontal and vertical components of the velocity of the ball?

b) What is the resultant velocity of the ball after 2 s?

Solution

a) Horizontal component of velocity = 60 cos 30° = 52 m/s.

Vertical component of velocity = 60 sin 30° = 30m/s.

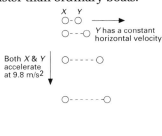

b) Horizontal component is unchanged, i.e. 52 m/s.

In the vertical direction the ball is subject to a retardation of 9.8 m/s^2.

Using $v = u + at$:

$v = 30 + (-9.8) \times 2 = 10.4$ m/s

Then:

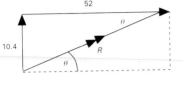

Using Pythagoras's theorem:
$$R = (52^2 + 10.4^2)^{\frac{1}{2}} = 53 \text{ m/s}$$
$$\theta = \tan^{-1}\left(\frac{10.4}{52}\right)$$
$$= 11.3° \text{ above the horizontal.}$$

Momentum Momentum is defined as the product of the mass of a body and its velocity. It is a vector quantity.

Units of Momentum Momentum has units of kg m/s (or Ns). A 1 kg mass moving at 20 m/s has the same momentum as a 10 kg mass moving at 2 m/s (i.e. 20 kg m/s).

Principle of Conservation of Momentum The principle of conservation of momentum states: providing no external forces act, when two or more bodies collide, the total momentum before impact measured in a particular direction is the same as the total momentum after impact measured in the same direction.

Explosions Momentum is also conserved in an explosion; for example, before a stationary bomb explodes, the momentum of the bomb is zero. After it explodes, the bomb fragments fly out in all directions. Since momentum is a vector, the total momentum of the bomb fragments in any given direction is also zero. A rifle firing a bullet is a simple example of an explosion. Before the rifle is fired the total momentum of the rifle and bullet is zero. After the bullet is fired it has a forward momentum, whereas the rifle gains an equal and opposite backward momentum.

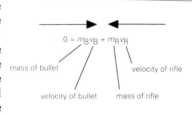

Rockets and Jets Rockets (and jet engines) burn fuel and emit (via the exhaust) gas at high velocity. The rocket (or jet engine) acquires a momentum that is equal in size (but acts in the opposite direction) to the momentum of the exhaust gas.

Elastic Collision In a perfectly elastic collision, momentum and kinetic energy are conserved.

Inelastic Collision In an inelastic collision, momentum is conserved but some kinetic energy is converted to other forms of energy (e.g. sound, heat, light etc.).
In either type of collision, total energy is always conserved.

Friction

Friction is the name given to forces providing resistance to relative motion between surfaces in contact. Friction can only stop a body once it is moving or prevent it from ever starting to move. It is always directed in the opposite direction to the motion.

For *solid surfaces* sliding, or attempting to slide across each other, friction is

1. independent of the area of contact
2. proportional to the load between the surfaces, and
3. dependent on the state of the surfaces in contact.

Examples of friction

Applying the brakes on a bicycle results in the force of friction between the brake block and the rim of the wheel stopping it. If the rim is wet, the brakes are less effective because the force of friction is less (the water acts as a lubricant). Friction can cause objects to heat up and to wear at their surfaces.

A film of oil or a thin layer of air at high pressure can reduce friction (and wear) preventing two surfaces sticking together. Oil is used to minimise frictional forces between the pistons and cylinders of an engine.

Heavy pieces of furniture are often fitted with castors because rolling friction is less than sliding friction. When motion does occur between solid surfaces, the size of the frictional force decreases slightly. This is not true of a body moving through a fluid. Here, the faster the body moves the greater the frictional force acting on it.

Free Fall

For a body in free fall the size of the frictional resistance increases roughly in proportion to the square of the speed. Eventually it equals the weight of the body, no net force acts and the body moves at constant velocity (its *terminal velocity*).

Terminal Velocity

The terminal velocity of a falling body depends on

1. its shape
2. its size, and
3. its mass.

A sky diver with a closed parachute attains a terminal velocity of about 56 m/s, whereas a sky diver with an open parachute attains a terminal velocity of about 5 m/s. The top speed of vehicles is limited by the same considerations. Dolphins (mammals) and fish have streamlined body shapes and smooth body surfaces. This minimises frictional resistance between their bodies and the surrounding water.

183

Floating and Sinking The pressure in fluid (a liquid or a gas) exerts forces on all sides of any body immersed in it. At any depth the horizontal force components have a resultant of zero. Vertically, the body weight W acts downwards and the weight of displaced fluid produces a net upward force or *thrust*, the *upthrust*, U, on the body.

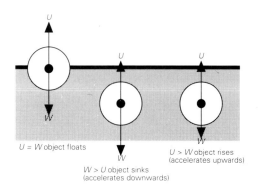

$U = W$ object floats

$W > U$ object sinks
(accelerates downwards)

$U > W$ object rises
(accelerates upwards)

Archimedes' Principle Archimedes' principle states that when an object is totally or partially immersed in a fluid it experiences an upthrust equal to the weight of fluid displaced.

Steel Ship 'Heavy' materials (e.g. a steel ship) can be made to float by making them hollow. Their average density is now less than the density of water since they contain a lot of air.

Submarine There is a constant upthrust on a submarine because its external volume is constant. Its weight however can be varied because it can fill its floatation tanks with air or water. This enables it to accelerate upwards or downwards or remain stationary at any depth. For a submarine moving forwards under the power of its propeller, the rudder and horizontal surfaces (corresponding to the elevators of an aircraft) can be deflected to produce loads on the submarine which propel it sideways or vertically. This is another way of changing the depth of the submarine.

Balloon A balloon experiences different upthrusts at different heights because

1. the density of the air varies with altitude, and
2. the external volume of the balloon varies.

When the upthrust on the balloon is equal to its weight, it will neither ascend nor fall.

Uniform Motion in a Circle   An object will continue moving in a straight line unless an unbalanced force acts on it. An object moving at a constant speed in a circular path experiences an acceleration because its velocity is continually changing (its direction of motion is continually changing and velocity is a vector quantity). It can be shown that this acceleration acts towards the centre of the circle. Since the object has mass, it follows that an unbalanced force F acts towards the centre of the circle. This unbalanced inward acting force is called a *centripetal force*. If m is the mass of the object and r the radius of the orbit, the centripetal force needed is given by:

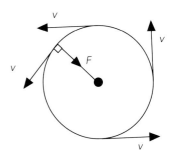

$$F = \frac{mv^2}{r}$$

Examples of motion in a circle
1. A ball whirled round in a circle. The tension in the string provides the inward acting centripetal force. If you let go of the string, because no force acts on it the ball flies off at a tangent to the circle at a constant velocity.
2. The Earth (and the other planets that make up the solar system) is held in orbit around the Sun by the gravitational pull of the Sun. Similarly, the Moon is held in orbit around the Earth by the gravitational pull of the Earth.
3. A vehicle can travel around a corner (i.e. part of a circle) because of the inward frictional force of the road on the tyres.

Satellites   The centripetal force needed to keep a satellite of mass m, travelling at speed v in an orbit of radius r equals $\frac{mv^2}{r}$. This centripetal force is provided by the gravitational pull of the Earth acting on the satellite. A satellite with a speed $\geqslant 8$ km/s but <11 km/s will remain in orbit. 8 km/s corresponds to a circular orbit. Sputnik I, launched by the Russians on 4th October 1957 was the first man-made satellite and orbited the Earth every 96 minutes. Telstar, launched in 1962, was the first communications satellite but could only be used when in range of the aerials of the user.

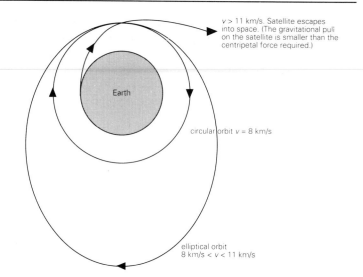

v > 11 km/s. Satellite escapes into space. (The gravitational pull on the satellite is smaller than the centripetal force required.)

circular orbit v = 8 km/s

elliptical orbit
8 km/s < v < 11 km/s

Weight-lessness A body is not truly weightless unless it is at a place where the gravitational field strength is zero. Astronauts in orbit around the Earth experience *the sensation of weightlessness* because they and their spaceship are in free fall towards the Earth. (Passengers in a lift accelerating down at g are falling with the same acceleration as the lift and experience the same sensation since no upwards push is felt.) The astronauts are moving with constant speed along the same orbit but have a centripetal acceleration of the same size as that of the spaceship and equal to the gravitational field strength at that height. There is no contact force between them and the spaceship but they do have weight. This weight provides the centripetal force required to keep them in orbit.

Tensile Force A tensile force tends to stretch a material.

force   force

Compressive Force A compressive force tends to squeeze or crush a material.

force   force

Shear Force A shear force tends to slide one face of a material over an adjacent face.

The cards are in shear. A shear force can cause a material to slide, bend or twist.

pack of cards
force
force
table

Elastic Materials	Elastic materials return to their original dimensions (within certain load limits) when the deforming load is removed.
Examples	Examples of elastic materials include copper, mild steel and rubber.
Plastic Materials	Plastic materials show no tendency to return to their original dimensions when the deforming load is removed.
Examples	Examples of plastic materials include plasticine and lead.
Ductile Material	A ductile material can be permanently stretched by tensile forces.
Examples	Examples of ductile materials include gold, copper and mild steel.
Hooke's Law	Hooke's Law states that provided some maximum load is not exceeded (the *limit of proportionality*), the extension of a material is directly proportional to the applied force.
Elastic Limit	The elastic limit is the maximum load a body can experience and still retain its original dimensions when the deforming load is removed. The elastic limit often coincides with the limit of proportionality.
Brittle Material	A brittle material breaks soon after the elastic limit has been reached.
Examples	Examples of brittle materials include cast iron, brick, glass, ceramics and concrete. Brittle materials tend to be strong in compression.

Crane
A crane can be reduced to three components:
1. a cable, X
2. a support, Y
3. a horizontal beam, Z.
X is in tension.
Y is in compression.
Z is in shear because it is acted upon by two equal and opposite forces, upwards from Y and downwards from X.

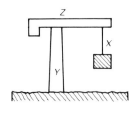

Beam
A beam is supported at each end.

The upper surface AB is in compression, and the lower surface CD is in tension.

187

Concrete Concrete is strong in compression but weak in tension.

Concrete Beam A concrete beam may break unless reinforced by including steel rods in the lower sections of the beam.

Cantilever A cantilever is a beam supported at one end only. If the beam were concrete we would introduce steel reinforcing rods in the upper sections because they are in tension.

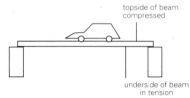

Simple Bridge A simple bridge comprises a beam or bridge deck supported at each end.

Bridges can be made from stone, steel or reinforced concrete.

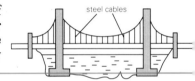

topside of beam compressed

underside of beam in tension

Suspension Bridge The supporting steel cables of a suspension bridge are under tension arising from the weight of the bridge and any loads on it (e.g. cars, lorries).

steel cables

Arch Bridge The beam in an arch bridge can be supported by an arch either from above as in the first picture or from below as in the second picture. The weight of the arch and any load it is carrying compress the material from which the arch is made. The arch bridge can be visualised as an upside-down suspension cable.

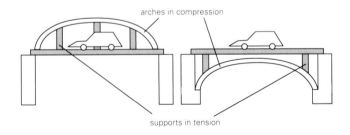

arches in compression

supports in tension

Equilibrium If a particle or body has zero linear acceleration and no tendency to rotate, then the particle or body is said to be in equilibrium.

Moments, Centre of Gravity and Machines

Moment of a Force about a Point The moment of a force about a point (torque) quantifies the turning effect of a force.

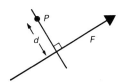

Formula

Moment of a force =	force × perpendicular distance
(about a point)	(from the line of action of the force to the point)

In the diagram, the moment of force F about point P is $F × d$.

Units of Torque The unit of torque is the newton-metre (Nm).

Riding a Bicycle Riding a bicycle involves applying a force to a pedal.

Length of crank = 20 cm or 0.2 m. For a downward vertical force of 25 N, the moment about the bearing O is $25\,x$ Nm.

$$\sin 30 = \frac{x}{\text{length of crank}} = \frac{x}{0.2\ \text{m}}$$

$\therefore x = 0.1$ m

$\therefore$ moment about bearing O

    = 25N × 0.1 m

    = 2.5 Nm

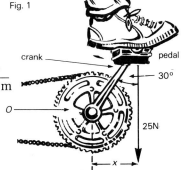

Fig. 1

crank

pedal

30°

25N

Turning the pedal to the correct position and applying the same force results in the maximum moment about the bearing.

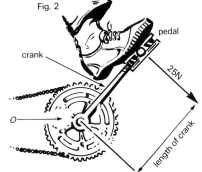

Fig. 2

pedal

crank

25N

length of crank

Moment about bearing is 25 N × 0.2 m, i.e. 5 Nm

The greatest moment exerted by the bicycle rider is with the pedal as in fig. 2.

189

Principle of Moments	The principle of moments states that for a body in equilibrium, the sum of the clockwise moments equals the sum of the anticlockwise moments.
Parallel Forces Acting on a Body	1. The sum of the forces in one direction equals the sum of forces in the opposite direction. 2. The principle of moments applies.
Centre of Gravity	The centre of gravity (c.g.) is the point through which the total weight of an object appears to act.

To Find the Centre of Gravity of an Irregular Shaped Lamina

1. Let the card hang freely from a pin held in a retort stand.
2. Hang a plumbline from the pin.
3. Mark the position of the plumb-line with crosses on the card. Draw a line through the crosses. The c.g. of the card lies somewhere on this line.
4. Rehang the card with the pin through another hole.
5. Repeat 3.

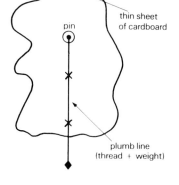

pin

thin sheet of cardboard

plumb line (thread + weight)

The intersection of the two lines locates the c.g. We can check this result by rehanging the card through a third hole and repeating 3 once more.

Stability of an Object	The stability of an object depends upon: 1. the location of its centre of gravity; and 2. its base area. Stable objects should have a low c.g. and a wide base area.
Racing Cars	Racing cars are built low. Their engines are usually mounted lengthways and nest in the middle of the rear of the car. They have a wide wheelbase and are shod with wide tyres. The risk of overturning when travelling around tortuous bends at high speeds is thus dramatically reduced.
Machine	A machine is a device for doing work.
Lever	A lever is a simple machine. A crowbar is the simplest form of lever.
Fulcrum	The fulcrum is the axis about which a rigid body is pivoted.
Effort (E), Load (L)	The effort E is the term used to describe a force applied at one point on the lever to overcome a force called the load L at some other point.

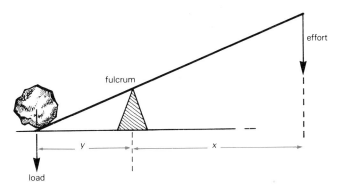

Equation of Moments about Fulcrum

The equation for load and effort about the *fulcrum* is:

$$L \times y = E \times x$$

where x = perpendicular distance of fulcrum to line of action of effort;

and y = perpendicular distance of fulcrum to line of action of load.

In practice $E \times x$ is *always* greater than $L \times y$ because of friction at the fulcrum and the weight of the lever.

Efficiency of a Machine

$$\text{Efficiency of a machine} = \frac{\text{work done on the load}}{\text{work done by the effort}}$$

Efficiency of lever above $= \dfrac{L \times y}{E \times x}$

The ratio is usually expressed as a percentage (multiply by 100).

Typical Levers

	Examples
Type 1. Fulcrum lies between effort and load	crowbar, claw hammer, pliers
Type 2. Load lies between effort and fulcrum	wheelbarrow, nutcrackers, car bonnet
Type 3. Effort lies between load and fulcrum	fishing rod, tweezers, sugar tongs

Type 2 Type 2 levers are known as force multipliers because a small effort moves a large load.

Type 3 Type 3 levers are known as distance multipliers because the load moves further than the effort. The distance is magnified. (N.B. The load is smaller than the effort.)

191

Wheel and Axle	The wheel and axle is a continuous lever. Examples include the brace, the screwdriver, a car steering wheel, and the winch.

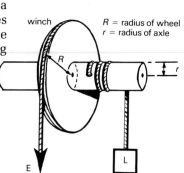

Circumference of a Circle	$C = 2 \times \pi \times$ radius Distance moved by effort $= 2\pi R$ Distance moved by load $= 2\pi r$

Equation of Moments about Axis of Rotation	The equation for load and effort about the *axis of rotation* is: $$L \times r = E \times R$$ $E \times R$ is always greater than $L \times r$ because of friction.

Gears	Gears can also be considered to be a continuous lever.

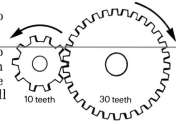

The small wheel needs to move anticlockwise through three full turns for the large wheel to move through one full turn (clockwise).

Driver	The small wheel here is known as the *driver*. The large wheel is being *driven*.

Reversing roles (large wheel driving small one) results in the small wheel rotating at a greater rate than the large one.

Single Fixed Pulley	A single fixed pulley is useful for raising small loads vertically. It is easier to pull downwards than upwards. The effort applied equals the load raised (neglecting the weight of the rope, elasticity of the rope and friction in the pulley bearings). The effort and the load move equal distances.

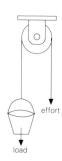

Single Moving Pulley The load is supported by the tension in two sections of string, i.e. the size of the effort applied need only be half the size of the load.*

Two-Pulley System The size of the effort here need only be half the size of the load.* The distance moved by the effort is twice the distance moved by the load.

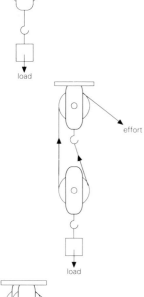

Block and Tackle A block and tackle comprises two blocks containing from two to eight pulleys in each. The pulleys in each block are mounted side by side.

Here the size of the effort need only be a quarter the size of the load. The distance moved by the effort is four times the distance moved by the load.*

*We neglect the weight of the pulley(s), the weight of the rope and friction.

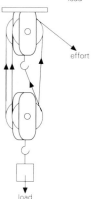

Efficiency The useful work done by the pulley is always less than the work done by the effort.

Efficiency of pulley system	= $\dfrac{\text{work ouput}}{\text{work input}}$
Efficiency	= $\dfrac{\text{load} \times \text{distance load moves}}{\text{effort} \times \text{distance effort moves}}$

Again the ratio is usually expressed as a percentage (multiply by 100).

23 Solids, Liquids and Gases

Kinetic Theory of Matter The kinetic theory of matter explains the existence and properties of the three states of matter – namely solids, liquids and gases. Electric forces acting between molecules (and ions) can be both attractive and repulsive. If two molecules are very close to each other they repel. At a particular distance the attractive and repulsive forces cancel. Beyond this distance attractive forces predominate. The size of the attractive force tails off quite sharply with increasing distance.

Solids Molecules within a solid can vibrate only about a mean fixed position. The average distance between adjacent molecules is such that attractive and repulsive forces cancel. In metals the distance between the centre of an ion and its nearest neighbour is approximately equal to the diameter of one ion. The distance between adjacent ice molecules is approximately equal to two molecular diameters.

Solids have a regular repeating molecular or ionic pattern, i.e. they are crystalline. Solids have a definite shape and volume.

Properties of Solids
1. Close molecular packing.
2. Low compressibilities.
3. Densities – high compared to gases.
4. Rigid – they do not easily change their shape under the action of small forces.

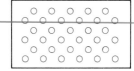

Liquids Liquid molecules have enough energy to move quickly over short distances and are never in the proximity of another molecule for a long enough period to be held in a fixed position. A liquid can flow and always takes the shape of its container.

Properties of Liquids
1. Comparatively close but disordered molecular packing.
2. Low compressibilities (~ same as solids).
3. Densities ~ same as solids.
4. No rigidity.
5. Have viscosities about one hundred times higher than gases.

Viscosity of a Medium A body moving through a medium has to keep pushing the medium aside to keep moving. If the force exerted on the body needs to be large to keep the body moving, the medium is said to have a high viscosity. Conversely, if only a small force is required, the medium is said to have a low viscosity.

Gases　Gas molecules are usually a large distance apart compared with their diameter. Typically the average distance between adjacent gas molecules is about ten times the distance between ions or molecules in a solid. Gas molecules are capable of speeds of hundreds of metres per second.

Properties of Gases
1. Irregular spatial arrangement.
2. Highly compressible over wide range of volume.
3. Low densities (a small number of molecules per m^3).
4. No rigidity.
5. Low viscosities.

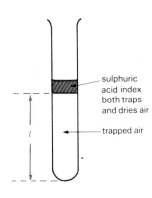

Units of Volume　The units of volume are mm^3, cm^3, m^3, litres (l), millilitres (ml).

Volume-Temperature Graph for a Fixed Mass of Gas　If we trap some air in a capillary tube with a sulphuric acid index and use a water bath to heat the air indirectly, we can raise the temperature of the trapped air. The pressure exerted by the air is approximately constant. The volume occupied by the air is directly proportional to *l* and so we can plot a graph of volume against temperature (see fig. 1).

sulphuric acid index both traps and dries air

trapped air

Pressure-Temperature Graph for a Fixed Mass of Gas　A flask containing a fixed volume of air is heated indirectly in a water bath and is connected to a pressure gauge. The variation of pressure with temperature is noted, and a graph of pressure against temperature is plotted (see fig. 2).

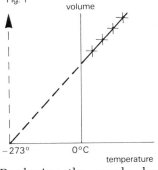

Fig. 1

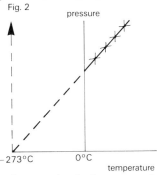

Fig. 2

Producing the graphs backwards we find they cut the temperature axis at − 273°C.

195

Absolute Zero   Absolute zero is the lowest temperature possible – the zero of the absolute or kelvin scale of temperature. It is equal to $-273\,°C$.

The Kelvin (K)   The kelvin is the unit on this temperature scale. A temperature difference of 1 K is the same size as a $1\,°C$ temperature difference.

Conversions   To convert from $°C$ to K, *add* 273.
For instance:
$-20\,°C = 253\ K$, $0\,°C = 273\ K$, $20\,°C = 293\ K$, $100\,°C = 373\ K$
To convert from K to $°C$, *subtract* 273.

General Gas Equation for a Fixed Mass of Gas

$$\frac{P_1 V_1}{T_1} = \text{a constant}$$

where P_1 = pressure exerted by the gas
V_1 = volume occupied by the gas
T_1 = temperature of gas in kelvin

If P_1 changes to P_2, V_1 to V_2 and T_1 to T_2, then:

$$\frac{P_1 V_1}{T_1} = \frac{P_2 V_2}{T_2}$$

Gas Laws   If the temperature of the gas is constant, $T_1 = T_2$, then:

$$P_1 V_1 = P_2 V_2 \qquad \text{(Boyle's Law)}$$

If the volume occupied by the gas is a constant, $V_1 = V_2$, then:

$$\frac{P_1}{T_1} = \frac{P_2}{T_2} \qquad \text{(Pressure Law)}$$

If the pressure exerted by the gas is constant, $P_1 = P_2$, then:

$$\frac{V_1}{T_1} = \frac{V_2}{T_2} \qquad \text{(Charles's Law)}$$

Density   Different substances with the same volume have different masses. 1 m^3 of water has a mass of 1000 kg. 1 m^3 of mercury has a mass of 13 600 kg. Mercury is said to be 13.6 times as dense as water.

Formula   The Greek letter rho, ρ, is used as the symbol for density.

$$\text{Density} = \frac{\text{Mass}}{\text{Volume}} \quad \rightarrow \quad \rho = \frac{m}{V}$$

Sometimes d is used instead of ρ.

Units   The unit of density is the kg/m^3 or the g/cm^3.

Pressure

Pressure Sometimes we have to consider not only the size of a force acting on a body but the area over which the force acts. Wearing snow-shoes or skis spreads a person's weight over a large area. The bigger the area over which a force acts, the less the pressure.

$$\text{Pressure} = \frac{\text{force}}{\text{area}} \quad \text{or} \quad P = \frac{F}{A}$$

Units of Pressure The unit of pressure is the N/m². 1 pascal (1 Pa) = 1 N/m².

Example Problem A rectangular block measuring 0.2 m × 0.3 m × 0.5 m has a mass of 20 kg. Calculate the minimum pressure exerted by the block on the ground.

Solution For the pressure to be a minimum, the area of contact should be a maximum. Taking the larger dimensions:
$A = 0.3\,\text{m} \times 0.5\,\text{m} = 0.15\,\text{m}^2$.
The force exerted by the block is equal to the weight of the block. Taking g to be 10 N/kg:

$$F = m \times g = 20\,\text{kg} \times 10\frac{\text{N}}{\text{kg}} = 200\,\text{N, and}$$

$$P = \frac{F}{A} = \frac{200\,\text{N}}{0.15\,\text{m}^2} = 1333.3\,\frac{\text{N}}{\text{m}^2} = 1333.3\,\text{Pa}$$

Pressure due to a Liquid

$$P = \text{depth of liquid} \times \text{density of liquid} \times g$$

$P = h \times \rho \times g$ (Take g to be 10 N/kg.)

At depth h:
$$P = 10\,h\rho$$

Note that the pressure due to a liquid is independent of cross-sectional area. The pressure exerted by a liquid at rest at a given depth acts equally in all directions.

Shape of a Dam The dam wall is thicker at the base. The arrows give a measure of the size of the thrust (force) on a given area at different levels within the water. (If we double the depth the pressure doubles.)

dam wall

Example Problem	A tank 5 m long, 4 m wide and 3 m high is filled to the brim with petrol (density 800 kg/m³). Calculate (a) the pressure exerted on the base, and (b) the thrust (force) on the base.
Solution	(a) $P = 10h\rho = 10 \times 3 \times 800$ Pa $= 24\,000$ Pa $= 24$ kPa (b) $F = P \times A = \dfrac{24\,\text{kN}}{\text{m}^2} \times 20$ m² $= 480$ kN (Since 1kPa = 1 kN/m²)
Mass of the Atmosphere	The total mass of the atmosphere is estimated to be of the order of 5000 billion tonnes. The atmosphere is held in place by the Earth's gravitational field and begins around 800 km above the surface. It increases in density as we approach the Earth's surface and three quarters of the world's air is contained within the first 11 km.
Evidence for the Existence of Atmospheric Pressure	1. *Collapsing can.* If we remove air from inside a can, it collapses because the pressure inside is now less than outside. 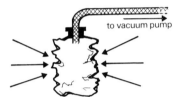
	2. *Magdeburg hemispheres.* In 1654 the German physicist Otto von Guericke, who was mayor of Magdeburg, evacuated the air from two large metal hemispheres to create a vacuum. Two teams of eight horses were unable to separate the hemispheres. Atmospheric pressure operating on the exterior of the hemispheres prevented them from moving apart until air was reintroduced.
	3. *The wind* is a result of a bulk movement of moving air molecules which contribute to atmospheric pressure.
Atmospheric Pressure Decreases with Altitude	The density of the atmosphere is a maximum at sea-level (1.2 kg/m³) and decreases with increasing altitude. If we assume an approximately constant gravitational field strength, then it follows that atmospheric pressure must decrease with altitude.
Pressurised Cabins	In aircraft cabins the air pressure is sufficiently increased to ensure the safety of the passengers. Cabin pressure is allowed to drop to around half of normal sea-level pressure when flying at around 11 000 metres.
Ear Popping	Ear popping is a consequence of a pressure difference across the ear-drum. Sweets offered to aircraft passengers promote swallowing, which facilitates pressure equalisation.
Spacesuits	Spacesuits are worn by astronauts in outer space and on the Moon (outside the pressurised space craft). They provide an appropriate 'atmosphere' for the astronaut. Without the suits, blood and body fluids would boil. Recall the boiling-point of

a fluid (such as blood) decreases with decreasing pressure. In space few molecules of any compound bombard an astronaut (without a suit) and so the pressure exerted on him would tend towards zero.

Barometer A barometer is an instrument which measures atmospheric pressure.

Simple Mercury Barometer A simple mercury* barometer is made by filling a glass tube (roughly 1 m long) with mercury, tapping out any air bubbles present and placing it upside-down in a mercury trough.

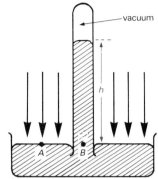

Atmospheric molecules bombard the trough surface exerting a pressure which supports a column of mercury in the tube.

Pressure at B = Pressure at A = Atmospheric pressure = $h\rho g$.

*Mercury is used rather than water because mercury is extremely dense (13.6 times as dense as water). A water barometer would be over 10 m high!

Standard Atmosphere A standard atmosphere corresponds with a height h of 0.76 metres or 76 cm or 760 mm. Atmospheric pressure is often quoted in millimetres of mercury (mm Hg). In a given location, the gravitational field strength and the density of mercury are taken to be constants and so the only variable is h. Atmospheric pressure at sea-level is about 760 mm Hg.

Bourdon Pressure Gauge A Bourdon pressure gauge works in a similar fashion to a rolled up party paper whistle which uncoils when you blow down it.

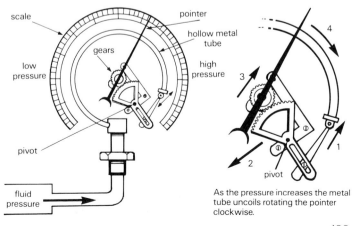

As the pressure increases the metal tube uncoils rotating the pointer clockwise.

Uses of Bourdon Gauge

A Bourdon gauge is used:
1. to monitor the pressure in boilers and gas cylinders; and
2. to monitor the oil pressure in motor vehicles.
Note that Bourdon gauges have to be calibrated before use.

Aneroid Barometer

An aneroid barometer comprises a partly evacuated flexible metal can with corrugated sides to increase its strength and allow it to expand or contract vertically. A strong spring prevents the can collapsing.

If the air pressure increases, the can caves in a little, resulting in the pointer rotating anticlockwise in the diagram. If the air pressure decreases, the spring pulls up the top of the can, causing the pointer to rotate clockwise.

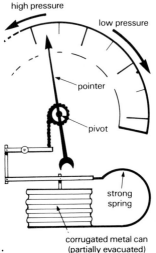

Uses of Aneroid Barometer

The aneroid barometer is used as:
1. a wall barometer for houses (high pressure implies good weather and low pressure implies poor weather); and
2. an altimeter for aircraft – the higher the aircraft, the lower the pressure.

U-Tube Manometer

A U-tube manometer is a device for measuring differences in fluid pressure. For larger pressure differences the operating liquid would be mercury and for small pressure differences we might use water or oil. Suppose that one end of the U-tube is connected to a gas supply.

The operating liquid is pushed around the U-bend by the pressure difference. The pressure exerted by the gas is greater than atmospheric by h cm of operating liquid. To convert to Pa we need to quote h in metres and multiply by 10ρ (i.e. $P = 10\,h\rho$).

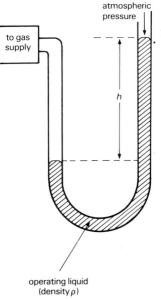

| Head of Liquid | The height h is sometimes called the *head* of liquid. |

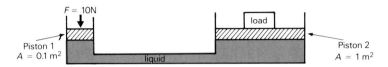

Pressure of gas = atmospheric pressure + $h\rho g$.

| Hydraulic Machines | When pressure is applied to a fluid in a given direction the fluid changes it into a pressure acting in all directions. |

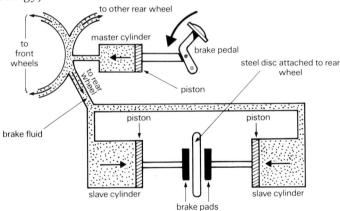

A is the cross-sectional area.
A downward force of 10 N acts on piston *1*.
The pressure transmitted through the liquid is given by:

$$P = \frac{F}{A} = \frac{10\text{N}}{0.1\text{m}^2} = 100 \text{ N/m}^2 = 100 \text{ Pa}$$

Thus a force of 10 N produces a force of 100 N.

N.B. The distance through which piston *2* moves is only $\frac{1}{10}$ of the distance that piston *1* moves through (conservation of energy).

| Simple Hydraulic Car Braking System | |

| Operation | 1. Depress brake pedal.
2. Master cylinder piston moves, forcing brake fluid through narrow pipes leading to the four wheels.
3. The slave cylinder pistons are pushed by the fluid.
4. Brake pads (normally held apart by a spring) are forced against the sides of a disc (which rotates with the wheel). The discs are not enclosed, and heat generated on braking is quickly dissipated into the atmosphere. |

| Air Bubbles | Air bubbles are compressible and if present in the system significantly reduce braking efficiency. |

25 Work, Energy, Power and Efficiency

Work　Work suggests the application of effort to some purpose. In Physics, work is said to be done when a force moves a body through a certain distance in the *direction of the force*.

Formula

Work = force × distance (in the direction of the force)

$$W = F \times s$$

Units of Work　In the S.I. system the unit of force is the newton, and the unit of distance is the metre, so the units associated with work are the newton-metre or Nm.

The Joule　The joule is defined in such a way that when a force of 1 newton moves a body 1 m in the direction of the force, 1 joule of work is said to be done (1 J = 1 Nm).

Energy　Energy implies a fuel or even *power* in semi-scientific language; but in Physics, energy is a difficult concept. There are formulae for computing some numerical quantities but the quantities are abstract. However, we know that no work of any kind can be done without some energy being used.

Definition of Energy　Energy provides the capacity or ability to do work and is expended when work is being done.

Units of Energy　The unit of energy is the joule (J) – the same as the unit of work.

Power　Power in Physics has a very precise meaning. Consider two different machines, A and B. Each machine can perform the same amount of work; but suppose that machine A can do five jobs in the same time that machine B does one, i.e. machine A is doing its work five times as fast as machine B. We say it has five times the power.

Definition of Power　Power is a measure of the rate at which work is done or the rate at which energy is converted from one form to another, i.e. work done per second.

Formula

$$\text{Power} = \frac{\text{work done}}{\text{time taken}} = \frac{\text{energy used}}{\text{time taken}}$$

Units of Power　The unit of work (or energy) is the joule and the unit of time is the second, so the unit of power is the joule divided by the second.

The Watt (W)　The watt is defined to be a rate of working of 1 joule per second. We would normally quote power in watts.

Useful Multiples of the Watt	One kilowatt = 1000 W (10^3W) One megawatt = 1 000 000 W (10^6W) One gigawatt = 1 000 000 000 W (10^9W)

There are many different forms of energy (light, wave, nuclear, electrical, chemical, heat, sound, mechanical and so on) and we believe today that:
1 energy can be converted from one form to another; and
2 in such conversions the total amount of energy that we finish up with is the same as that we started with, i.e. we believe that energy can be neither created nor destroyed.

Principle of Conservation of Energy The principle of the conservation of energy states that in an energy conversion, the total amount of energy present is a constant.

Efficiency A perfect machine would be 100% efficient. In practice no machine is 100% efficient, since energy is always wasted overcoming friction between the moving parts of the machine. The input energy to a machine is *always* greater than the machine's output energy. If the input energy to a motor is 2000 J and the output energy is 1200 J, then the efficiency of the machine expressed as a fraction is:

$$\frac{1200\,\text{J}}{2000\,\text{J}} = \frac{120}{200} = \frac{12}{20} = \frac{6}{10} = 0.6$$

Note, efficiency has *no* units (joules on the numerator cancel with joules on the denominator). We would normally express efficiency as a percentage. To do this we multiply our result by 100 so the machine described above is 60% efficient.

Definition of Efficiency

$$\text{Efficiency} = \frac{\text{useful output energy}}{\text{input energy}} = \frac{\text{useful output power}}{\text{input power}}$$

Kinetic Energy Kinetic energy (k.e.) is the energy a body has because of its motion. The faster a body moves the more k.e. it has.

Formula

$$\text{k.e.} = \frac{1}{2}mv^2$$

where m = mass of body (in kg)
v = velocity of body (in m/s)

Units of Kinetic Energy The unit of kinetic energy is the joule (J).

Temperature The temperature of a body is a measure of its 'hotness'. It is a property of an object that determines the direction of heat flow when the object is brought into contact with other objects. Heat energy flows from regions of high to low temperature. Temperature is a measure of the kinetic energy of the particles (atoms, molecules or ions) that constitute matter.

Heat Heat is energy possessed by a substance in the form of particle kinetic energy. The unit of heat energy is the joule (J).

203

Potential Energy	Potential energy (p.e.) is the energy *associated* with a body because of its position or condition.
Elastic Potential Energy	Elastic potential energy is the energy stored in an elastic object after work has been done on the object in changing its shape.
Gravitational Potential Energy	A body above the Earth's surface is considered to have associated with it an amount of gravitational p.e. equal to the work done by the force used to raise it (against gravity).

To lift a body of mass m through a *vertical* height h requires a *force* equal and opposite to the weight of the body. If the local gravitational field strength is g, then the weight of the body is given by mg and the force required is equal to mg.

Recall our definition of *work*:

Work = force × distance (in the direction of the force)

Here, work done by force = force × vertical height

$$= mg \times h$$
$$= mgh$$

Formula	Therefore: $\boxed{\text{p.e.} = mgh}$
Units of Potential Energy	The unit of potential energy is also the joule. N.B. We call the quantity gh the *potential* of the gravitational field at the height h.
Gravitational Potential Difference	Consider two locations in space above the earth (namely A and B) where the local gravitational field strength is g. Locations A and B are heights h_a and h_b above ground. A mass m held at A has associated with it a potential energy mgh_a joules. The potential at A is gh_a joules/kg.

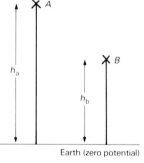

Earth (zero potential)

The potential differences between locations A and Earth, and B and Earth, are respectively:

$$V_a(= gh_a) \text{ and } V_b(= gh_b)$$

The potential difference between location A and B is $V_a - V_b$.

The gravitational potential difference between two points may be defined as the energy released per kilogram when an object falls from one point to the other.

Units of Potential Difference	The unit of gravitational potential difference is the joule per kilogram (J/kg).

Thermal Energy

Conduction of Heat	Heat conduction is the transfer of heat energy through matter due to a *temperature gradient*. There is no movement of the matter as a whole.
Metals	Metals comprise relatively fixed ions in a sea of electrons. Heating one part of a metal results in a localised electron kinetic energy increase. These energetic electrons transfer some of their energy to atoms in cooler parts by collisions raising the temperature of these parts. Metals are the best conductors of heat.
Non-Metals	Non-metals contain no free electrons. The atoms at the hot part of a non-metal vibrate vigorously, transferring energy by collisions to cooler neighbouring atoms. However, this is a relatively inefficient process and non-metals tend to be poor conductors.
Fluids	In fluids (liquids and gases), high energy molecules collide with an energy transfer to 'cooler' molecules. Gases are much poorer conductors than liquids.
Convection	Convection is the process by which heat energy flows from one part of a fluid to another by the actual movement of the fluid. This movement is due to density differences.
Air	Air is a very poor conductor. Houses may be built with double-glazed windows (two sheets of glass separated by an air gap) and cavity walls (two walls separated by an air gap). Air is a poor conductor but a good convector, so plastic foam (containing air bubbles) is sometimes injected into the cavity. Loft insulation (fibreglass) contains trapped air and minimises heat energy loss through the house roof.
Radiation	Radiation is the way in which energy in the form of electromagnetic waves (mostly infra-red) flows from one place to another at the speed of light. A very hot object (e.g. a star) emits infra-red and ultraviolet light.

When radiation strikes an object:
1. some energy is reflected;
2. some energy passes through; and
3. some energy is absorbed.

The absorbed energy raises the temperature of the object.

Rate of Conduction of Heat Energy	The rate of conduction of heat energy through a material depends on:
1. the nature of the material – copper is a better conductor than aluminium, which in turn is better than steel;

205

2. its area A – the bigger the area, the greater the rate of heat energy conducted; and
3. the *temperature gradient* – this is the ratio of the temperature difference across the material divided by the thickness of the material. The bigger the temperature gradient, the greater the rate at which heat energy is conducted. If we characterise the nature of the material by k and the temperature gradient by G we can write:

> Heat energy conduction rate $= kAG$

Units of Conduction Rate

The unit of heat energy conduction rate is the joule/second or the watt, and k is known as the thermal conductivity of the material.

Radiation Detection

When heat energy falls on the junction of two different metals (e.g. bismuth and antimony) connected to the terminals of a galvanometer, we note a deflection of the galvanometer needle. Heat energy has been converted to electrical energy. The size of the deflection gives us a measure of the heat energy received. If we join many junctions together in series we magnify the effect. A cone with a highly reflecting surface is fitted over the end. It is called a thermopile.

Thermopile

Leslie's Cube

A hollow metal cube can be filled with hot water and each of its four vertical sides has a different finish. The radiation from each side can be monitored with the thermopile.

A dull matt surface is a good radiator, especially if black, whereas a highly polished silvery surface is a poor radiator (e.g. a kettle or teapot).

Good Radiators

> Good radiators are good absorbers.

Vacuum Flask

A vacuum flask keeps hot liquids hot or cold liquids cold. It consists of a double-walled glass vessel with a vacuum between the walls.

Radiation loss is reduced by silvering the inner (vacuum) faces of the walls. Any radiation in the vacuum gap is reflected back across the vacuum. The vacuum gap and the plastic stopper minimise heat energy losses due to convection. The materials that make up the flask are poor thermal conductors – glass, vacuum, plastic.

cap
plastic stopper
case
padding
hot liquid, e.g. coffee
vacuum
silvered surfaces
seal

| Greenhouse | Glass transmits short wavelength infra-red radiation. This is emitted by the sun and is absorbed by plants and soil inside a greenhouse which in turn emit infra-red but of longer wavelength. (Only very hot bodies are capable of emitting short wavelength infra-red.) The longer wavelength infra-red cannot penetrate the glass and the temperature inside increases. | 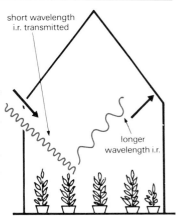 |

Specific Heat Capacity (*c*)
The specific heat capacity of a substance is the amount of heat energy in joules required to produce a 1°C or 1 K temperature increase in 1 kg of the substance.

Units of S.H.C.
The unit of specific heat capacity is the J/(kg°C) or the J/(kgK). The s.h.c. of water is 4200 J/(kg°C). The s.h.c. of mercury is 140 J/(kg°C). This means that we need to supply thirty times more heat energy to raise the temperature of 1 kg of water than we would for mercury.

Formula

> Energy required = mass × s.h.c. × temperature change

> $Q = m \times c \times \Delta\theta$

The Greek symbol Δ denotes 'change'.

Example Problem
How much heat energy is needed to raise the temperature of 0.2 kg of water from 15°C to 20°C?

Solution
Given: $\Delta\theta$ = 5°C; m = 0.2 kg; and s.h.c. of water = 4200 J/(kg°C)

$$Q = 0.2 \text{ kg} \times \frac{4200 \text{ J}}{\text{kg} \times °C} \times 5°C = 4200 \text{ J}$$

Note how the units drop out to leave J. However, the kilojoule (kJ) is often used in the unit of s.h.c. and for Q itself; hence Q = 4.2 kJ. Note the kJ *is not* the S.I. unit of energy, whereas the kg *is* the S.I. unit of mass.

S.H.C. of Sea-Water
The s.h.c. of sea-water is approximately five times bigger than the s.h.c. of land. This means that it takes a relatively long time for the sea to heat up but a relatively long time also for it to cool down. This explains why islands do not suffer dramatic seasonal temperature changes whereas large land masses do.

Car Engine Cooling System
A car engine cooling system often uses water because of its high s.h.c. It is capable of taking in a large amount of heat energy from the engine before boiling takes place.

Central Heating System

A central heating system normally uses water. This has a high s.h.c., and so can transfer heat energy rapidly from the boiler, through the radiators, into the building.

Night Storage Heater

Night storage heaters contain large concrete blocks, which are heated by elements at night when electricity is cheaper. The heat energy stored per unit volume

$$\frac{Q}{V} = \frac{mc}{V} \cdot \Delta\theta = \left(\rho c\right) \Delta\theta$$

is proportional to ρc, which is greater for concrete than for water, and is released slowly during the following day.

Determination of S.H.C. of a Metal Block by an Electrical Method

A 100-W electrical heating coil and a thermometer are placed in two appropriate cylindrical holes bored in a well-lagged metal block. In 3 minutes we observe a temperature rise of 40°C.

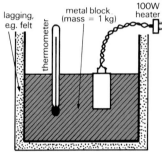

Solution

Heat energy supplied = $\dfrac{100\,\text{J}}{\text{s}} \times 3 \times 60\,\text{s} = 18\,000\,\text{J}$

So, for the formula $Q = m \times c \times \Delta\theta$, we know:
$Q = 18\,000\,\text{J}; \Delta\theta = 40°\text{C}; m = 1\,\text{kg}$.
To find s.h.c. (or c), rearrange:

$$c = \frac{Q}{m \times \Delta\theta}$$

$\therefore$ s.h.c. $= \dfrac{18\,000\,\text{J}}{1\,\text{kg} \times 40°\text{C}} = 450\,\text{J/kg}°\text{C}$

This is a little higher than it should be since we have not allowed for heat energy losses to the surroundings.

Heat Engines

Heat engines convert heat energy into mechanical work.

Car Engine

The car engine (internal combustion engine) is a type of heat engine. Petrol and air are mixed in a cylinder and compressed by a piston which slides freely in the cylinder. The mixture is ignited by a spark, burns, and expands forcing the piston outwards. A rod connecting the piston to a crankshaft converts the piston's vertical movement into a rotary one. The crankshaft rotation is transmitted to the wheels.

Energy Sources

Non-Renewable or Finite Energy Sources	Non-renewable or finite energy sources are the fossil fuels (namely, coal, oil and natural gas) and nuclear fuels such as uranium. These deposits are essentially fixed in quantity because they take millions of years to replenish naturally.
Renewable or Infinite Energy Sources	Renewable energy sources may arise from the sun directly (wind, wave, solar, tidal) and indirectly (biomass, geo-thermal), or be man-made (hydroelectric).
Nuclear Fusion	Nuclear fusion occurs when the nuclei of light elements merge forming more massive nuclei with an accompanying substantial energy release. Deuterons (nuclei of heavy hydrogen ^2_1H) fuse readily into helium nuclei at temperatures of millions of degrees kelvin (temperatures existing in the Sun's interior). Thermonuclear fusion is the primary mechanism responsible for the Sun's radiant energy output and is also the basis for the hydrogen bomb.
	Research into providing a controlled thermonuclear environment could eventually lead to a cheap power source.
Coal	Coal occurs mainly in large underground deposits. It consists of carbon and various carbon compounds. It was formed by the decomposition and compression of vegetable matter over many millions of years. On burning coal, stored energy, which came originally from sunlight, is released.
Oil	Early plants received sunlight energy and converted it into starch and cellulose. Marine organisms ate the plants and, when they died, their unused chemical energy remained. Over millions of years their rotting bodies yielded mineral oil.
Natural Gas	Natural gas is another source of chemical energy, formed from the plant and animal life of millions of years ago. It consists of about 95% methane. It can be piped and is widely used in industry and in the home for heating and cooking.
The Energy Crisis	Oil and natural gas reserves have a predicted lifetime of under fifty years. Coal will last perhaps a few hundred years. Nuclear power stations have a very short lifetime (under fifty years) and building new ones is very expensive. Research into alternative energy sources has thus begun.
Biomass	Biomass is the name for organic (and other) material from which biofuels can be obtained. For example, alcohol is derived from sugar cane. In Brazil, many cars run on alcohol instead of petrol.

Solid Biofuels Solid biofuels include wood and straw. They are burnt for heating.

Liquid Biofuels Liquid biofuels include methane gas and alcohol. They burn more efficiently at low temperatures.

Photosynthesis Photosynthesis is the process whereby plants take in CO_2 and water from their surroundings in the presence of sunlight, and convert them into oxygen and carbohydrates (starches and sugars).

Efficient Fuel Crops Efficient fuel crops include sugar-cane and sugar-beet which convert about 6% of the solar energy that falls on them into stored carbohydrate energy, unlike most plants in temperate climates which convert less than 1%.

Eating Carbohydrates Eating carbohydrates synthesised by plants in the form of a plant or the flesh of a plant-eating animal results in a chemical reaction with oxygen which provides us with the food energy we need for all our body and brain functions.

Energy Values of Fuels and Food

Fuel	MJ/kg	Foodstuff	MJ/kg
Coal	30	Fresh fruit	2
Natural Gas	56	Green	
Petrol	50	vegetables	1.5
Wood	15	Milk	3
		Cheese	17
		Eggs	7
		Sugar	16
		Bread	10
		Chocolate	23
		Beef	6

'Average' Person The average person requires an energy input $\simeq$ 10MJ/day.

Wind Wind is a large-scale atmospheric convection effect. Cloudless regions, heated more by sunlight than cloudy regions, have lower density and thus lower pressure (since pressure is directly proportional to density). Air flows as wind from higher pressure cloudy regions to lower pressure cloudless regions.

Windmills These can convert wind energy into electrical energy.

Windmill Types
1. Horizontal axis machines are the most common.
2. Vertical axis machines respond to wind from any direction (see Darrieus type on page 211).

Windmill Power If D is the windmill diameter, V is the wind speed and ρ is the air density, then the power can be shown to be proportional to $D^2 V^3 \rho$.

Darrieus Type Windmill The Darrieus type windmill is a sophisticated vertical axis windmill (curved blade, egg whisk shaped).

Offshore Wind Turbines Wind speed offshore is greater than it is over land. In water depths of 5 to 35 m, offshore wind turbines could produce enough electricity to supply all the needs of the U.K. However, investment capital, operation and maintenance is at present too expensive.

Problems with Wind Turbines
1. Large wind turbines may be environmentally unacceptable.
2. The alternative is an array, or wind farm, comprising several hundred smaller turbines.
3. The spacing and configuration of such an array has its own problems, in that wind turbines operating downwind of others suffer an output reduction.
4. Tens of thousands of small wind turbines would be needed to match the annual energy output of a major power station.

Geothermal Energy Geothermal energy is energy obtained from hot rocks. U-238, U-235, Th-232 and K-40 are naturally occurring radioactive elements concentrated especially in crustal rocks. These elements undergo continuous spontaneous decay and are responsible for the Earth's internal heat.

Aquifer An aquifer is a water-bearing stratum (e.g. sandstone or limestone).

Hot Aquifer A hot aquifer is an aquifer in contact with hot rocks.

Geothermal Heat Source A geothermal heat source is indicated by the presence of volcanoes, earthquake activity, natural geysers and hot springs.

Tapping Geothermal Energy
1. A hot aquifer may be tapped directly.
2. An explosion may be detonated in hot solid rock below an aquifer, shattering the rock. Water from the aquifer seeps deeper into the hot solid rock, producing steam at a higher

211

pressure. A second borehole feeds in fresh water to maintain aquifer pressure.

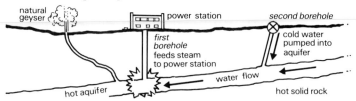

N.B. Temperature of the Earth's crust increases with depth.

Lardarello Lardarello in Italy is the site of the world's first geothermal power-station, operational since 1904. The field produces superheated steam which is fed directly to turbines to produce electricity.

Indirect Space Heating In Paris, hot saline water at depths ~ 2 km is extracted, passed through a heat exchanger (to eliminate corrosion problems) and reinjected into a second borehole. Hundreds of apartments are heated indirectly using this technique.

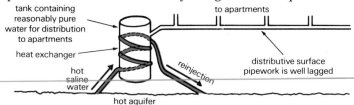

Problems 1. It is known from geological surveys in the U.K. that very few hot deep aquifers lie conveniently close to major cities.
2. It is expensive to transport over long distances the hot water given out.

Solar Energy Solar energy is energy received directly from the Sun mainly in the form of light, infra-red and ultraviolet radiation. Solar energy has the advantage of being inexhaustible, non-polluting and free.

Solar Cell A solar cell is a device for converting sunlight directly into electricity. A conversion efficiency of 10% is typical. A light meter uses solar cells, and so do communication satellites which power radio transmitters and receivers.

Solar Panel A solar panel is a device for producing domestic hot water. In the northern hemisphere it is typically installed on the south-facing roof of a house.

Short wavelength infra-red from the sun penetrates the glass cover and most of it is absorbed by the blackened copper piping. The i.r. re-radiated is longer in wavelength (because of the low temperature) and cannot penetrate the glass.

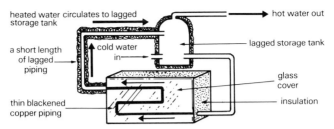

Thin blackened* copper piping contains the water to be heated. (Copper has a high thermal conductivity.) The piping is coiled in such a way that the area presented is a maximum. The rate at which heat energy is transferred depends directly on the surface area presented.

*Black surfaces are good absorbers.

Solar Furnace

A solar furnace is a device for concentrating the sun's rays on very small targets in order to produce high temperatures. A parabolic mirror focuses the rays on to a small target area in front of the mirror. In this way, temperatures in excess of 3000°C can be achieved. A boiler placed at the focus produces steam which can drive a turbine. A generator coupled to the turbine can produce electricity.

Factors influencing the Amount of Solar Energy Received

The amount of solar energy received at a point on the Earth's surface is affected by: the altitude; the time of day; the season; the latitude; and the degree of cloud cover.

Solar Power Station

A solar power station could comprise a large satellite (operating in continuous sunlight) in a geostationary orbit*, carrying thousands of solar cells to collect solar energy and convert it to electricity. This, in turn, would be beamed to a receiving station on the Earth in the form of microwaves.

*Orbiting at such an altitude that it remains stationary over a given point on the Earth.

Tidal Power

Tidal power is a result of:
1. a gravitational attractive force between the Moon and the Earth (the Sun and the planets also play a lesser role); and
2. a rotating Earth – different parts of the Earth pass in and out of a bulge at different times – hence tides.

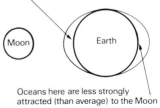

Oceans here are more strongly attracted (than average) to the Moon

Oceans here are less strongly attracted (than average) to the Moon

N.B. Take the centre of the Earth as under average pull.

A river estuary or inlet is dammed in such a way that high tide water is trapped. At low tide the water flows out. The potential energy of the water falling from a high to a low level is converted to kinetic energy by rotating a turbine, which in turn drives a generator, producing electrical energy.

Problems

The power output depends on the tides (which vary on a daily basis) and is consequently intermittent. Economically justifiable tidal energy conversion requires:

1. a high tidal range;
2. a large number of estuaries or inlets which can be dammed; and
3. highly efficient turbo-generators that can operate at a low head of water.

Wave Energy

Wave energy is a result of winds blowing across the sea causing waves. Floats moving up and down with the waves could convert this movement into electricity. However, tens of kilometres of floats would be needed to match the power output of a major power station.

Hydroelectric Power

Rain-water stored in dams is piped (a tunnel through a hill or a mountain is equivalent to a pipe) from a high level to a low level. The mechanism for conversion to electrical power is the same as that described for tidal power.

The power available is directly proportional to:

1. the head of water – the vertical height through which the water falls; and
2. the water flow rate.

Pumped Storage

Because steam pressure takes time to build up in a furnace, the power output of a large thermal power-station (one using coal, oil or uranium) cannot be quickly altered. It therefore maintains a baseload, that is, it never completely shuts down. At night, when demand is less than the baseload, surplus electrical energy operates pumps which raise water at mountain power-stations from the low level to the high level reservoir. When demand rises in daytime, the water previously pumped up is fed down to power turbines which are coupled to generators. The baseload is supplemented. This is known as pumped storage.

Wave Properties

Wave Motion   Wave motion is the propagation of a periodic disturbance carrying *energy*. A periodic oscillation about an average position takes place at any point along the path of a wave motion. Sound waves in air are a consequence of oscillating air molecules. Similarly, water waves are a consequence of oscillating water molecules.

Progressive Wave   A progressive wave is one that travels through a medium and transfers energy from one location to another. In a material medium (i.e. a non-vacuum), the particles of the medium oscillate and by virtue of this oscillation transmit energy.

Transverse Wave Motion   A transverse wave motion involves particles or fields vibrating at right angles to the direction of wave propagation.

Examples include water waves and electromagnetic waves.

Longitudinal Wave Motion   A longitudinal wave motion involves particles vibrating in the same direction as the wave.

A tuning-fork or a loudspeaker cone generates a sound wave in air. Air particles oscillate about some mean position as a wave passes, but the mean position of the air molecules does not move. Alternate layers of air at a pressure slightly higher than atmospheric pressure (compressions) and slightly lower (rarefactions) result.

Undisturbed Layers of Air (Before Passage of Sound Wave)

Situation After a Sound Wave Passes

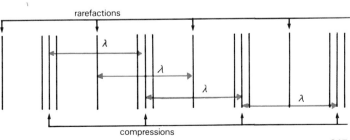

215

Slinky Spring   A slinky spring is capable of exhibiting both longitudinal and transverse modes of propagating energy.

Amplitude   The amplitude is the maximum displacement of a particle from the rest position. In a progressive wave, the particles of the medium oscillate with the same amplitude, but out of step with their neighbours.

Wave Profile Schematic for a Transverse Wave

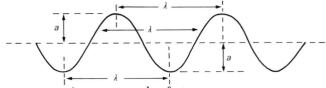

A water wave is one example of a transverse wave.

a = amplitude = height of a crest or depth of a trough above or below the average water level.

Wavelength   The wavelength is the distance between two successive crests or troughs or between two successive points on the wave which are in step with each other. Wavelength is usually denoted by the Greek letter λ (lambda).

N.B. for sound waves, λ is the distance between the centres of successive compressions or rarefactions.

Frequency   The frequency is the number of vibrations made per second by the wave source and hence also by the wave itself. The unit of frequency is the hertz (Hz). The unit was formerly cycles per second (c.p.s.). Frequency is usually denoted by f.

Velocity = $f \times \lambda$

Velocity =	frequency f	×	wavelength λ
(m/s)	(in hertz)		(in metres)

The velocity of propagation of a given type of wave depends upon the nature of the medium. Sound waves travel at around 330 m/s in air, 1500 m/s in water and 6000 m/s in steel. In a given medium the velocity is a constant, and it thus follows that if the frequency increases the wavelength decreases, and vice versa.

Reflection of Plane Wavefronts at a Plane Surface

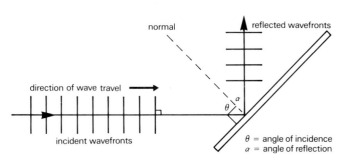

θ = angle of incidence
α = angle of reflection

Generate plane or straight waves in a ripple tank or a bath of water with a rectangular block of wood that is long compared to its width. Allow the waves to collide with a straight metal barrier.

We find that θ is equal to α.

Reflection of Circular Wavefronts at a Plane Surface Generate circular pulses in a ripple tank, using a syringe. Observe what happens to the pulses when they impinge upon a straight metal barrier.

The reflected pulse appears to come from Y which is as far behind the barrier as X is in front.

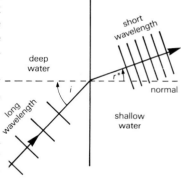

straight metal barrier

Deep Water/ Shallow Water Interface Generate plane waves in a ripple tank. The frequency at which the plane waves are being generated is fixed. Since the wavelength λ has decreased in the shallow water, it follows that the velocity of propagation has also decreased, since $v = f \times \lambda$.

The direction of propagation of the water waves in the shallow region is bent towards the normal. This 'bending' is termed refraction.

i = angle of incidence
r^* = angle of refraction

When the water waves meet the shallow region they are slowed down. So as the wave in the deep water travels the distance WX, the wave in the shallow region travels the shorter distance YZ.

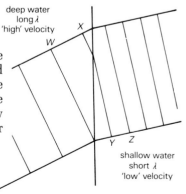

217

29 Mechanical Oscillations

Mass Spring System The mass spring system consists of a loaded spring attached to a support.

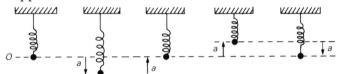

Displacing the load downwards through a distance a results in the load oscillating about O.

One Complete Oscillation One complete oscillation involves the load moving through a distance $4a$ in a complete to and fro vibration between two points a distance $2a$ apart.

Amplitude of Oscillation The amplitude of the oscillation is the maximum displacement attained by the load and is equal to a.

Time Period for One Oscillation (T) The time period for one oscillation is the time taken to cover $4a$. In practice one would need to time, say, 20 oscillations and divide by 20 in order to arrive at a realistic value for T. This is because the 'reaction time' involved in switching on and off a stopwatch can be of the same order of magnitude as T.

Frequency of Oscillation (f) The frequency of oscillation is the reciprocal of the time period T. It is the number of oscillations made per second. f is measured in hertz (Hz). It can be shown that f is inversely proportional to the square root of the mass of the load.

Formula

$$f \propto \frac{1}{\sqrt{m}}$$

The natural frequency of vibration of the spring also depends on the nature of the spring – what it is made of, and how thick it is.

Pendulum Bob A pendulum bob pushed gently to one side of the vertical also oscillates with a natural frequency. Here, f depends on the length of the pendulum.

Barton's Pendulums

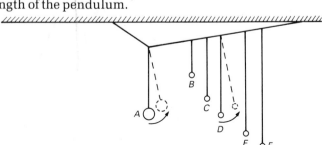

Set *A* oscillating. Pendulums *B-F* oscillate as a result. Pendulum *D* having the same length as *A*, and thus the same natural frequency, is set into large amplitude of vibration by *A*. We say that *D* has been set into *resonance* by *A*.

Resonance

Resonance occurs when a system is made to oscillate at its natural frequency as a consequence of oscillations received from another source of the same frequency.

A Child on a Swing

The child experiences increasingly bigger oscillations if the 'forcing frequency' of the parent is the same as the natural frequency of the child plus swing.

Domestic Spin Driers

Driers invariably pass through a speed equal to the natural frequency of vibration of the tub's elastic mounting causing it to vibrate violently for a few seconds.

An Unbalanced Car Wheel

The wheel eventually rotates at a speed equal to the natural frequency of vibration of the suspension system. The vehicle resonates and a sudden increase in noise is heard in the car.

A Diver

A diver gains substantial uplift by jumping repeatedly at the end of a diving-board. Eventually, the forcing frequency of the diver and the natural frequency of vibration of the board are equal, and resonance results.

Bridges

Bridges collapse if the frequency of one of the upward and downward forces resulting from incident wind matches one of its natural frequencies of vibration.

Soldiers

Soldiers crossing a suspension bridge should break step to minimise the possibility of setting the bridge into resonance.

Singers

Singers can shatter wine glasses if the frequency of the note is equal to the natural frequency of the glass.

Diatomic Molecules

Diatomic molecules such as HCl can be thought of in terms of a mass H connected by a tethered spring to Cl.

Molecules such as this can be made to resonate by subjecting them to infra-red radiation of a particular (known) frequency. The bigger the resonant frequency, the stiffer the molecular bond.

Minor Resonances

Minor resonances can occur in machines with rotating parts, if the (variable) machine frequency coincides with the natural frequency of one of its parts, or a simple multiple of this.

219

30 Sound Waves

Sound

Sound is a physiological sensation received by the ear. Vibrating bodies produce sound waves which are transmitted as a longitudinal pressure wave through a material medium. The ear detects sound waves and converts the pressure fluctuations into electrical impulses which are then decoded by the brain.

Sources of Sound

Typical examples include: the violin, the human voice, pneumatic drills, and church bells.

Sound Waves Require a Material Medium for their Propagation

This is another way of saying that sound cannot travel through a vacuum. This can easily be demonstrated.

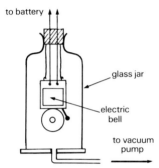

1. Switch on the bell.
2. Gradually remove air from the glass jar.
3. Although the striker continues to hit the gong, the sound slowly dies away.

Limits of Audibility

Humans are capable of hearing sounds with frequencies in the range 20 Hz – 20 000 Hz. The upper limit varies between individuals and generally declines with age. Some animals communicate by sound vibrations outside this frequency range either by ultrasonic waves above 20 000 Hz or by infrasonic ones below 20 Hz. Whales, dolphins, bats and many insects can hear well beyond the human upper frequency limit.

Echoes

Hard flat surfaces reflect sound waves well. An echo is the sound heard after reflection.

Echo-Sounding

Echo-sounding is used by ships to find the depth of the sea, i.e. to locate the sea-bed.

Example Problem

A ship transmits a sound wave, receiving an echo after 4 seconds. What is the depth of the water?

Solution

It takes 2 seconds for the sound wave to reach the sea-bed. Take the speed of sound in water to be 1500 m/s.

Using: $\boxed{\text{Speed} = \dfrac{\text{distance}}{\text{time}}}$

Rearrange: Distance = speed × time

$$= \frac{1500 \text{ m}}{\text{s}} \times 2 \text{ s} = 3000 \text{ metres}$$

Ultrasonic Echo Location Bats emit ultrasonic pulses and navigate by listening to the resulting echoes. Blind bats navigate equally as well as those with sight. They also detect and intercept flying insects by the same means. Blind bats do not go hungry!

Oscilloscope An oscilloscope is a useful device for pictorially depicting transverse waves having the same frequency as the longitudinal sound waves associated with a sound source.

Loudness 1. Connect a microphone to the oscilloscope.
2. Whistle a soft note into the microphone.
3. Now whistle the same note louder.

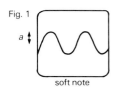

Fig. 1

soft note

a and *a'* represent amplitudes. The *loudness* of a note depends on the amplitude of the wave.

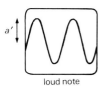

loud note

$a' > a$

Pitch 4. Sound a low-frequency tuning-fork.
5. Sound a high-frequency tuning-fork.
The pitch of a note depends on the frequency of the sound source. A high-pitched note has a high frequency.

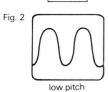

Fig. 2

low pitch

high pitch

'Pure' Note A pure note (a single frequency) is emitted by a tuning-fork and a signal generator connected to a loudspeaker. Generally, notes consist of a main frequency, called a *fundamental*, mixed with higher frequencies, called *overtones*.

Harmonic A harmonic is a note whose frequency is an exact multiple of the fundamental.

Overtone An overtone is a harmonic that accompanies the fundamental. It is usually 'weak' compared to the fundamental.

221

Quality The quality of a note is dictated by the number and strength of the overtones. This explains why a guitar and a violin playing the same note at the same loudness sound different.

Simple Method of Determining the Speed of Sound in Air

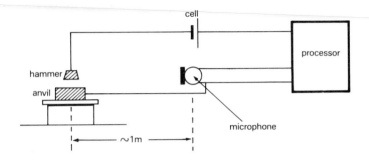

1. Hammer strikes anvil.

2. Processor receives a pulse from cell and a 'clock' in the processor begins to count.

3. A sound wave travels outwards and is picked up by the microphone. It converts sound energy into electrical energy.

4. A voltage-time analog of the incoming sound waves is monitored by the processor.

5. The first peak voltage reading is linked with a later time (recorded by the processor).

6.
$$\text{Speed of sound in air} = \frac{\text{distance travelled}}{\text{time taken}}$$

VELA Vela is an acronym for Versatile Laboratory Aid and is a single multi-purpose microprocessor-based instrument which can be used in the above experiment.

Stringed Instruments A string or wire, mass per unit length μ, stretched to tension T between fixed supports of separation l, when disturbed may emit notes of pitch or frequency f given by:

$$f = \frac{n}{2l} \sqrt{\frac{T}{\mu}}$$

As the length of string is decreased, by placing a finger at higher fret positions on a guitar for example, the frequency of the note is increased. If the tension in a string is increased, by adjusting the tuning pegs (or using the wah bar on electric guitars), the frequency is once again increased. Finally the thicker strings on a guitar have a greater mass per unit length than the thinner strings and produce notes of lower frequency. Generally if the mass per unit length of a string is increased, the frequency of the note is reduced. Other examples of stringed instruments are the violin, the harp, the zither, the piano and the mandolin. The quality of the note is determined mainly by the construction and shape of the resonance chamber (and to some extent the effects available in the amplifier circuitry). The resonance chamber is the body of the instrument and is generally placed behind the strings.

Structure of the Ear See page 33.

Noise The risk of damage to hearing due to noise depends on:

1. length of exposure, and
2. loudness.

Noise can:

1. instantaneously deafen or damage ears – in extreme cases the eardrum can be ruptured
2. reduce the ear's sensitivity to sounds of certain frequencies
3. numb the ears for a limited period
4. cause accidents
5. cause pyschological disturbance
6. impair communications.

Aircraft, machinery, personal stereos and discos can damage our hearing. Many heavy metal bands and their supporters wear earplugs during a performance.

Industrial Deafness Industrial deafness is usually associated with inner ear damage. This may go unnoticed for many years until it is chronic. Frequencies above 4 kHz cannot usually be detected. Since speech is in the 0.5 kHz to 2 kHz range, it is only when a worker finds it difficult to follow speech that the damage is detected. Noise inside buildings can be reduced by replacing hard surfaces which reflect sound by soft surfaces which absorb sound.

Hearing Tests A hearing test is carried out by an otolaryngolist in a sound-proofed room. Test sounds are sent to each ear separately through earphones. Frequencies from 250 to 8000 Hz are used and at each frequency the volume is raised until the patient just hears the sound. The hearing thresholds can then be plotted on a chart and compared to normal hearing thresholds.

223

The hearing aid

The hearing aid comprises a tiny microphone, amplifier, battery and earphone. It can be made small enough to fit inside the ear or built into the frame of a pair of spectacles. It sends an amplified (often distorted) sound to the eardrum. If the eardrum or middle ear is damaged vibrations can be sent to the cochlea directly through the bones of the skull. Deafness cannot at present be readily corrected if the cochlea or auditory nerve is damaged. It is possible to implant an artificial cochlea (an electronic device programmed by computer outside the body) but it has neither the range nor the sophistication of a real cochlea.

Ultrasonics

Ultrasonics is the study and application of frequencies beyond the upper limit of hearing of the average healthy human ear, i.e. frequencies > 20kHz. Ultrasonic waves have a short wavelength and can be sent out in a straight beam. An ultrasound generator placed in a liquid creates waves that move the liquid back and forth hundreds of thousands of times each second.

Applications

1. Paint manufacturers use ultrasound to mix and blend colours effectively.
2. Some washing machines and dishwashers use ultrasonic waves to drive soap-suds back and forth rapidly resulting in clean clothes and dishes.
3. Ophthalmic opticians and camera companies use ultrasonic waves to clean lenses. Surgical instruments are sterilised in hospitals using ultrasonic cleaners.
4. Ultrasound can be used for cutting and drilling hard materials. The part to be cut is covered with a scouring paste. Ultrasonic waves set up in the paste by a tool attached to an ultrasonic generator wear away the material at that place. The tool never touches the material and little heat is produced. Some dentists' drills work in the same way. Since no pressure or heat is developed the drill is practically painless.
5. Hidden cracks or flaws inside metal machine parts can be found using ultrasonic sonar.
6. Ultrasonic body scanning can form images of unborn babies. No damage to the mother or unborn child results.
7. Some car alarm systems fill the car interior with ultrasonic waves which, if disturbed, activate a siren. Gusts of air from air vents can trigger sensors to activate if the alarm is badly adjusted or located.
8. Ultrasonic waves can be used to study the Earth's crust. Mineral and oil deposits can be located.

Light and the Electromagnetic Spectrum

Electro-magnetic Spectrum

The electromagnetic (e.m.) spectrum comprises a family of transverse wave-like radiations carrying energy. Light is one of the members of this family.

The wavelength λ dictates the colour of the light*. Blue light has $\lambda \sim 400$ nm whereas red light has $\lambda \sim 700$ nm. This is the only portion of the e.m. spectrum that we can see. (1 nm = 1 nanometre = 10^{-9} m).

*Strictly speaking, colour resides in the eye-brain system and is not a property of wavelength.

Luminous Sources

Luminous sources produce their own light. The Sun, electric lamps and candles are luminous sources.

Non-Luminous Sources

Non-luminous sources do not produce their own light. They rely on luminous sources to reflect light from them in order that we can see them. Most things we see are non-luminous.

Mono-chromatic Waves

Monochromatic waves comprise light waves restricted to a very narrow band of wavelengths – ideally, one wavelength.

Ray of Light

A ray of light defines a specific path along which waves travel, and is perpendicular to a wavefront.

Shadow Formation

1. Point Source

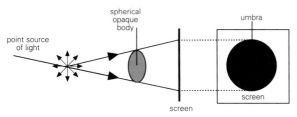

The point source of light gives rise to a well defined circular shadow with a sharp clearly defined edge; this region of total shadow is the umbra.

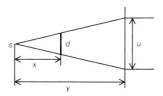

Let the diameter of the spherical opaque body be d.

Thus: $\dfrac{u}{y} = \dfrac{d}{x}$

225

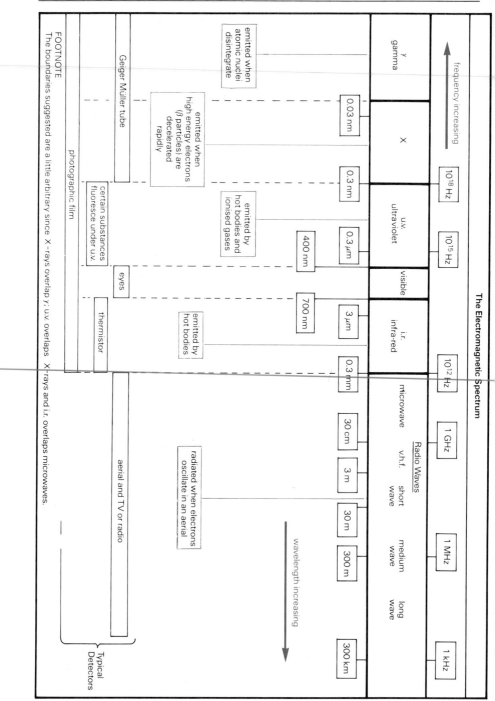

The Electromagnetic Spectrum

2. Extended source (opaque body larger than source)

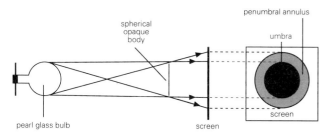

The penumbral annulus becomes brighter towards its outer edge. (A penumbra is a region of partial shadow.)

3. Extended source (opaque body smaller than source)

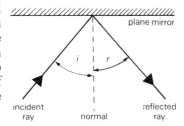

The nature of the shadow depends on the position of the screen. For this configuration, the shadow is wholly penumbral (becoming gradually brighter towards the outer edges).

Laws of Reflection   Using a ray-box and a card with a single slit in it we can direct a ray of light at a plane mirror. Having drawn a normal (a perpendicular) to the mirror at the point of incidence we can monitor the path of the reflected ray.

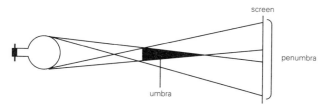

We find:
1. the angle of incidence equals the angle of reflection, $\angle i = \angle r$; and
2. the incident ray, the reflected ray and the normal all lie in the same plane.

These are known as the laws of reflection.

Regular Reflection   Parallel rays of light incident on a highly polished metal surface are reflected according to the laws of reflection.

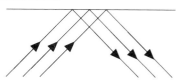

227

Diffuse Reflection Parallel rays of light incident on a matt (rough, not shiny) surface are reflected, or scattered in all directions.

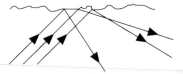

Formation of an Image by a Plane Mirror Any object can be said to comprise a number of points. Consider one of these points. It could be a luminous point source, or alternatively we can think of light being reflected from it. Let us say we are dealing with a luminous point source. Light from the source will travel in an infinite number of directions. Place a plane mirror in front of the object and consider two arbitrary directions, i.e. allow two rays from the source to impinge upon the plane mirror.

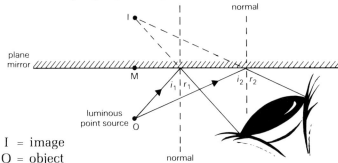

I = image
O = object

The two rays are reflected from the plane mirror according to the laws of reflection. When produced backwards the intersection point locates the image of the object point. In this way we can build an image of an object that comprises more than one point.

OM = IM The image of an object point in a plane mirror is the same distance behind the mirror as the object is in front.

Virtual Image I is a *virtual* image of O. The rays of light only appear to come from I. They do not actually intersect in the image. Any ray of light from O will after reflection appear to originate from I. (See page 239 for *real image*.)

Lateral Inversion A lateral inversion is a sideways reversal of an image. A driver in a car followed by an ambulance will see the word AMBULANCE on looking at the image of it in either his interior mirror or wing mirror because the word has previously been sideways reversed.

228

Characteristics of an Image Formed by a Plane Mirror

1. Image is as far behind mirror as object is in front.
2. Image is upright.
3. Image is same size as object.
4. Image is virtual.
5. Image is laterally inverted.
6. A point object and image lie on the same normal.

Periscope

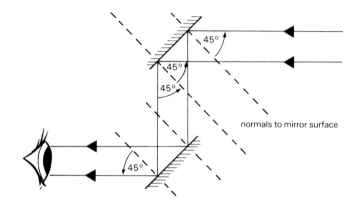

normals to mirror surface

A simple periscope consists of two parallel plane mirrors fixed at 45°.

Refraction When a ray of light impinges upon a transparent medium such as glass, some of the light is reflected according to the laws of reflection, whilst the rest is transmitted. Unless the incident ray is normal to the surface, we find that the direction of the ray inside the medium is different from that of the incident ray. This change of direction or bending of the light is called refraction.

Experiment to Demonstrate Refraction (Glass Block in Air)

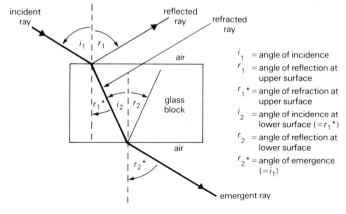

i_1 = angle of incidence

r_1 = angle of reflection at upper surface

$r_1{}^*$ = angle of refraction at upper surface

i_2 = angle of incidence at lower surface $(=r_1{}^*)$

r_2 = angle of reflection at lower surface

$r_2{}^*$ = angle of emergence $(=i_1)$

Spherical or Circular Glass Block, Semicircular Glass Block

A ray of light passing through the centre of a sphere must meet the surface normally (i.e. at right angles). From the principle of reversibility of light, a point source of light placed at the centre of a sphere must radiate rays in such a way that they meet the surface normally. Similarly, a ray directed towards the centre of a circular glass block must meet the surface normally. No refraction takes place at either surface.

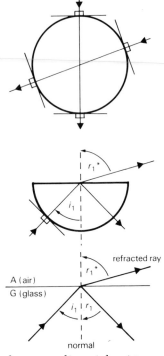

Now bisect the circular block.

Direct a ray of light towards the centre – the ray must meet the curved surface normally, i.e. no refraction occurs at the curved surface and we can concentrate our attention on the plane surface.

We are moving from an optically dense medium (glass) to an optically rarer medium (air). The light ray is bent (refracted) away from the normal. From the principle of reversibility of light, moving from air to glass would result in the light being bent towards the normal.

Critical Angle and Total Internal Reflection

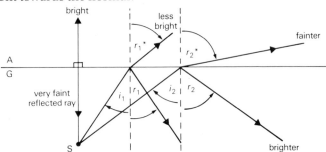

S = luminous point source

As the angle of incidence (i) increases, the angle of refraction increases, the refracted ray becoming increasingly faint and the reflected ray increasingly bright. Eventually, the angle of incidence becomes such that the refracted ray (very faint) just escapes, grazing the interface whilst the reflected ray inside the glass is bright.

Critical Angle

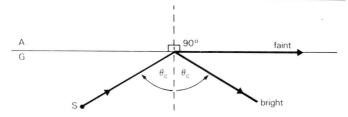

This threshold angle of incidence (θ_c) beyond which total internal reflection takes place (100% reflection) is known as the critical angle.

Total Internal Reflection

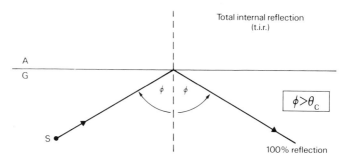

Deviation of a Monochromatic Light ray by a Triangular Prism

i_1 = angle of incidence (face 1) i_2 = angle of incidence (face 2)
r_1^* = angle of refraction (face 1) r_2^* = angle of refraction (face 2)
d_1 = angle of deviation (face 1) d_2 = angle of deviation (face 2)

Case 1 $i_2 <$ critical angle (θ_c)

a = apical angle
d = angle of deviation = $d_1 + d_2$
Deviation is a minimum when the ray passes symmetrically through the prism (i.e. $r_1^* = i_2$ and $i_1 = r_2^*$).

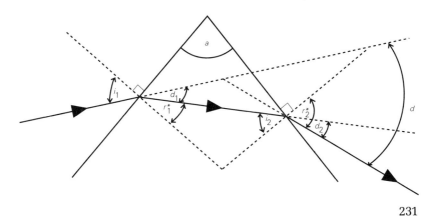

Case 2 i_2 = critical angle (θ_c)

a = apical angle
d = angle of deviation = $d_1 + d_2$

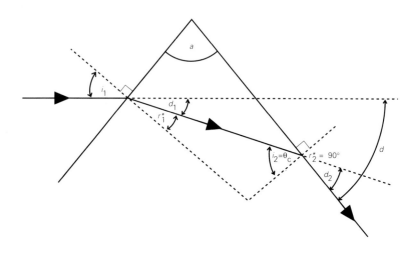

Case 3 $i_2 >$ critical angle (θ_c)

a = apical angle
d = angle of deviation = $d_1 + d_2 + d_3$

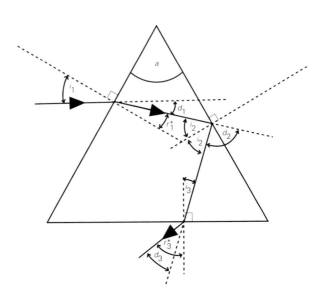

Multiple Images A plane mirror has a finite thickness and as a result several faint images due to partial reflection and refraction accompany a prominent image. The thicker the glass the more widely separated the images.

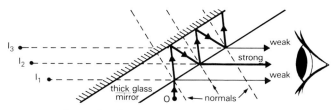

Total Reflecting Prisms Because of multiple or 'ghost' images, high-quality periscopes do not employ plane mirrors but use right-angled isosceles prisms (90°, 45°, 45°).

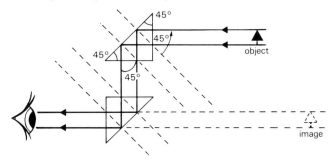

These rays are totally internally reflected because the angle of incidence at the glass/air boundary (45°) is greater than the critical angle between glass and air (42°).

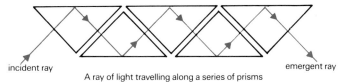

incident ray   emergent ray

A ray of light travelling along a series of prisms

Optical Fibre

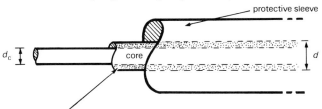

cladding – glass or plastic optically less dense than the core

Core diameter, $d_c \simeq 0.5\,\mu\mathrm{m}$
d = diameter of core + cladding $\simeq 125\,\mu\mathrm{m}$.

233

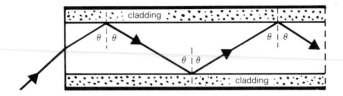

Light from a source impinging upon the core/cladding interface at an angle θ at least equal to the critical angle for this pair of media will be successively totally internally reflected as shown.

Information in the form of a large number of extremely rapid pulses can be sent down a fibre. The light source could be a light-emitting diode (l.e.d.) based on the semiconductor gallium arsenide (GaAs), or a semiconductor laser.

Industrial Counter

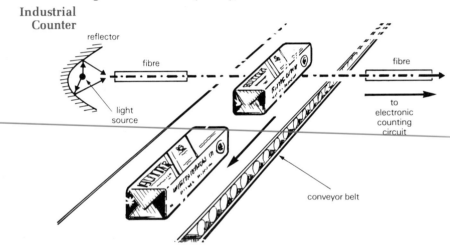

When an object breaks the beam, an electronic counter 'counts'.

Communications

Optical fibres are increasingly replacing copper wire in the telephone system. Thousands of telephone conversations can be transmitted at the same time by a single fibre. They are also capable of carrying TV pictures and teletext in the form of coded information.

Medicine

Optical fibres are used by doctors to see inside patients' throats, lungs and stomachs. Light is sent down some of the fibres which comprise the bundle, and reflected light from the area of concern is viewed by the doctor through the remainder of the bundle.

Spectrum   Allow a shaft of sunlight to meet a triangular glass prism.

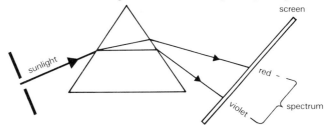

The sunlight (white light) splits up into a band of colours called a spectrum. The splitting of white light into **Dispersion**   component colours is called dispersion. The component colours are conventionally identified, Red, Orange, Yellow, Green, Blue, Indigo and Violet (ROY G BIV). (Strictly, there is a very slow gradation of colours from one end to the other.) Dispersion is a result of the different colours travelling with slightly different speeds in the glass.

Colour   Colour is subjective – the colours we see are qualities of our mental image. A person whose colour vision is defective may not be able to discriminate between red and green and so it follows that these colours cannot appear to him or her as they do to a normal observer.

The colour of an object depends on:
1. the nature of the illuminating light;
2. the nature of the surface and surroundings; and
3. the observer.

However, for convenience we assign wavelengths to the colours that a normal observer would perceive.

> Blue light has a wavelength ∼ 400 nm
> Red light has a wavelength ∼ 700 nm

Coloured   Surfaces look coloured because
Paper   they *reflect* some colours of the spectrum and absorb others! White surfaces are good reflectors of all colours of light. Black surfaces are good absorbers of all colours of light. *Blue paper* viewed in white light reflects mainly blue (and a smaller percentage of the colours bordering blue).

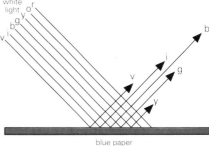

Blue paper only appears blue if the illuminating light has a blue component. If a coloured surface is viewed in coloured artificial light its appearance changes, e.g. blue paper viewed

235

in the yellow light of a sodium lamp appears brown (a sodium lamp does not emit blue light).

Coloured Glass If white light is viewed through blue glass, the colour blue is mainly *transmitted* (a small percentage of the spectral colours bordering blue are also transmitted).

Filters When illuminated with white light:
a green glass filter transmits green light;
an impure yellow glass filter transmits mainly yellow and some red and green;
a cyan glass filter transmits blue and green;
a magenta glass filter transmits red and blue (which are seen together as magenta).
The colours that are not transmitted by the filters are absorbed.

Filter Combinations

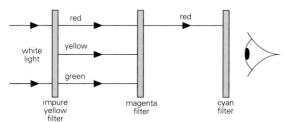

Here the magenta filter only transmits red light (there is no incident blue light), and the cyan filter transmits nothing (there is no incident blue or green light).

Visual Sensitivity The eye is not equally sensitive to the different colours of light in the visible spectrum. Visual sensitivity varies with wavelength. The maximum visual effect is obtained with light of wavelength 555 nm (yellow-green).

Brightness For a given colour (i.e. wavelength) the perceived brightness depends upon the intensity of the wave. This is proportional to the square of its amplitude.

Speed of Electromagnetic Waves The speed of electromagnetic waves in a vacuum is a constant. It is usually given the symbol c, where $c = 3 \times 10^8$ m/s.

$$c = f \times \lambda$$

Radio Waves If radio waves in the medium waveband have a wavelength of 300 m,
$$\text{then } f = \frac{c}{\lambda} = \frac{3 \times 10^8 \text{ m/s}}{300 \text{ m}} = 10^6/\text{s}, \quad \text{i.e. } f = 1 \text{ MHz}.$$

Electromagnetic Waves Need No Material Medium for Propagation Unlike sound waves which cannot travel through a vacuum, e.m. waves can. Think of the e.m. radiation in the form of heat and light reaching the Earth from the Sun. There is 150×10^6 km of near-perfect vacuum between ourselves and the Sun.

236

Uses of Electro-magnetic Waves:

Microwave Ovens

Microwaves are absorbed by food and liquid. They penetrate ~ 3 cm into the food, after which heat energy is transferred via the mechanism of conduction and convection. The inner walls of a microwave oven are made of metal because microwaves are reflected by metals. A spinning metal paddle reflects the waves in all directions around the oven, and the food is placed on a rotating turntable to ensure uniform cooking.

Radar

Radar is an acronym of Radio Detection And Ranging. Distant objects which cross the path of a directed beam of microwaves reflect the pulses back to the transmitter (which also acts as a receiver). The time taken for a pulse to travel to the object and back enables the distance to the object to be calculated.

Satellites

Microwaves are used in satellite communication (see also Solar Power Station, page 213).

X-Rays

1. Short wavelength X-rays are used in hospitals to kill cancer cells.
2. Less penetrating (longer wavelength) X-rays penetrate flesh but not bone and are used in dental X-ray photography. Hidden faults inside metal castings can be located using X-ray photography.

Infra-red

1. Infra-red (i.r.) photographs can detect poor blood circulation.
2. In warfare the i.r. emitted from the hot engine of an aircraft can be tracked.
3. Infra-red photographs can be taken in the dark. The image formed by a thermal imaging camera is initially in shades of grey. A computer assigns a colour to each shade, resulting in a colour picture. Such cameras can detect temperature differences as small as 0.1°C.
4. The remote control of TV and video uses i.r.

Ultraviolet

1. Ultraviolet (u.v.) radiation can produce a sun-tan.
2. The coated inner surface of fluorescent tubes radiates visible light when u.v. (emitted by mercury vapour inside the tube) impinges.
3. Clothes washed in detergents fluoresce in sunlight as a result of the u.v. which the sunlight contains.

Light Detection and Ranging (LIDAR) Laser light in the form of a narrow collimated (parallel) beam is increasingly being used as a range-finder by the armed forces. The system consists of a pulsed laser, a telescope (to collect the reflected light), a photodetector and an accurate timer. The Apollo space missions left *retroreflectors* on the surface of the Moon, and the distance to the Moon has been measured using this technique.

Convex Lens, Positive Lens, Plus Lens, Converging Lens The four terms on the left are alternative ways of describing a lens that is thick in the middle and thin around the edge. The centre of the lens is known as the *optical centre* C, and a line through C at right angles to the lens is known as the *principal axis*.

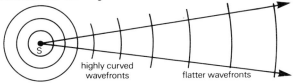

We can think of reflected light from a non-luminous point object S radiating out as a series of spherical waves. In two dimensions we can represent these waves as circles.

highly curved wavefronts   flatter wavefronts

The diagram suggests that the wavefronts impinging upon a convex lens from a distant object will be plane, i.e. rays emanating from the object will be parallel.

Principal Focus, Focal Length When a beam of light parallel to the principal axis passes through a convex lens it is refracted so as to converge to a point on the axis called the *principal focus*, labelled F. The distance CF is called the *focal length* of the lens. Since light can fall on either face of a lens, it has two principal foci, one on each side.

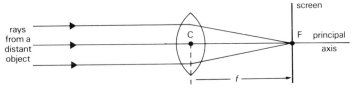

A screen placed in the plane of F will catch a real image of a distant object.

Rays Used in Image Construction
1. A ray of light parallel to the principal axis of a convex lens is refracted through a principal focus.
2. A ray of light passing through the optical centre is undeviated.

238

3. A ray passing through a principal focus is refracted parallel to the principal axis.

Usually only rays *1* and *2* are required to locate the image of an object.

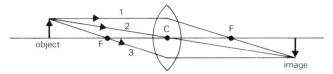

Real Image   A real image is one that can be projected on to a screen.

Using a Single Convex Lens as a Projection Lens

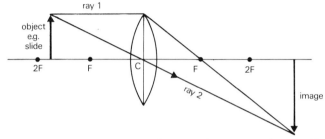

2F is a point on the principal axis a distance twice the focal length from C.

The image is:
1. magnified;
2. inverted – if the slide is turned upside-down, the image of it will appear the right way up; and
3. real.

The size of the image can be changed by changing the slide/lens distance.

Using a Convex Lens as a Magnifying Glass

Place an object (e.g. print on a page) between F and C.

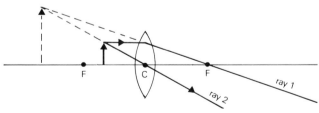

Rays *1* and *2* are divergent. We produce the rays backwards to locate the image.

The image is:
1. magnified;
2. upright; and
3. virtual, i.e. the rays of light only appear to come from it.

239

Virtual
Image

A virtual image is one that cannot be formed on a screen.

Concave
Lens

Concave lens, negative lens, minus lens and diverging lens are four alternative ways of describing a lens that is thin in the middle and thick around the edge. When a beam of light parallel to the principal axis passes through a concave lens it is refracted so as to appear to come from a point in front of the lens on the axis called the principal focus, labelled F.

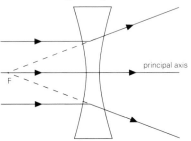

Rays Used in
Image
Construction

1. A ray of light parallel to the principal axis of a concave lens is refracted as though it came from F.
2. A ray of light passing through the optical centre is undeviated.

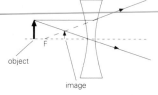 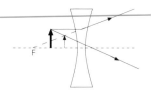

Note that the image is always upright, virtual and diminished.

Structure of
the eye

See page 31.

Binocular
Vision

Each eye has a slightly different field of vision. The brain fuses the two images together to give binocular vision which enables us to perceive depth.

Nature of the
Image at the
Retina

The images are real, diminished and inverted. The brain is responsible for turning the images the right way up.

Cataracts

The transparent lens gradually turns opaque. The condition is treated by removing the lens and giving the patients powerful spectacles or contact lenses.

Contact
Lenses

Contact lenses are lenses placed in direct contact with the eye.

Advantages of Contact Lenses over Spectacles

1. The eye receives images through the same section of the lens giving the wearer a greater field of corrected view.
2. Contact lenses move with the eyes.

Near Point

The distance from the unaided eye to the nearest object on to which it can focus is called the near point. For a normal eye the near point is taken to be 25cm from the eye.

Far Point

The distance from the unaided eye to the farthest object that can be focused upon. For a normal eye the far point is at infinity.

Defects of Vision

1. Short sightedness (Myopia)
    The eyeball is too long or the focal length of the eye is too short. The far point is nearer than infinity and the near point is very close to the eye. Very near objects can be seen clearly but not distant objects. Diverging spectacle lenses are used to correct the defect.

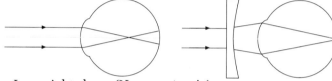

2. Long sightedness (Hypermetropia)
    The eyeball is too short or the focal length of the eye is too long. The eye's near point is farther away than 25 cm and so close objects cannot be seen clearly. Also distant objects cannot be seen clearly *if the ciliary muscle is relaxed.* Converging spectacle lenses are used to correct the defect.

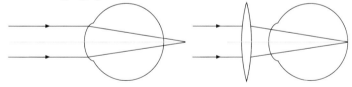

Note: The last two diagrams illustrate the situation with the ciliary muscles relaxed.

Surgical developments

Laser beams directed at the cornea can reshape it. Directed at the centre of the cornea, they can correct short sightedness. Directed at the eye's periphery (giving the cornea a more acute curve) they can correct long sightedness.

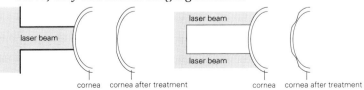

241

Wavefronts and Secondary Wavelets

Each point on the wavefront WF is considered to be a new source of secondary waves called *wavelets*. The wavefront WF envelops the wavelets which created it. For all points on a particular wavefront the wave has travelled from S for the *same time* and over the same distance. All points on a particular wavefront are said to be in the *same phase*.

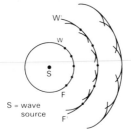

S = wave source

Diffraction

Diffraction is the name given to the phenomenon by which wave energy (whatever its nature) resulting from the superposition of secondary wavelets appears in a region of geometrical shadow. When a wave moves through a gap, or past an obstacle it spreads out from the edges.

Diffraction at a Gap

1. Circular wavefront impinging upon a gap. (Gap width $< \lambda$)

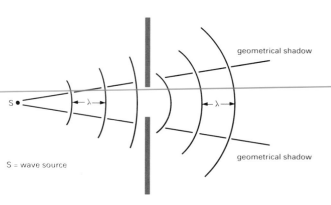

2. Plane wavefronts impinging upon a gap.

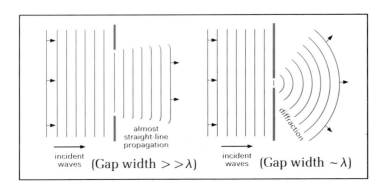

When the gap width is wide compared with the wavelength of the waves, they pass through in parallel straight lines (there is a very slight bending round at the edges). When the gap is of the same order of magnitude as the wavelength, a pronounced circular shape is observed. The waves spread out in all directions. Sound waves (λ = 1m) are diffracted when passing through doors or windows about 0.5 m wide.

A person at Y can hear a person at X talking because of diffraction. Microwaves (λ = 3cm) are diffracted by gaps about 1 cm wide.

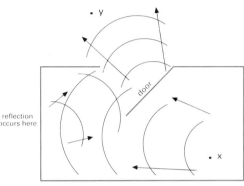

reflection occurs here

door

Interference

Interference is a term used to describe the effects which occur when two separate wave motions overlap.

Constructive Interference

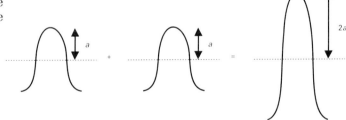

a = amplitude of the wave

When the displacements due to two waves combine such that the wave crests overlap, a larger displacement results. The waves are *in phase* (in step) with each other.

Destructive Interference

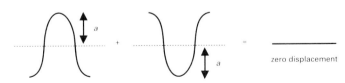

zero displacement

When the displacements due to two waves combine such that the wave crest of one overlaps with the trough of another, no displacement results. The waves are *in antiphase* (completely out of step) with each other.

243

Interference Pattern

Consider two dippers attached to the same vibrating rod in a ripple tank. The frequency of the vibrating rod dictates the frequency of the periodic circular waves produced by each dipper (equal to each other). Where the wavefronts overlap a pattern of *nodes* and *antinodes* called an *interference pattern* results.

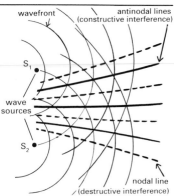

Young's Double Slit Experiment

Antinodal and nodal lines denote where constructive and destructive interference has taken place respectively.

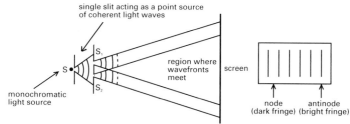

Slit width $\sim 6 \times 10^{-5}$m.   Single slit/double slit separation ~ 0.15 m.
Slit separation $\sim 4 \times 10^{-4}$m.   Double slit/screen separation ~ 1 m.

S_1 and S_2 act as independent sources of waves with identical amplitudes and wavelengths.

As a result of the diffraction that occurs at the double-slit system, an interference pattern of visible fringes is produced. The bright fringes (antinodes) and the dark fringes (nodes) correspond to positions where the waves interfere constructively and destructively, respectively.

Providing the two slits (S_1 and S_2) are equidistant from the single slit they will receive light (simultaneously) in the same phase. Any sudden phase changes that occur in the light from the single slit will affect the two slits equally. Light from the double slit system is said to be *coherent*.

If the single slit were absent, the two slits would receive light from different parts of the source. Light from an ordinary light source suffers random changes about once every 10^{-8}s. The conditions for constructive interference, destructive interference or some intermediate state would thus last for times of the order 10^{-8}s. Since the eye cannot follow such short-term changes, no interference effects would be observed. Light emerging from each of the double slits would be in different and constantly varying phase. In order to produce a stable interference pattern the individual waves (associated with the two slits) must maintain a constant phase relationship with one another. This is achieved by introducing the single slit.

Polarisation   Electromagnetic waves (including visible light) contain mutually perpendicular electric and magnetic fields which oscillate perpendicular to the direction of travel (in every possible orientation). The electric field in the wave exerts a much greater force than the magnetic field and is much more important in producing the observed effects of light. Light is usually unpolarised, i.e. the electric disturbances are in *all* directions at right-angles to the direction of travel.

A polaroid sheet produces plane-polarised light from unpolarised light. It only transmits those components of the electric field which are in a particular direction. Any components at right angles to this direction are absorbed. The arrangement of atoms in polaroid gives it a ribbed structure, equivalent to a large number of parallel slots.

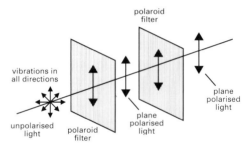

If two pieces of polaroid are placed one behind the other, light passes through both when their slots are parallel but is completely cut off if they are crossed.

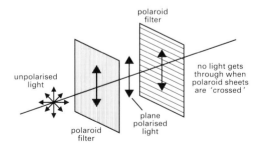

However, if a third sheet of polaroid is inserted between the crossed polaroids sandwiched at some angle $\theta(0 < \theta < 90°)$, some light gets through. Consider this third (middle) sheet of polaroid.

245

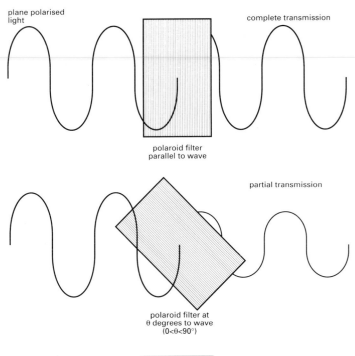

plane polarised light

complete transmission

polaroid filter parallel to wave

partial transmission

polaroid filter at θ degrees to wave (0<θ<90°)

zero transmission (complete absorption)

polaroid filter at right-angles to wave

Light from the Sky
Light from the sky is partially plane polarised (small particles in the atmosphere scatter light). Partially plane polarised light is also obtained when light is reflected from unsilvered glass or a water surface.

Polaroid Sunglasses
Polaroid sunglasses reduce or eliminate completely (depending on the viewing angle) the sun's glare reflected from, for example, water.

Machine Parts
The stresses distributed in machine parts can be investigated using polarised light. A plastic model of the machine part is subjected to appropriate stresses while placed between crossed polaroid sheets. The stress patterns can thus be observed.

Electricity

Conductor   A conductor is a substance which readily allows electrons to flow through it. Silver and copper are especially good conductors.

Insulator   An insulator is a substance which does not readily allow electrons to flow through it. Most non-metals are good insulators. Dry air, glass, rubber, porcelain and plastics such as polythene are good insulators.

Charging by Rubbing   If a strip of polythene is rubbed with dry wool, electrons are transferred from the cloth to the polythene, leaving the polythene negatively charged. Rubbing a perspex rod with dry wool transfers electrons from the perspex to the cloth, leaving the perspex positively charged. Prior to rubbing, the polythene and the perspex are electrically neutral. Materials which are positively charged have a deficiency of electrons.

Like Charges Repel

Unlike Charges Attract

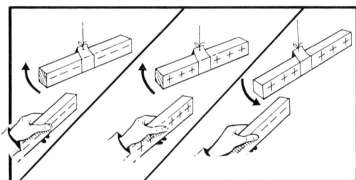

Electrostatic Attraction   Electrostatic attraction is the attraction that opposite electrical charges have for each other.

Charged Objects Attract Uncharged Objects   A plastic comb which has been pulled through your hair becomes charged and can pick up tiny scraps of paper. If the comb is negatively charged, electrons in the atoms of the paper redistribute themselves so that the paper facing the comb is effectively in deficit of negative charge (i.e. positively charged) and attraction takes place.

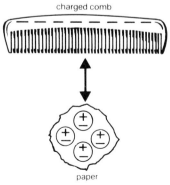

Paper is an insulator. There are no free electrons in paper.

247

Similarly, pulling out a plastic record from a paper sleeve charges the record. Dust is an insulator and dust particles redistribute their electron concentration so that they are attracted to the record. Charges are said to be induced in the paper or the dust.

Electrostatic Precipitation
Electrostatic precipitation is a means of controlling the pollution of air. Effluent gases that would normally pollute the atmosphere are subjected to an electrostatic field which is provided by a series of overlapping positive and negative electrodes. Depending upon the type of pollutant, solid or liquid particles suspended in the gas are attracted to one or other of the sets of electrodes.

Metallic Conductor
A metallic conductor can be thought of as a highly structured array of ions in a sea of electrons. The free electrons move randomly.

Current Flow
A current flow consists of a bulk drift of electrons moving randomly in one direction.

Electric Current
An electric current consists of moving electric charges – namely electrons.

Primary Cell
A primary cell is a device which maintains (by chemical action) a surplus of electrons at one terminal (the negative) and a deficit at the other (the positive). A continuous current flow can be maintained if:

1. there is a complete circuit through which current can flow;
2. the circuit contains a device which maintains a difference in the state of charges between its terminals (e.g. a primary cell).

Secondary Cell
A secondary cell is one that can be recharged by passing a current through it in the opposite direction to which it would normally discharge.

Units
The ampere (A) is the S.I. unit of electrical current.

The coulomb (C) is the unit of electrical charge. It is equal to the charge on about 6×10^{18} electrons. (The charge on one electron is far too small for practical purposes.) The coulomb is defined in terms of the ampere – it is that amount of charge passing any point in a circuit when a steady current of 1 ampere flows for 1 second. Mathematically we can describe the relationship between the charge in coulombs and electrical current in amperes as follows:

$$Q = I \times t$$

where Q = charge in coulombs,
I = electrical current in amperes, and
t = time in seconds.

A charge of 6C would pass each point in 3 s if the current was 2 A (i.e. $I \times t = 2 \times 3 = 6$).

Semi-conductor A semiconductor (s.c.) is a material having an electrical conductivity between that of insulators and metallic conductors. The resistance of a s.c. decreases with increasing temperature and the presence of impurities. Typical s.c.'s include germanium, silicon, selenium and lead telluride.

Direct Current A direct current (d.c.) is an electric current which always flows in the same direction.

Thermionic Emission Thermionic emission is the release of electrons from a solid as a result of its temperature. For example, heating a fine tungsten wire by connecting a battery across it gives the electrons in the tungsten enough energy to break through the surface of the metal. The electrons exist outside the wire as a 'cloud.' The number of electrons emitted increases with increasing temperature (voltage).

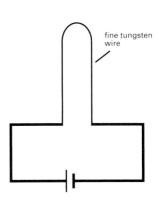

fine tungsten wire

X-ray Tubes Electrons 'boiled off' from a hot tungsten filament are focused on to a metal target (usually tungsten or copper) in an evacuated tube, so the electrons are not slowed down in the path to the target. The target metal is embedded in a copper block kept at a high potential difference (100 kV or more) relative to the filament. When highly energetic electrons collide with the target, most of their kinetic energy is transferred as heat but some energy is emitted from the target as X-rays. High voltages produce extremely penetrating or 'hard' X-rays. Lower voltages produce less penetrating or 'soft' X-rays.

Alternating Current An alternating current (a.c.) reaches a maximum in one direction, decreases, then reverses to reach a maximum in the opposite direction. The cycle is continuously repeated.

Frequency of an Alternating Current The frequency of an a.c. is the number of cycles per second. Three cycles are shown here. The frequency of the mains (operating at 240 V) is 50 cycles per second or 50 hertz (50 Hz).

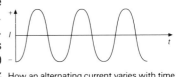

How an alternating current varies with time

249

Standard Symbols for Electrical Components

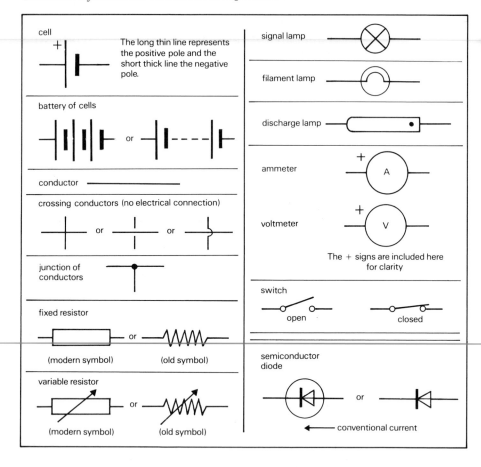

cell — The long thin line represents the positive pole and the short thick line the negative pole.	signal lamp
battery of cells — or	filament lamp
	discharge lamp
conductor	ammeter + A
crossing conductors (no electrical connection) — or — or —	voltmeter + V
	The + signs are included here for clarity
junction of conductors	switch — open — closed
fixed resistor — or — (modern symbol) (old symbol)	semiconductor diode
variable resistor — or — (modern symbol) (old symbol)	or ⬅ conventional current

Conventional Current Flow

Prior to the discovery of the electron, scientists *agreed* to think of electrical current flowing around a circuit in the direction in which positive charges would flow, i.e. in the direction from positive to negative of a battery. This is referred to as *conventional current flow* and the agreement still holds.

Consider this simple circuit comprising a cell and a lamp.

The electrons actually flow from the negative terminal of the supply to the positive terminal whereas conventional current flow is in the opposite sense.

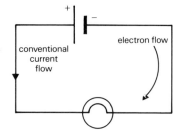

Potential Difference

Earlier we recognised the existence of the Earth's gravitational field wherein different locations above ground possess different potentials, depending on the level above the ground. We defined the potential difference (p.d.) between two points as the energy released per kg when an object falls from one point to another.

An analogous situation occurs in electricity but now we must think in terms of electron movement. A battery has a p.d. across its terminals. Joining a conductor across the terminals results in positive charge moving (if it could) from the positive to the negative terminal – or (what amounts to the same thing) negative charges (electrons) moving from the negative to the positive terminal. Connecting a lamp across the terminals results in electrons moving through the filament releasing energy in the form of light and heat.

The Volt

The volt is defined to be that p.d. between two points in a circuit if 1 joule of electrical energy is converted into other forms of energy (e.g. light and heat) when 1 coulomb passes from one point to the other:

1 volt	= 1 joule per coulomb
2 volts	= 2 joules per coulomb
10 volts	= 10 joules per coulomb

If we represent the p.d. by V, the energy changed (i.e. the work done) by W, and the charge in coulombs by Q we can write:

$$V = \frac{W}{Q}$$ i.e. Potential difference $= \dfrac{\text{Work done}}{\text{Charge moved}}$

or, rearranging:

$$W = V \times Q$$

Also, if Q is in the form of a steady current I (amperes) flowing for a time t (seconds), then since $Q = I \times t$:

$$W = I \times t \times V$$

Measuring Current

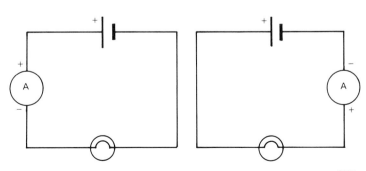

An ammeter is an instrument for measuring electric current.

1. The ammeter should be connected *in series*.
2. The ammeter *must* be connected in the circuit in such a way that its positive terminal is connected to the positive terminal of the supply irrespective of the number of components between the ammeter and the battery.
3. Ammeters have a very low resistance. The *perfect* ammeter would absorb no energy. The p.d. across it would be zero.

Cells and Batteries

Strictly, a group of cells connected together is called a battery.

Fig. 1 *Series connection*

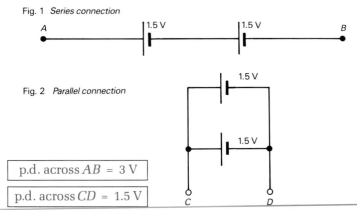

Fig. 2 *Parallel connection*

p.d. across AB = 3 V

p.d. across CD = 1.5 V

The arrangement in fig. 2 behaves as a larger cell, has a longer life, and allows us to draw a larger current. To avoid the possibility of discharge due to current circulating in the battery itself, it is prudent after use to disconnect such a combination.

Measuring Potential Difference

A voltmeter is an instrument for measuring p.d. Unlike an ammeter which is connected *in series* in a circuit, a voltmeter is connected *across* that part of the circuit where the p.d. is required.

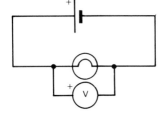

1. The voltmeter is connected *in parallel.*
2. Voltmeters (like ammeters) have to be connected into the circuit in such a way that the positive terminal should be connected to the positive terminal of the supply irrespective of the number of components between the voltmeter and the supply.
3. Voltmeters should have a very high resistance. The *perfect* voltmeter should take no current and absorb no energy, i.e. it should have an infinite resistance.

Resistance (R) The measure of the opposition of the atomic structure of a substance to the flow of electrons is called its resistance (*R*). Insulators strongly oppose the movement of electrons whereas conductors offer little opposition.

Units of Resistance The unit of resistance is the ohm (Ω). This is the resistance of a conductor which is such that a p.d. of 1 volt applied across it produces a current flow of 1 ampere through it. Hence

$$R = \frac{V}{I}.$$

Consider a cylindrical copper wire (*kept at a constant temperature*) of length *l* and cross-sectional area *A*. The resistance is directly proportional to the length of the conductor:

$$\boxed{R \propto l}$$

Keeping the length of copper wire constant and doubling the cross-sectional area (at constant temperature) halves the resistance to electron flow. Trebling the cross-sectional area reduces the resistance encountered by a factor of three. The resistance is said to be inversely proportional to the cross-sectional area:

$$\boxed{R \propto \frac{1}{A}} \qquad \text{(N.B. } A = \frac{\pi d^2}{4} \text{ where } d = \text{wire diameter)}$$

Resistance Varies with Temperature An increase of temperature increases the resistance of most metals. You can think of the atoms within a metal gaining energy with increasing temperature, resulting in an overall increase in amplitude and rate of vibration, thus making it more difficult for the electrons to flow.

The resistance of non-metals, carbon and most semi-conductor materials decreases with increasing temperature. Certain alloys such as constantan and manganin are unusual in that their resistance is reasonably constant over a wide temperature variation.

Ohm's Law The size of the electrical current through a conductor is directly proportional to the applied p.d. across its ends *if the temperature is constant*. For a constant p.d. *V*, if *I* decreases, it follows that *R* increases; and if *I* increases, *R* decreases. For most metallic conductors at constant temperature, *V/I* always has the same value when *V* is varied and the corresponding value of *I* found. Doubling V doubles *I*, trebling V trebles *I* and so on. Thus $\frac{V}{I} = R$. This is Ohm's Law. We can express

Ohm's law in two other ways: $I = \frac{V}{R}$ or $\boxed{V = I \times R}$

If *V* is in volts, and *I* is in amps, then *R* is in ohms.

Ohmic Components	Ohmic components are components that obey Ohm's Law. Most metals, certain alloys and electrolytic (conducting) solutions obey Ohm's law.
Non-Ohmic or Non-Linear Components	Non-ohmic components are components that do not obey Ohm's Law. Transistors, thermistors, valves and semiconductor diodes do not obey Ohm's Law, or obey Ohm's Law only over certain specified ranges of applied potential difference.
Resistors in Series	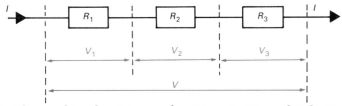

Let the combined resistance of resistors R_1, R_2, and R_3 be R. The same current flows through each resistor. Let this current be I. The total p.d. V across all three is equal to the sum of the separate p.d.'s across them, i.e.

$$V = V_1 + V_2 + V_3$$
$$IR = IR_1 + IR_2 + IR_3$$

Thus: $\boxed{R = R_1 + R_2 + R_3}$

Use of $R = R_1 + R_2 + R_3$	If $R_1 = 3\,\Omega$, $R_2 = 5\,\Omega$ and $R_3 = 2\,\Omega$, then $R = 10\,\Omega$.
Resistors in Parallel	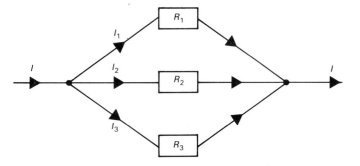

The sum of the currents in the branches of a parallel circuit is equal to the current entering or leaving the parallel section:

$$I = I_1 + I_2 + I_3$$

The p.d. between the ends of each resistor is the same. Let us label this p.d. V.

So, $I_1 = \dfrac{V}{R_1}$ $\qquad I_2 = \dfrac{V}{R_2}$ $\qquad I_3 = \dfrac{V}{R_3}$

Let R be the combined resistance.

Since $I = \dfrac{V}{R}$, then: $\quad \dfrac{V}{R} = \dfrac{V}{R_1} + \dfrac{V}{R_2} + \dfrac{V}{R_3}$

Thus:

$$\dfrac{1}{R} = \dfrac{1}{R_1} + \dfrac{1}{R_2} + \dfrac{1}{R_3}$$

Use of $\dfrac{1}{R} = \dfrac{1}{R_1} + \dfrac{1}{R_2} + \dfrac{1}{R_3}$

If $R_1 = 3\,\Omega, R_2 = 5\,\Omega$ and $R_3 = 6\,\Omega$,

then: $\dfrac{1}{R} = \dfrac{1}{3} + \dfrac{1}{5} + \dfrac{1}{6} = \dfrac{10}{30} + \dfrac{6}{30} + \dfrac{5}{30} = \dfrac{21}{30}$

$\therefore R = \dfrac{30}{21} = 1.43\,\Omega$

Useful Multiples and Sub-Multiples of Basic Electrical Units

Current (I)	Voltage (V)	Resistance (R)
1 ampere = 1 A	1 volt = 1 V	1 ohm = 1 Ω
1 milliamp = 1 mA = 10^{-3} A	1 millivolt = 1 mV	1 kilohm = 1 kΩ = $10^3\,\Omega$
1 microamp = 1 μA = 10^{-6} A	1 microvolt = 1 μV	1 megohm = 1 MΩ = $10^6\Omega$
	1 kilovolt = 1 kV = 10^3V	

N.B. $10^{-3} = \dfrac{1}{1000}$, and $10^3 = 1000$; $\quad 10^{-6} = \dfrac{1}{1\,000\,000}$, and $10^6 = 1\,000\,000$

Terminal Potential Difference The terminal p.d. of a cell is the reading on a voltmeter connected across the cell terminals.

Open Circuit Open circuit terminal p.d. is the reading obtained when the cell is not supplying current to any component(s).

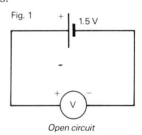

Fig. 1

1.5 V

Open circuit

voltmeter reading = 1.5 V

Closed Circuit Closed circuit terminal p.d. is the reading obtained when the cell is supplying current to other component(s) connected to it.

Fig. 2

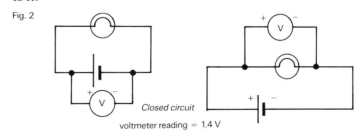

Closed circuit

voltmeter reading = 1.4 V

Potential Difference The terminal p.d. on closed circuit (see fig. 2) is the p.d. applied to the lamp, i.e. 1.4 V in our example.

255

Closed circuit terminal p.d. can be regarded as the number of joules of electrical energy *changed* per coulomb in the external circuit. In fig. 2, 1.4 J of electrical energy is changed into heat and light per coulomb.

Open circuit terminal p.d. is the number of joules of electrical energy a cell or battery gives to each coulomb. If a battery gives 1.5 J of electrical energy to each coulomb on open circuit we say it has an electromotive force (e.m.f.) of 1.5 V.

Electromotive Force
Electromotive force (e.m.f.) measures *energy* per coulomb. (The term is misleading since we might expect it to measure force per coulomb!) The e.m.f. of a cell or battery (or other electrical energy source) is its terminal p.d. on open circuit.

'Lost' Energy per Coulomb
The lost energy per coulomb is due to the cell having resistance (internal resistance). Each coulomb wastes 0.1 J (in our example) in order to get through the cell itself.

Internal Resistance
The internal resistance of a cell is labelled r.

Ohm's Law Applied to Complete Circuits
The energy supplied per coulomb by cell or battery is equal to the energy changed into other forms (e.g. heat and light) in the external circuit plus the energy wasted per coulomb on cell resistance.

e.m.f. = useful p.d. + 'lost' p.d.

The e.m.f. of an electrical energy source can be regarded as the sum total of the p.d.'s which it can produce across all the various components of a circuit, including the p.d. required to drive the current through the cell itself.

Circuit Equation
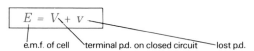

$$E = V + v$$

e.m.f. of cell · terminal p.d. on closed circuit · lost p.d.

which may also be written: $E = IR + Ir = I(R + r)$

where R is the total equivalent resistance of any resistive components in the external circuit, and r is the internal resistance of the cell.

Example Problem
A cell of e.m.f. 1.5 V and internal resistance 1 Ω is connected to a resistor of 5 Ω. Find the current in the circuit.

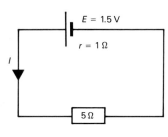

Solution
Using: $E = I(R + r)$
$1.5 = I(5 + 1) = I(6)$
$\therefore I = \dfrac{1.5}{6.0} = \dfrac{1}{4} = 0.25$ A

Experiment to Determine Resistance by Use of Voltmeter-Ammeter Readings

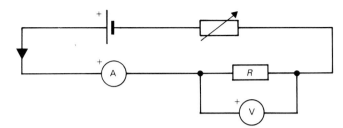

1. The current through R is measured by the ammeter.
2. The p.d. across R is measured by the voltmeter.
3. For a given setting of the variable resistor, the ratio of V to I gives R, i.e. $R = \dfrac{V}{I}$
4. Changing the size of the variable resistor alters both I and V. However, $\left(\dfrac{V}{I}\right)$ will be a constant if the temperature is constant.

V/I and I/V Graphs for a Metal at Constant Temperature

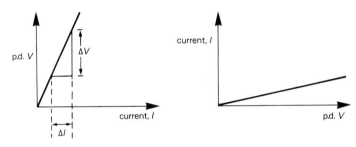

The slope of the V/I graph, $\left(\dfrac{\Delta V}{\Delta I}\right)$, yields R.

Characteristic Curve

However, it is usual to plot the value of I resulting from an applied p.d., V, as shown in the second graph. This form of graph for any device is called a *characteristic curve* and will be used from now on.

Characteristic Curve for a Filament Lamp

Provided I is low (low temperature), the ratio of V to I is constant. But as the temperature increases (I increases), V increases more rapidly than I so that $\dfrac{V}{I} (=R)$ increases. As the lamp filament gets hotter its resistance increases.

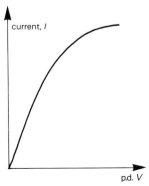

257

Characteristic Curve for a Semi-conductor Diode

A diode permits a current to flow (to any extent) *only one way.* When connected in this way in a circuit it is said to be *forward biased.* When the diode is connected in the opposite sense it is said to be *reverse biased.* Virtually no current flows through the diode when reverse biased.

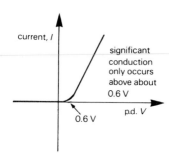

Characteristic Curve for a Thermistor

The characteristic curve denotes a thermistor whose resistance *decreases* with *increasing* temperature .

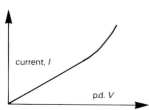

$P = I \times V$

Earlier we saw that an electric lamp converts electrical energy (in joules) to heat energy and light energy. The change in electrical energy, $W = I \times t \times V$. Dividing both sides of this equation by t tells us that the electrical energy changed per second $\left(\dfrac{W}{t}\right)$ into heat and light equals $I \times V$.

Power is defined to be the rate of energy conversion.

Power P (in watts)	=	current I (in amps)	$\times$	p.d. V (in volts)

The Kilowatt-Hour (kWh)

The kilowatt-hour is a unit of energy. It is the energy supplied when a rate of working of 1 kilowatt is maintained for 1 hour. Electricity meters are marked in kWh. The amount of energy used in kWh equals the power (in kW) × time (in hours).

Example Problem

A 3-kW immersion heater is used for 10 hours at a cost of 5p per kilowatt-hour. The heater is designed for use on 240 V mains. Find (a) the current taken from the mains;

(b) the resistance of the heater;

(c) the energy used in 1 hour;

(d) the cost of using the heater for 6 hours.

Solution

(a) $P = 3\,\text{kW} = 3000\,\text{W}$
$P = V \times I$
$3000 = 240 \times I$
$I = \dfrac{3000}{240} = 12.5\,\text{A}$

(b) $V = I \times R$
$R = \dfrac{V}{I}$
$R = \dfrac{240}{12.5} = 19.2\,\Omega$

(c) 3 kW = 3000 W, and 1 W = 1 J/s
∴ 3000 W = 3000 J/s
3600 s = 1 hour
∴ Energy used in 1 hour = 3000 × 3600 J
= 10 800 000 W = 10.8 MW

(d) Number of kWh = 3 × 6 = 18 kWh
Cost at 5p per kWh = 90p

Symbol for a Fuse

(modern symbol)   (old symbol)

Fuse A fuse consists of a short length of metal wire of low melting-point (tin or tinned copper). When the current exceeds a particular value the fuse wire melts or blows and breaks the circuit. Incorporating a fuse minimises the risk of (i) fire owing to the wiring overheating, and (ii) damage to appliances.

A 2-kW fire used at 240 V draws 8.33 A. A 5A fuse plugged into the circuit will blow, break the circuit and protect the wiring. If the live wire makes contact with neutral or touches a part of the equipment that is earthed, an extra large current flows through the wiring and the fuse blows.

M.C.B.'s. These are Miniature Circuit Breakers which switch the circuit off if the current exceeds a particular value. They can be used instead of fuses.

E.L.C.B.'s. Earth Leakage Circuit Breakers.

R.C.C.B.'s. Residual Current Circuit Breakers.

R.C.D.'s. Residual Current Devices.

These continuously check that the amount of current flowing along the live wire is matched by the return flow along the neutral wire. Any imbalance (current escaping) results in an automatic current cut-off. (N.B. These imbalances may not be big enough to blow a fuse or trip an M.C.B.)

R.C.C.B. units fitted into modern consumer units protect the whole electrical system of a household, or outlets incorporating R.C.C.B. can replace conventional socket outlets. Outdoor appliances including lawn mowers, hedge trimmers and power tools should not be used without R.C.C.B. protection.

Electric Cables Electric cables are also rated for the current they can pass. The rating is lower for a completely coiled cable than when the cable is unwound since the heat energy produced disperses more slowly.

259

Simplified House Wiring Diagram

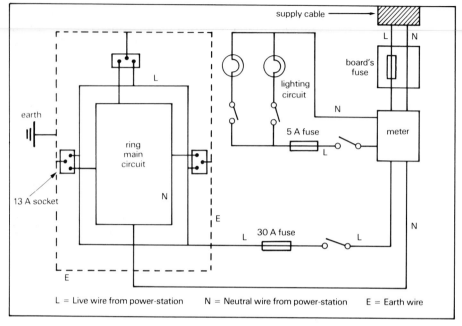

L = Live wire from power-station   N = Neutral wire from power-station   E = Earth wire

Ring Main   The ring main is a cable comprising live, neutral and earth wires each forming a 'ring' around the house. Both the live and neutral wires carry current but the neutral is earthed at a local sub-station and is at zero potential. The ring main is protected by a 30 A fuse and each power point is protected by a fuse inside the plug.

The ring mains fuse restricts the amount of power that can be drawn from it. It can supply only 7200 watts (7.2 kW) at any time. ($P = V \times I = 240\,V \times 30\,A = 7200\,W$).

If the ring is overloaded, the mains fuse blows and there is no further supply to any sockets. In modern house wiring systems, before the fuse blows, a switch is tripped to break the circuit so the fuse doesn't have to be replaced.

Advantage of Domestic Ring Main   Thinner cable can be used, since current to each socket flows by two paths.

Lighting Circuit   The lighting circuit is protected by a 5A fuse.

Earth Wire   The earth wire is connected to a *metal* water pipe in the house or to a supply cable earth. The earth wire *only* carries current if there is a fault. If a live wire touches the metal case of an appliance (which has little resistance), a large current flows through the fuse (in the live wire) to earth via the earth pin on a three-pin plug which is connected to the case. The fuse blows and the appliance is turned off until the fault can be rectified. If there were no earth connection, anyone touching the case might receive a *fatal* electric shock, since the current would then flow through that person to earth.

Switches and Fuses Switches and fuses are found solely in the *live wire*. Inserting them into the *neutral wire* (at the lower potential) would mean that lamp and power sockets would be potentially lethal even when switches were turned to *off* or after fuses had blown.

Threshold of Muscular Decontrol The threshold of muscular decontrol is about 15 mA 50 Hz a.c. and 70 mA d.c. Severe muscular contractions make it difficult for the casualty to release his/her hold. An increase in current beyond 20 mA 50 Hz a.c. or 80 mA d.c. can be fatal. The electrical resistance of the body (which governs the size of the current) varies from a few hundred ohms to thousands of ohms and depends on whether the skin is moist or dry.

Fuse Ratings The rule is always to use a fuse of the lowest possible value that will still allow the current drawn by the appliance to flow.

Examples of How to Work Out the Correct Fuse Value

1. Electric Iron (600 W)

   Supply Voltage = 240 V

   $P = V \times I$

   $I = 2.5$ A

   Therefore, use a 3 A fuse (rather than a 5 A or 13 A fuse).

   Generally, appliances rated at <720 W require a 3 A fuse (coloured red), unless a high starting current is required (e.g. a spin-drier or vacuum cleaner), in which case the manufacturer's instructions should be followed.

2. Immersion Heater (3 kW = 3000 W)

   Supply Voltage = 240 V

   $P = V \times I$

   $I = 12.5$ A

   Therefore, use a 13A fuse.

Colour Code The colour code specified has the advantage of being distinguishable by people who are red/green colour-blind.

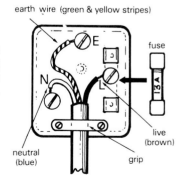

earth wire (green & yellow stripes)

E

fuse

N

live (brown)

neutral (blue)

grip

How to Wire a Fused Three Pin Plug

1. Slit outer sheath of flex with a sharp knife.
2. Strip insulating plastic from the three wires. Twist the strands of each wire together. Trim to correct length.
3. *For pillar terminal plugs*
   For small diameter wires fold the bared ends back to double them up. Push each wire into its appropriate terminal and screw down tightly allowing as much slack as possible for the earth conductor. (If the flex is pulled from the plug, the earth wire must be the last to disconnect should the grip fail.)

pillar terminal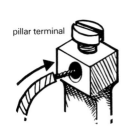

   For stud terminal plugs
   Twist the bare threads of each wire into a clockwise loop. Screw the trimmed wires firmly around the appropriate terminals. Ensure the wires are trapped under the washers whilst tightening the studs.

stud terminal

4. Check that the fuse is of the correct rating for the appliance.
5. Fix flex firmly in grip.
6. Ensure there are no loose strands of wire within the plug. These could cause short circuits.
7. Replace plug top.

Electrical Energy Is Transmitted at High Voltage

Electrical energy is transmitted at high voltage because this gives a greatly reduced power loss (as heat) in communicating cables.

Power Lost as Heat in a Cable

Power lost as heat in a cable can be calculated using:

$$P = I^2R$$

where P = heat energy lost per second
R = resistance of the cable, and
I = current transmitted in amps.

Imagine we wish to transmit 5 kW (5000 W) of power through a cable of resistance 5 Ω.
We could transmit, for example, 1 A at 5000 V or 100 A at 50 V. In the first case the power loss would be 5 W and in the second 50 kW!

Magnetism and Electromagnetism

Lodestone (Fe_3O_4)	A lodestone (magnetic iron oxide) is a natural magnet. When freely suspended it points North-South.
Magnetic Substances (Ferromagnetic)	Magnetic substances are substances that attract other metals or other magnets. They include iron, cobalt and nickel, and alloys such as steel, and also alloys of other metals which, on their own, are not magnetic.
Magnetically Hard Material	A hard magnetic material is one that is difficult to magnetise (low susceptibility) but retains its magnetism well (high retentivity), e.g. steel.
Magnetically Soft Material	A soft magnetic material is one that is easily magnetised (high susceptibility) but retains little magnetism on removing the magnetising field (low retentivity), e.g. iron.
Permanent Magnets	Permanent magnets are formed from magnetically hard material, and are usually horseshoe-shaped or in the form of a rectangular bar.
Freely Suspended Bar Magnet	A freely suspended bar magnet aligns with the Earth's magnetic field. 
North-Seeking Pole (North Pole)	The North-seeking pole is the end of a magnet which points approximately geographic North. The other end is called the south pole. The attracting power of a magnet is greatest at its poles.
Like Poles Repel	Two N or two S poles repel.
Unlike Poles Attract	A N and a S pole attract.
Compass	A compass consists of a magnetised needle pivoted at its centre.
Unmagnetised Material	An unmagnetised material is attracted to *both* poles of a magnet.
Attraction and Repulsion	Let both poles of a permanent magnet be brought in turn near to one pole of a suspended magnet. We should observe attraction and repulsion. Repulsion is the only sure way of discovering whether an object is a magnet or not.
Magnetic Field	A magnetic field is a force field surrounding a magnet. It can also be found in the vicinity of a conductor through which current is flowing.

263

Magnetic Domain

A magnetic domain is a region in a ferromagnetic material where each atom can be thought of as a tiny magnet and all atoms in the region point in the same direction. A magnet comprises many domains. In a magnetised steel bar all the domains line up in approximately the same direction.

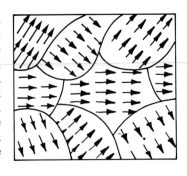

Strength of a Magnet

The strength of a magnet is determined by how well the domains are lined up.

Magnetic Induction Precedes Attraction

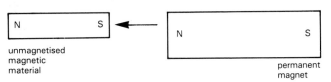

unmagnetised magnetic material

permanent magnet

An unmagnetised magnetic material has magnetism induced in it as a consequence of being brought into the vicinity of a magnetic field. In the above diagram the magnetic field is provided by the permanent magnet. Note the polarity of the unmagnetised material.

The Earth's Magnetic Field

The Earth's magnetic field can be thought of as being provided by a giant bar magnet within the Earth whose S pole points magnetic North.

Angle of Declination

The angle of declination is the angle between magnetic North and true geographic North.

Direction of a Magnetic Field

The direction of a magnetic field is the direction in which the N pole of a plotting compass points.

Lines of Magnetic Force (Flux) around a Bar Magnet

Lines of flux can be mapped with a plotting compass.

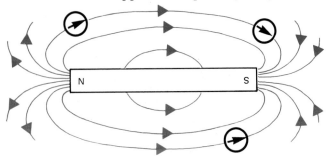

Magnetic Shielding

Magnetic shielding of electrical devices that could be adversely affected by stray or unwanted magnetic fields is achieved by surrounding the device in a soft iron container.

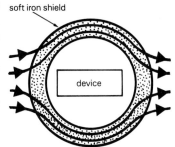

soft iron shield

Lines of magnetic force concentrate in the soft iron.

Making a Magnet:

By Stroking One pole of a permanent magnet is used to stroke a steel knitting-needle, for example, end to end in the same direction.

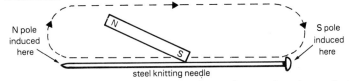

The magnet must be raised well above the steel at the end of each stroke. The polarity of the end of the steel where the magnetising pole leaves is opposite in polarity to the magnetising pole.

By Magnetic Induction In magnetic induction, a magnetic pole induces an unlike pole near to it and a like pole away from it.

Using a Solenoid A solenoid is a cylindrical coil of insulated copper wire.
1. Place steel rod in solenoid.
2. Connect solenoid to low-voltage *d.c.* supply.
3. Briefly switch current on. Switch off.
The steel rod is now a magnet.

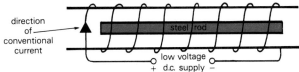

The polarity of the magnet depends on the direction of the current. View one end of the solenoid end-on.

If the conventional current in the coil, when viewed *externally*, is flowing aNticlockwise that end of the enclosed rod becomes a N pole. If current flows clockwiSe, then the end becomes a S pole.

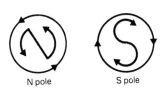

265

Demagnetising a Magnet

Demagnetising a magnet involves placing it inside a solenoid through which *a.c.* is flowing. The magnet is very slowly moved a few metres from the solenoid. The solenoid is placed with its axis pointing East-West.

Electric Current Produces a Magnetic Field

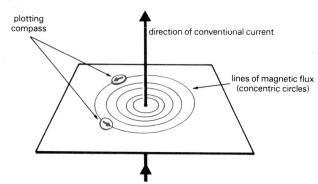

Field due to a Straight Wire

A plotting compass or compasses can map out the direction of the field at different points.

The Right-Hand Screw Rule

The right-hand screw rule predicts the direction of the field. The direction of rotation of a right-handed screw moved in the direction of conventional current flow gives the field direction.

Field due to a Solenoid

The field due to a solenoid is similar to that of a bar magnet.

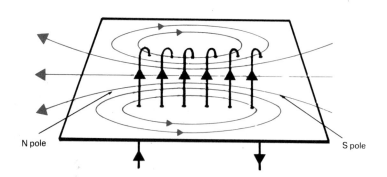

Electromagnet

An electromagnet is a solenoid wrapped around a *soft iron* core. The soft iron is magnetised *only* when current flows in the windings. It can thus be switched on and off.

To Increase the Strength of an Electromagnet

1. Increase the number of coil turns.
2. Increase the current.
3. Bring poles closer together (see Horseshoe Electromagnet).

Horseshoe Electromagnet The coil is wound such that the current flows in opposite directions in each limb, producing opposite poles.

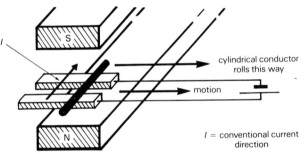

N pole   S pole

Some Uses of an Electromagnet Electric bell; lifting iron objects in a scrapyard; magnetic relays; telephone receivers; motors; loudspeakers.

Current-Carrying Conductor A current-carrying conductor placed in a magnetic field experiences a force.

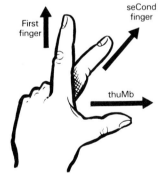

cylindrical conductor rolls this way

motion

I = conventional current direction

Fleming's Left Hand Rule (F.L.H.R.) If the thumb, first and second fingers of the left hand are held at right angles to each other so that:
the First finger points in the direction of the magnetic Field,
the seCond finger in the direction of conventional Current,
then the thuMb points in the direction of Motion.

First finger

seCond finger

thuMb

The *maximum* force is exerted when the conductor is perpendicular to the magnetic field. The force on a current-carrying straight conductor in a magnetic field is a result of the interaction of its own magnetic field with the one in which it is placed. It increases with increasing field strength and with increasing current.

Microphone   A microphone is a device for converting sound energy into electrical energy.

Circuit symbol for a microphone

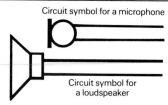

Loudspeaker   A loudspeaker is a device for converting electrical energy into sound energy.

Circuit symbol for a loudspeaker

Moving-Coil Loudspeaker   Varying electric currents from a radio or record player pass through a short cylindrical *voice coil*, which is free to move. The turns of the coil lie perpendicular to the strong radial field in the annular (ring-shaped) gap between the central pole and the surrounding ring pole. As the coil current varies, the coil moves in and out, with motion determined by Fleming's Left Hand Rule. The attached cone of specially treated paper moves with the coil and sets up vibrations in the neighbouring air layers. Waves are produced and detected as sound by the ear.

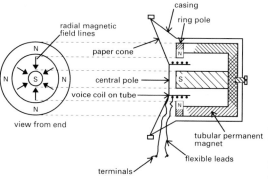

casing
radial magnetic field lines
ring pole
paper cone
central pole
voice coil on tube
view from end
tubular permanent magnet
flexible leads
terminals

Principle of Moving-Coil (or Dynamic) Microphone   In principle, the moving-coil loudspeaker could be used as a microphone. Incoming sound adjacent to the paper cone vibrates the cone and thus the coil. The coil cuts the radial magnetic field and, electromagnetically induces (see page 270) an alternating e.m.f. in it which appears at the terminals for amplification before *it* is fed to the coil of a loudspeaker. In practice, the bulk of a moving-coil loudspeaker makes it inconvenient for this purpose.

Current-Carrying Coil   A current-carrying coil wrapped around a soft iron cylinder and placed between the concave poles of a permanent magnet experiences a turning effect. If current enters and leaves the coil by springs, it rotates until stopped by the springs.

The coil is pivoted in jewelled bearings A and B.

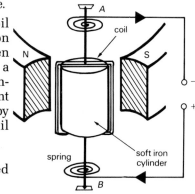

A
coil
N
S
+
spring
soft iron cylinder
B

Moving Coil Galvanometer A moving coil galvanometer consists of a current-carrying coil with a pointer attached to it.

Turning Effect of a Current-Carrying Coil in a Magnetic Field The turning effect of a current-carrying coil in a magnetic field increases with:
1. the strength of the magnetic field;
2. the current;
3. the number of turns on the coil; and
4. weaker hair springs.

Radial Field A radial field is one where the field lines are directed towards the centre of the cylinder. The concave pole pieces and the soft iron cylinder produce such a field in the air gap.

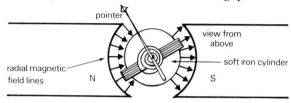

Linear Scale A linear scale is one where the divisions are the same size. A radial field ensures a linear scale over which the pointer moves.

Springs The springs determine the angle of rotation of the coil. They enable the coil to return to its original position when the current is switched off. Strong springs allow a coil to rotate through a smaller angle than weak springs.

Simple Electric Motor A simple electric motor consists of:
1. a coil;
2. a magnetic field; and
3. a split-ring commutator (a split copper ring) against which carbon brushes press.

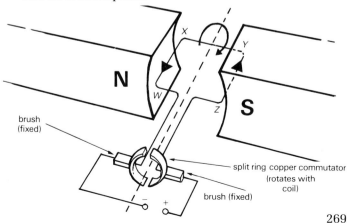

No forces act on WZ and XY since they are parallel to the field. WX experiences an upward force and YZ experiences a downward force (apply F.L.H.R). The coil rotates until the commutator halves change contact from one brush to the other. The current through the coil reverses, WX now experiences a downward force whilst YZ experiences an upward force. The coil rotates clockwise.

Efficiency of a Motor

$$\text{Efficiency of a motor} = \frac{\text{useful mechanical power output}}{\text{electrical power input}}$$

Electro-magnetic Induction

Electromagnetic induction describes the effect of producing electricity from magnetism.

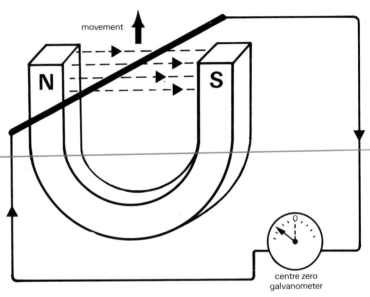

A conductor (connected by wires to a galvanometer) is moved in the direction shown between the poles of a permanent magnet. The magnetic lines of flux between the poles are cut. A potential difference is induced between the ends of the conductor. The size of the induced p.d. depends on the rate at which lines of flux are being cut. The greater the rate, the greater the p.d. The induced p.d. depends upon:
1. the length of wire in the field;
2. the strength of the magnetic field; and
3. the speed at which the wire moves.
The p.d. becomes zero when the motion stops. The p.d. results in a tiny current which gives rise to a deflection on the galvanometer.

Fleming's Right Hand Rule (F.R.H.R.)

Fleming's Right Hand Rule gives the direction of the induced current for a straight wire moving at right angles to a magnetic field.
If the thumb, first and second fingers of the right hand are held at right angles to each other so that:
the First finger points in the direction of the magnetic Field,
the thuMb in the direction of Motion,
then the seCond finger gives the direction of conventional Current.

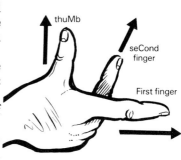

Inducing an Electromotive Force (and thus a Current in a Coil)

Inducing an e.m.f. can be achieved by moving a magnet towards or away from the coil. Lines of magnetic flux associated with the magnet are being cut by the turns of the coil.

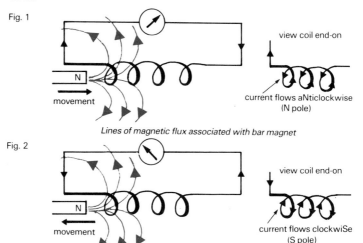

Fig. 1

view coil end-on

current flows aNticlockwise (N pole)

movement

Lines of magnetic flux associated with bar magnet

Fig. 2

view coil end-on

current flows clockwiSe (S pole)

movement

The direction of the induced current flows in the coil in such a way as to oppose the movement of the magnet. In fig. 1 the turns of the coil take on the appearance of a N pole and in fig. 2 a S pole. If the induced currents caused opposite poles to those that they do, electrical energy would be created from nothing violating the principle of conservation of energy (see page 203).

Direction of the Induced E.M.F.

The direction of the induced e.m.f. is specified by that of the induced current.

Lenz's Law Lenz's Law states that the induced current always flows in a direction which opposes the change responsible for inducing it.

Size of the Induced E.M.F. The size of the induced e.m.f. increases if we increase:
1. the rate at which lines of magnetic flux are being cut – increase the speed of the magnet relative to the coil (or vice versa);
2. the area of the coil;
3. the strength of the magnetic field; and
4. the number of coil turns.

Bicycle Dynamo A bicycle dynamo consists of a magnet on an axle in the vicinity of a stationary coil wrapped around a soft iron core connected to a lamp.

The induced current in the coil makes the lamp light. A faster rotation means that the rate at which lines of magnetic flux are being cut by the coil is increased, resulting in a bigger induced e.m.f. (and current). The lamp becomes brighter.

Simple A.C. Generator A simple a.c. generator consists of:
1. a coil;
2. a magnetic field; and
3. two slip rings (on the axle of the coil) against which carbon brushes press.

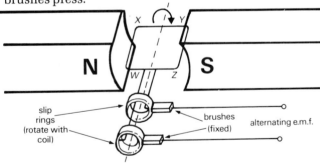

When the coil is rotated it cuts the magnetic field lines. An alternating e.m.f. is induced in the coil. The e.m.f. is a maximum when the coil is horizontal, since WX and YZ are cutting lines of flux at the greatest rate. When the coil becomes horizontal again, WX will be moving downwards and YZ upwards. The direction of e.m.f. will reverse.

Variation of E.M.F. over One Revolution

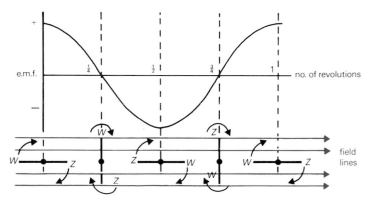

If the coil rotates twenty times per second, the a.c. will have a frequency of 20 Hz.

Mutual Induction

Mutual induction describes the effect of inducing an e.m.f. and current in a coil as a result of switching on, or off, or *changing* a current in a neighbouring coil. Subjecting a coil to a continuously varying magnetic flux pattern is analogous to a coil being cut by lines of magnetic flux as a result of moving a magnet (carrying its own fixed magnetic field pattern) toward or away from it.

The simplest way of doing this is to arrange for an a.c. to run through one of the coils. The magnetic field pattern associated with it will be continuously changing direction. A second coil in the vicinity of the first (preferably wrapped around a common soft iron core to minimise flux leakage) will experience a continuously changing magnetic flux pattern. A continuously changing e.m.f. (and current) will be induced in the second coil.

Transformer

A transformer transforms an alternating e.m.f. from one value to another of greater or smaller value. Primary and secondary coils are wound one on top of the other or on separate limbs of a common soft iron core. An alternating e.m.f. E_p applied to the primary coil induces an alternating e.m.f. E_s in the secondary given by

$$\boxed{\frac{E_s}{E_p} = \frac{N_s}{N_p}}$$

N_s = number of turns on secondary coil
N_p = number of turns on primary coil

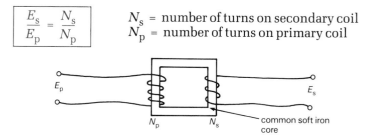

273

Circuit
Symbol for a
Step-Up
Transformer

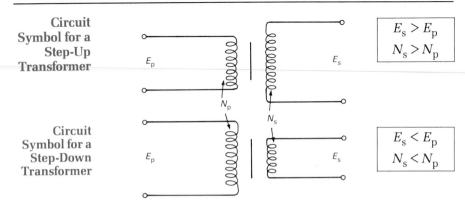

$$E_s > E_p$$
$$N_s > N_p$$

Circuit
Symbol for a
Step-Down
Transformer

$$E_s < E_p$$
$$N_s < N_p$$

Transformer Core The transformer core is made up of sheets of soft iron. Each sheet is insulated from adjacent sheets by varnish which increases the resistance. Heat energy losses inside the iron (a consequence of circulating induced currents inside it called eddy currents) are thus minimised.

Perfect Transformer The perfect transformer would ensure that all the electrical energy given to the primary appears in the secondary. For a 100% efficient transformer,

| Power in primary = power in secondary |

i.e.

| $E_p \times I_p = E_s \times I_s$ | where I_p = current in primary, and
I_s = current in secondary.

Thus:

$$\frac{E_s}{E_p} = \frac{N_s}{N_p} = \frac{I_p}{I_s}$$

Mains Transformer Hum Mains transformer hum is a result of its vibrating ferromagnetic core (vibrating bodies provide sound waves). A change in dimensions of ~ 3 parts in 10^5 results from a ferromagnetic substance being magnetised (magnetostriction). For every cycle of a.c., ferromagnetic domains are continually being aligned in one direction and then the other. Since the core has its maximum length when magnetised in either direction, the frequency of the sound waves is $2 \times 50\,\text{Hz}$ which is $100\,\text{Hz}$.

Example If $\dfrac{N_s}{N_p} = 50$, then $\dfrac{I_p}{I_s} = 50$, i.e. $I_s = \left(\dfrac{1}{50}\right) \times I_p$

That is to say, if a step-up transformer has a turns ratio of 50:1, the current is stepped down in the ratio 1:50. Thus the terms step-up and step-down for a transformer refer to E, not I.

An Actual Transformer
Because of electrical and magnetic losses, the perfect transformer does not exist. These losses are:
1. eddy currents – it is impossible to eliminate them completely;
2. heat energy produced in the coil windings;
3. the magnetic flux lines produced by the primary may not all cut the secondary – some escape from the core; and
4. hysteresis loss in the magnetic core due to its continued magnetisation and demagnetisation.

Energy Transfer of a Transformer
The energy transfer of a transformer can be over 90% efficient. In calculations we assume a 100% efficiency.

The National Grid
The National Grid transmits power at high voltages (high tension) and low current to minimise power losses in long-distance cabling.

A.C. Power Transmission
Transmission by a.c. enables us to use transformers which *efficiently* step alternating p.d.'s up and down.

U.K. Electricity Distribution System (National Grid)

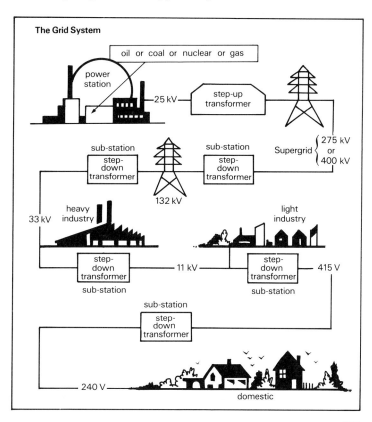

The Grid System

275

34 Electronics

The Potential Divider Circuit

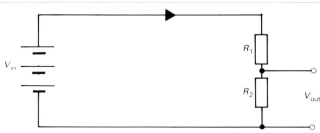

The p.d. across R_1 and R_2, $V_{in} = I(R_1 + R_2)$ ... ①

Also, $V_{out} = IR_2$ ... ②

Potential Divider Equation

$$V_{out} = V_{in}\frac{(R_2)}{(R_1 + R_2)}$$

[Divide equation ② by ① and multiply by V_{in}.]

Example

$$\left.\begin{array}{l} V_{in} = 6\text{ V} \\ R_2 = 100\ \Omega \\ R_1 = 50\ \Omega \end{array}\right\} \Rightarrow V_{out} = 4\text{ V}$$

L.E.D. (Light-Emitting Diode)   A light-emitting diode is a semiconductor diode which converts electrical energy into light. To light up, a p.d. of 2 V across it is needed.

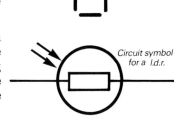

Circuit symbol for a l.e.d.

current flows this way to light

Protective Resistor   A protective resistor is *always* placed in series with a l.e.d. to limit the current through it and the p.d. across it. A p.d. much bigger than 2 V will damage it.

Uses   Uses of l.e.d.'s include:
1. indicator lamps; and
2. seven segment l.e.d. displays in calculators and clocks.

Seven Segment Display   The figure *eight*. All numbers from nought to nine can be made by illuminating different combinations of the seven segments.

L.D.R. (Light Dependent Resistor)   A light-dependent resistor is a resistor whose resistance decreases with increasing light intensity. The more intense the light, the better the l.d.r. conducts electricity.

Circuit symbol for a l.d.r.

Thermistor A thermistor is a s.c. whose electrical resistance generally decreases rapidly with increasing temperature. Its resistance can vary from 100 kΩ at room temperature to a few ohms at 100°C.

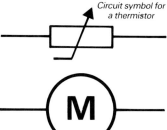

Circuit symbol for a thermistor

Circuit Symbol for a Motor A motor is represented as shown.

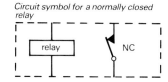

Relay A relay is an electromagnetic switch. A small current in one circuit operates a switch (via an electromagnet) in a second circuit. The second circuit often carries a much larger current.

Switching a Motor on via a Relay

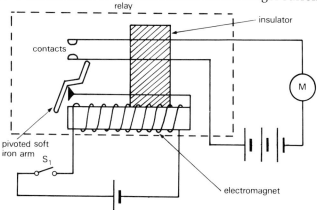

Operation
1. Close S_1.
2. Electromagnet energises.
3. Soft iron arm (called an armature) is pulled towards electromagnet.
4. Contacts close.
5. Current flows through motor.

Circuit Symbol for a Normally Open or Normally Closed Relay

Circuit symbol for a normally open relay

Circuit symbol for a normally closed relay

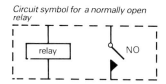

Transducer A transducer is a device for converting a non-electrical quantity (e.g. light, heat, sound) into electrical signals. Examples include l.d.r.'s, thermistors and microphones.

Transistor A transistor is a current amplifying device. It is often used as a high-speed switch.

| NPN Transistor | An npn transistor has three terminals: collector c base b emitter e. |

| Transistor as a Switch | OFF when no collector current flows.
 ON when sufficient collector current flows to give a small collector-emitter voltage. |

A minimum base-emitter voltage of about 0.6 V is necessary.

Switching on a Transistor Using a Potential Divider

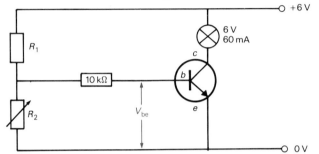

V_{be} depends on the resistance of R_2 compared with R_1. When $V_{be} > 0.6$ V the transistor switches on and the lamp lights. A very small base-emitter current allows a much larger collector-emitter current to flow. The 10 kΩ resistor ensures only a small current is allowed to flow into the base.

Electronic Systems

Electronic systems have an input sensor, a processor and an output device. The input sensor (e.g. l.d.r. or thermistor) detects changes in the environment. The processor (e.g. potential divider circuit used in conjunction with transistor/logic gates) controls what action to take. The output device (e.g. lamp or buzzer) is controlled by the processor.

Light-Dependent Switch

(i) Indicator Lamp On in the Dark

The light level sensitivity control is R_1.

R_1 dictates how dark it needs to be before the indicator lamp switches on.
The 2.2 kΩ protective resistor ensures that should R_1 ever tend to zero, the current through the transistor will still be low. If the l.d.r. is covered its resistance is high and V_{be} is high enough for the transistor to switch on. The lamp lights. Varying R_1 changes V_{be}.

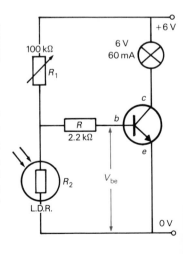

(ii) Indicator Lamp Off in the Dark

> The light level sensitivity control is R_2.

R_2 dictates how dark it needs to be before the indicator lamp switches off.
If light is incident on the l.d.r. its resistance drops and V_{be} is high enough for the transistor to switch on. The lamp lights.
Covering the l.d.r. results in a high R_1 (compared to R_2). The transistor switches off and the lamp goes out.
Varying R_2 changes V_{be}.

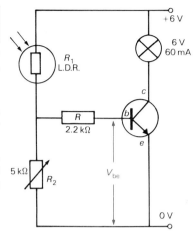

Temperature-Dependent Switch

(i) Indicator Lamp on in the Cold

> The light level sensitivity control is R_1.

R_1 dictates how cold it needs to get before the indicator lamp switches on.
As the thermistor gets colder its resistance increases, so its share of the 6 V increases and the transistor switches on. The lamp lights.

(ii) Indicator Lamp Off in the Cold

> The light level sensitivity control is R_2.

R_2 dictates how cold it needs to get before the indicator lamp switches off.
As the thermistor gets hotter its resistance decreases and its share of the 6 V decreases. V_{be} increases until the transistor switches on. The lamp lights.

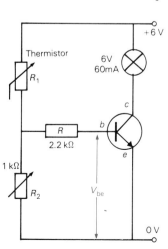

Light-Dependent Switch Operated by a Relay

Lamp On in the Dark

The sensitivity control is R_1

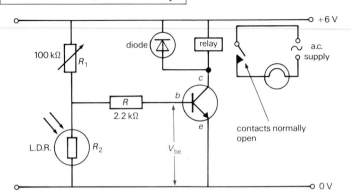

The darker it gets the bigger the resistance of the l.d.r. and the bigger its share of the 6 V. V_{be} increases. The transistor switches on. The relay* switches on. The contacts close. The lamp lights. R_1 dictates how dark it needs to get before the lamp lights.

*A *reverse biased* diode is connected in parallel with the relay to divert current away from the transistor when the relay is switched off. Switching off the relay results in lines of magnetic flux collapsing in a very short time. This gives rise to a large e.m.f. induced in the coil of the relay. The e.m.f. gives rise to a current which could destroy the transistor.

Logic Circuits Logic circuits use electrical signals for inputs and outputs.

Logic Gates Logic gates can be either OFF or ON.

Logic 0 Logic 0 stands for OFF. It corresponds to an input p.d. of 0 Volts.

Logic 1 Logic 1 stands for ON. It corresponds to an input p.d. > 0 Volts.

T.T.L. Levels Transistor-Transistor Logic Levels. Logic 0 is < 0.4 V. Logic 1 is between 2.4 V and 5 V. 0.4 V to 2.4 V is avoided.

Truth Table for an AND Gate

inputs

A	B	output
0	0	0
0	1	0
1	0	0
1	1	1

circuit symbol

input A

AND output

input B

The output is ON (Logic 1) only when both input A AND input B are ON.

Truth Table for a NOT Gate	input	output	circuit symbol
	0	1	
	1	0	

A **NOT** gate is an *inverter*. The output is the opposite of the input.

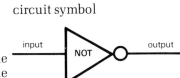

Truth Table for an OR Gate	inputs			circuit symbol
	A	B	output	
	0	0	0	
	0	1	1	
	1	0	1	
	1	1	1	

The output is ON (Logic 1) when either or both inputs *A* and *B* are ON.

Combining an AND Gate with a NOT Gate

Output of **AND** gate is input to **NOT** gate. This combination can be replaced by a single gate known as a **NAND** gate.

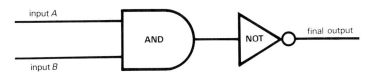

Truth Table for a NAND Gate	inputs			circuit symbol
	A	B	output	
	0	0	1	
	0	1	1	
	1	0	1	
	1	1	0	

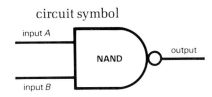

Combining an OR Gate with a NOT Gate

Output of **OR** gate is input to **NOT** gate. This combination can be replaced by a single gate known as a **NOR** gate.

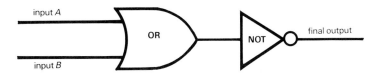

281

Truth Table for a NOR Gate	inputs			circuit symbol
	A	B	output	
	0	0	1	
	0	1	0	
	1	0	0	
	1	1	0	

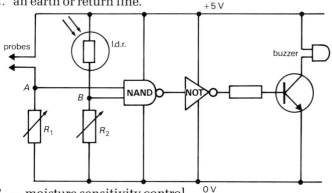

Logic Gate Application

Students should appreciate that logic gates require:
1. a power supply input; and
2. an earth or return line.

Circuit for Detecting Moisture in Daylight

R_1 = moisture sensitivity control
R_2 = light level sensitivity control

For the buzzer to 'buzz' we require (working backwards):
1. the output from the **NOT** gate to be a logical 1;
2. the input to the **NOT** gate to be a logical 0 (see Truth Table for **NOT** gate);
3. the output from the **NAND** gate to be a logical 0;
4. the two inputs to the **NAND** gate to be logical 1 (see Truth Table for **NAND** gate);
5. the resistance of the l.d.r. to be low for the potential at B to be high. (We want most of the voltage drop to be across R_2.) The resistance of a l.d.r. decreases with increasing light intensity, so we want DAYLIGHT;
6. the resistance between the detector probes to be low for the potential at A to be high. (We want most of the voltage drop across R_1.) Hence the detector probes should be moist.

N.B. The **NAND** gate followed by the **NOT** gate in the above circuit could be replaced with an **AND** gate.

Simple Capacitor

A simple capacitor is made up of two metal plates separated by a thin layer of air or insulating material called a *dielectric*. When connected to a battery it will store charge.

Capacitance of a Capacitor

The capacitance of a capacitor is a measure of its ability to store charge. To increase the capacitance:
1. increase the area of the plate overlap;

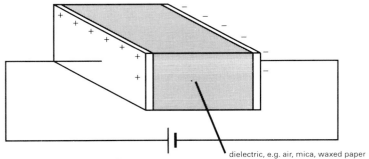

dielectric, e.g. air, mica, waxed paper

2. decrease the plate separation;
3. change the nature of the dielectric, e.g. replacing air with mica to increase the capacitance by a factor of seven.

Units of Capacitance   Capacitance is measured in farads (F). Practically, this unit is too large and capacitors are measured in microfarads ($1\mu F = 10^{-6}F$) or picofarads ($1pF = 10^{-12}F$).

Polarised or Electrolytic Capacitors   Electrolytic capacitors are made in sizes up to $\sim 10^5 \mu F$. Connecting them the wrong way round in a circuit will damage them.

Non-electrolytic or Non-polarised Capacitors   Non-electrolytic capacitors are made in small sizes up to about $1~\mu F$. It does not matter which plate is connected to the positive side of the battery.

Variable Capacitors   Variable capacitors comprise two sets of interleaved plates. Turning one set of plates so that they overlap more increases the capacitance. They are made in sizes up to 1 nF ($1~nF = 10^{-9}F$). Air is the dielectric.

Charging/ Discharging a Capacitor

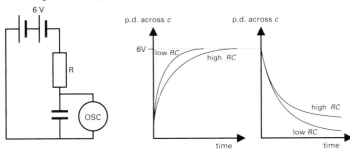

When a current flows in an uncharged capacitor, charge is stored and the p.d. across the capacitor increases until it reaches the same value as the supply voltage. A large capacitor can store more charge and so it takes longer to reach the supply

283

p.d. A large resistor only allows a small current to flow on to the plates. It is the product RC, the *time constant*, which determines the time taken for the capacitor to charge up to its maximum p.d. The bigger the time constant, the longer it takes the capacitor to charge up to its maximum p.d. When a resistor is connected across a charged capacitor, a current flows from the capacitor, and the p.d. across the capacitor decreases. RC also determines the time taken for the capacitor to discharge through the resistor.

Simple Timer A capacitor and resistor can be used as a simple timer in electronic systems. When combined with the output from the sensor, processing of the output from the sensor is delayed. A burglar alarm circuit can be designed incorporating such a simple timer which takes a pre-specified time (ensuring an appropriate time delay) to charge up to, for example, 0.6 V to switch on a transistor which in turn enables the alarm.

NAND Gate Flip-Flop Recall that the output of a NAND gate is only 0 if both inputs are 1, i.e. the output is always 1 unless *both* inputs are 1. Two NAND gates cross-connected is called a *bistable* or *flip-flop* because it has *two* stable states, the set state and the re-set state.

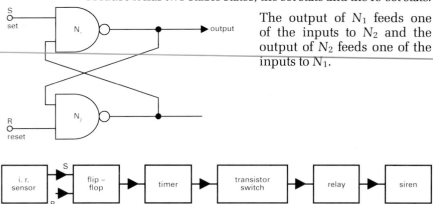

The output of N_1 feeds one of the inputs to N_2 and the output of N_2 feeds one of the inputs to N_1.

Block diagram for a burglar alarm Imagine you leave home with S and R = 1. Previous output of N_1 = 0. The siren is off. A burglar arrives and breaks the i.r. beam. The table (facing) describes what happens when a burglar breaks into a house and the owner returns and resets the alarm.

With 9 we are now back to where we started – obviously somehow the householder has to leave the dwelling without triggering the system! A time delay associated with the SET and RESET facilities enables the householder to reconfigure the system (without being deafened) and leave without triggering the system.

Activity	N_1's previous output	R	N_2's output	S	N_1's output	Comment
1. Householder leaves	0	1	1	1	0	siren enabled
2. Burglar enters i.r. beam	0	1	1	0	1	siren on
3. Burglar leaves i.r. beam	1	1	0	1	1	siren still on
4. Householder returns – turns RESET off (hopefully to an intact home after scaring intruder)	1	0	1	1	0	siren off
5. Householder turns RESET on	0	1	1	1	0	siren off
6. Householder turns SET off	0	1	1	0	1	siren on
7. Householder turns SET on	1	1	0	1	1	siren on
8. Householder turns RESET off	1	0	1	1	0	siren off
9. Householder turns RESET on.	0	1	1	1	0	siren off

Conclusions

We can see from the tabulation that the only way to change the output of the bistable (flip-flop) from ON to OFF is to change the RESET input (see 4 and 8). The output stays OFF even when the RESET input is changed back again (see 5 and 9). Similarly, to change the output of the flip-flop from OFF to ON the SET input needs to be changed (see 2 and 6). The output then stays ON even when the SET input is changed back again (see 3 and 7). The circuit 'remembers' the first change to the SET input.

Practical considera-tions

1. Infra-red radiation is preferable to light because it is invisible to the human eye.

2. Transmitter and receiver should be housed in identical cases to eliminate possible identification of the units.

3. Additional dummy housings further complicate attempts to defeat the system.

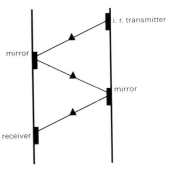

4. If an intruder is aware of the presence and path of the ray he may attempt to physically avoid it, for example, by crawling underneath it. 'Lacing' the ray zig-zag fashion using mirrors as shown here) makes evasion impossible.

5. Infra-red radiation will penetrate clear glass so protection can be extended through glass partitions and windows.

35 The Solar System and the Universe

Phases of the Moon
The Moon (i) spins on its axis
(ii) revolves around the Earth.
Since the two periods (27.3 days) are the same, the Moon always presents the same face to us. The Moon has no light of its own and depends entirely upon light reflected from the Sun. As the Moon travels in orbit around the Earth different parts of it are illuminated. These changing aspects are called its *phases*.

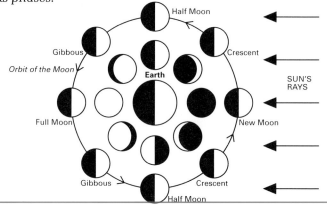

Day and night
The Earth spins on its own axis every day (24 hours). The half of the Earth which faces the Sun is in daylight; the other half of the Earth is in darkness (night).

The Seasons

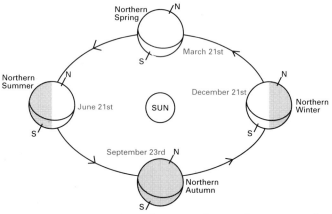

The seasons come about because the Earth's axis is tilted at 23° 27′ to the perpendicular (which is the same as saying the equator is tilted by 23° 27′ to the plane of the orbit). About December 21st, the axis is tilted so that the North Pole is tilted

THE PLANETS

1AU = 150 000 000 km = 1 Astronomical Unit.
This is the mean distance between the centre of the Earth and the centre of the Sun.
The mass of the Earth is 6.0×10^{24} kg.

Planet	Symbol	Mean surface temp °C	Dist. from Sun (AU)	Escape speed km/s	Time to go round Sun once	Axial rotation	Volume (relative to Earth) E=1	Mass (relative to Earth) E=1	Diameter E=1	Surface gravity E=1	Density (water=1)	No. of natural satellites	Nature
Mercury	☿	350 (day) −170 (night)	0.4	4.2	88d	58.65d	0.056	0.06	0.38	0.38	5.5	0	tenuous atmosphere rocky volcanic
Venus	♀	480	0.7	10.2	224d	243.16d	0.86	0.8	0.95	0.90	5.25	0	dense atmosphere − mainly CO_2 rocky (basaltic) volcanic
Earth	⊕	22	1.0	11.1	1 year	23h 56 min	1.0	1.0	1.0	1.0	5.52	1 The Moon	nitrogen/oxygen atmosphere 70% water, rocky (basaltic), volcanic
Mars	♂	−23	1.5	5.1	2y	24h 37min	0.15	0.1	0.53	0.38	3.94	2 Phobos & Deimos	thin CO_2 atmosphere dusty, arid, rocky (basaltic), volcanic
Jupiter	♃	−150	5.2	59.4	12y	9h 50min	131	317	11.3	2.64	1.33	⩾16	mainly hydrogen and helium
Saturn	♄	−180	9.5	35.2	29y	10h 39min	744	95	9.4	1.16	0.71	21	mainly hydrogen and helium
Uranus	⛢	−210	19.0	22.2	84y	17h	67	14.5	4.1	1.17	1.7	15	thick atmosphere of hydrogen and methane
Neptune	♆	−220	30.5	24.2	165y	18h	57	17	3.9	1.2	1.8	8	
Pluto	♇	−230	39.5	v. low	248y	6d 9h	?	0.002	0.24	<0.1	v. low	1	may be covered with frozen methane gas

furthest away from the Sun and the South Pole is tilted closest to the Sun. It is midwinter in the northern hemisphere and midsummer in the southern hemisphere.

Six months later, about June 21st, the North Pole is tilted closest to the Sun and the South Pole furthest away from it. It is midsummer in the northern hemisphere and midwinter in the southern.

At places on the hemisphere tilted closest to the Sun:

1. the period of daylight is longer than that of darkness
2. the Sun rises higher in the sky so more energy is received from the Sun, and
3. the weather is warmer.

If the Earth's axis were not tilted, there would be 12-hour days everywhere and no seasons. Mars (angle of tilt, 23° 59') has seasons, but Venus (angle of tilt, 178°) does not. Uranus (angle of tilt, 98°) is effectively tipped on its side so that at any given time one pole is pointed at the Sun. The poles are warmer than the equator. Since Uranus takes 84 Earth years to go round the Sun once, it follows that daylight at the Uranus poles lasts for 42 Earth years followed by an equally long night.

Solar Eclipse (Occultation) The Sun and the Moon appear almost the same size in the sky. When the Moon passes between the Earth and the Sun and all three are in a straight line, the Moon may for a few minutes blot out the Sun's visible disc. The phenomenon is universally called a *total solar eclipse*. To be precise it is an *occultation*. In a true eclipse (e.g. a lunar eclipse), the eclipsed body is invisible or darkened because it is in shadow. The Sun's surrounding halo (the *corona*) becomes visible during a total eclipse.

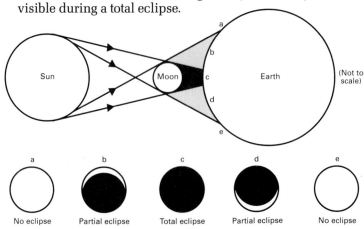

Sun's appearance

a	b	c	d	e
No eclipse	Partial eclipse	Total eclipse	Partial eclipse	No eclipse

Annular Eclipse If the Moon is at its greatest distance from the Earth when lining up occurs, the lunar disc appears smaller than that of the Sun and an *annular eclipse* occurs.

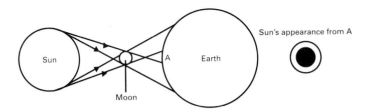

Lunar Eclipse	Since the Moon revolves around the Earth, there are times when the Moon passes into the shadow cast by the Earth. We would expect the Moon to be completely invisible when it is in the umbra of the Earth but, because some sunlight is refracted on to its surface by the Earth's atmosphere, it merely turns into a dim coppery colour.

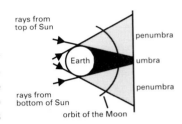

Constellation This is a group of stars forming a pattern that does not change noticeably over the years. Their name is supposed to reflect the shape of the pattern. Examples of their Latin names and English equivalents include Aries the Ram, Cancer the Crab, Scorpius the Scorpion and Leo the Lion.

The Planets The planets visible to the naked eye look like stars but are not self-luminous. We see them because they reflect light from the Sun. The name planet means 'wanderer'. They appear to wander against the background of 'fixed' stars. The orbits of the planets around the Sun are slightly squashed circles (ellipses) with the Sun quite close to the centre.

Meteorites Meteorites are carbonaceous, iron or stony rocks that survive the drop to the ground. They may produce a crater. The most massive meteorite known weighs $\sim 10^4$N. The sacred black stone at Mecca (The Kaaba) is almost certainly a meteorite.

Shooting Star (Meteors) When meteors (small particles of dust) crash into the Earth's upper atmosphere at speeds up to 70 km/s, they become heated by friction with air molecules and produce a luminous effect. Shooting stars are neither stars nor meteorites.

The Asteroid Belt The asteroid belt comprises lumps of rock orbiting the Sun. They are found between Mars and Jupiter and range in size from one km to hundreds of km across.

289

Comets Most comets describe eccentric orbits about the Sun. They are non-luminous aggregates of rock, dust and ice. When a comet approaches the Sun, ice inside its nucleus vaporises, giving rise to the formation of a head or *coma*. Larger comets may develop two tails – a gas tail, and a dust tail. Tails point away from the Sun and can extend to millions of kilometres in length.

The Oort Cloud The Oort cloud is a cloud of thousands of millions of comets that orbit the Sun beyond the orbit of Pluto or Neptune. (Neptune will be the outermost planet of our solar system until 1999.)

Halley's Comet Halley's comet describes an elliptical orbit that goes beyond the orbit of Pluto. It has a period of 76 years (although it has been as low as 74 years and as high as 79). It is depicted in the Bayeux tapestry which records the Norman conquest of 1066. It will be next seen in 2061.

Escape Speed A projectile fired from the Earth's surface requires a speed which just exceeds the *escape speed* of 11.1 km/s to leave the Earth completely for outer space. Since air molecules have far smaller average speeds than this, the Earth's gravitational field maintains an air atmosphere. Planets with low escape speeds have lost their free molecules and have thin atmospheres. Jupiter has a high escape speed and has been able to retain even hydrogen. A certain amount of energy is required to escape from the Earth. Multi-stage rockets burn their fuel relatively slowly, developing a large power over long time periods. They are launched from zero velocity and need not attain the escape speed to reach outer space.

Factors which Limit Space Travel
1. *Cost*: The Viking landing on Mars cost $1 billion. The Galileo probe (heading for Jupiter) cost $1.4 billion. (Galileo had to travel to Venus and back to Earth twice, using 'gravity-assist' at each planet in order to gain enough speed to reach Jupiter and its moons.) A single manned mission to Mars will cost $20 billion. This is one month's expenditure on armaments by the USA.

2. *Medical*: The heart grows weaker and shrinks. Muscles atrophy in 'zero' gravity. Bones become brittle. (On Earth bones renew themselves about every six months, and although calcium in an astronaut's bones, in 'zero' gravity, disappears at the same rate as on Earth, it is renewed at a much slower rate.) The immune systems malfunction.

3. *Cosmic ray bombardment*: Astronauts are bombarded by cosmic rays to an unprecedented extent compared with their counterparts on Earth. These rays may damage cells or genes.

4. *Spacecraft environment*: Maintaining conditions within the spacecraft needed to sustain life for long periods, including food, oxygen, water, warmth and sanitation is also a limiting factor.

Satellite Speed

The speed of a satellite is inversely proportional to the square root of the radius of the orbit i.e. $V \propto \sqrt{\frac{1}{R}}$ and therefore small orbits mean high speeds and large orbits mean slower speeds.

Polar Orbiting Satellites

Polar orbiters circle the Earth at a height of 850 km and make about 14 orbits every 24 hours. During the 90 minutes between successive orbits, the Earth has rotated 25° longitude. They can scan the whole Earth each day.

Geostationary Satellites

Geostationary satellites are usually put into orbit 36 000 km above the *equator*. They have to be above the equator to remain in a geostationary orbit. The height of this orbit is such that satellites orbit at the same rate the Earth turns. They appear to be stationary to somebody on the Earth's surface. Meteosat (a European weather satellite) stays over the Gulf of Guinea near West Africa, an excellent position for Africa and quite good for Europe. Communication satellites are geostationary.

Remote Sensing Satellites

Remote sensing satellites can:

1. help scientists understand the make-up of underlying terrain;
2. estimate wind strength and direction;
3. provide high-resolution images of icebergs (useful for ship and oil tanker traffic);
4. measure the amount of infra-red radiation from the sea's surface (data can be converted to temperature readings);
5. monitor ocean currents, hurricanes, the state of the ozone hole over Antarctica;
6. investigate the chemistry, dynamics and wind patterns of the upper atmosphere to provide upper air information over the oceans for use in computer forecasting;
7. track changes in coastal topography;
8. monitor the destruction of the rain forests;
9. provide people on Earth with information about their precise location – in terms of latitude, longitude and altitude – to within one metre;
10. help cartographers draw up detailed and precise maps.

291

Astronomy Satellites	Astronomy satellites monitor and process information in the form of electromagnetic radiation from astronomical objects. Short-wavelength radiation (ultraviolet X-rays and γ-rays) cannot penetrate the Earth's atmosphere and even light waves from a star can be absorbed by the atmosphere. To eliminate the effect of obscuring gases in the atmosphere, we need to get above it. X-rays are emitted from hot regions of space. The pulsar (a rapidly varying radio source, now known to be a neutron star) at the centre of the Crab Nebula gives off weak X-rays as well as radio waves, indicating a temperature of some 2 000 000 °C. The brightest γ-ray regions in the sky are those where cosmic dust is most dense, such as the Orion Nebula.
IRAS	The Infra-Red Astronomical Satellite (IRAS) has produced some evidence for planetary systems forming around other stars. Infra-red telescopes have enabled the temperature of the lower atmosphere of Venus to be mapped.
IUE Satellite	The International Ultra-Violet Explorer satellite has observed the u.v. spectra of nearly all the planets and their moons. IUE can help scientists deduce the kind of stars galaxies contain and the rate at which new stars are being formed. Hot young stars tend to be strong sources of u.v.
HST	The Hubble Space Telescope (a conventional reflector telescope) launched by NASA in 1990 should have seen further and better than any Earth-based telescope but unfortunately its primary mirror was slightly misshapen. In December 1993, the crew of space shuttle Endeavour undertook a successful repair mission on behalf of NASA. The orbiting telescope was fitted with a mechanism containing four small relay mirrors designed to cancel the error in the curvature of HST's primary mirror by creating an error of equal and opposite size.
The Sun	The Sun shines because of nuclear reactions taking place in its core. Vast amounts of energy are generated which flow to its surface, eventually radiating into space. The Sun is composed mainly of hydrogen ($\approx 73.5\%$ of its mass) and helium ($\approx 25\%$). There is also a small fraction of heavier elements. At the Sun's centre, gas is compressed to a density some 160 times greater than water. The core temperature is $\sim 2 \times 10^7$ K. The pressure exerted by the gases is about 10^8 atmospheres. Hydrogen nuclei collide so violently in these conditions that one in 10^{30} encounters results in helium being formed. The mass of a helium nucleus is about 0.7% less than the mass of the four nucleons that formed it. The difference in mass is converted to energy according to $E = mc^2$. Our Sun is an average star. It has a mass of 2×10^{30} kg and a power output of 4×10^{26} W.

In order to maintain this output, 4.4×10^6 tons of matter are destroyed per second. The Sun has been shining for 5×10^9 years and it will be as long again before it exhausts its supply of hydrogen fuel.

Galaxies Galaxies contain many billions of stars, together with interstellar material in the form of gas and dust. Many are spiral-like catherine wheels; others are elliptical, spherical or irregular.

The Galaxy (The Milky Way) The Galaxy (ours!) is a loose spiral-type with the Sun and Solar system located at the edge of one of the spiral arms. The diameter of the Galaxy is about 10^5 light years, having a maximum breadth of 2×10^4 light years. There are about 10^{11} stars in the Milky Way but there are billions of separate galaxies in the Universe. The distance between 'adjacent' galaxies is often millions of times bigger than the size of the galaxies themselves. The age of the Milky Way is $\sim 10^{10}$ years.

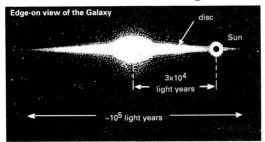

The centripetal accelerations experienced by high velocity stars (far from the galactic centre) depend on the mass concentrated at its nucleus. The gravitational pull on these stars enables the mass of the Galaxy to be deduced. 90% of this mass cannot be accounted for. Similarly, the red shifts of galaxies enable the Universe to be massed. 99% of the mass cannot be accounted for.

Birth of a Star A star is a result of a cloud of gas (almost entirely hydrogen and dust) shrinking because of gravitational attraction between the particles that make it up. The cloud shrinks, becomes denser, heats up and dimly glows. The shrinking results in the hot gases spinning at a faster rate and glowing more brightly. It will eventually take the shape of an oblate ball with disc-like rings of gas and dust surrounding it. Eventually, after further shrinkage, thermonuclear reactions are initiated at its centre. The heat produced results in an outward radial force caused by radiation pressure.

Stable Star In a stable star, the force of gravity is balanced by the force due to radiation pressure. The size of the star remains constant.

Expanding Star Eventually, the fuel at the centre of a star is exhausted and the nuclear burning moves outwards. The star gets hotter and the force due to radiation pressure becomes greater than gravity. It will expand to become a red giant.

Red Giant	A red giant is so called because the maximum intensity of its radiation lies in the red part of the spectrum (corresponding to a temperature ~ 4000 K). Its diameter would be about 100 times that of our Sun. Its luminosity would increase by a factor of 10^2 to 10^4 and its density would decrease by a factor of 10^4 to 10^7.
Collapsing Star	When stars no longer have fuel to burn they finally collapse. The force of gravity becomes dominant.
White Dwarf	If a star's mass does not exceed 1.4 solar masses, it may evolve into a white dwarf. Matter becomes completely ionised with electrons and nuclei packed extremely close together. The density is $\sim 10^8$ to 10^{11} kg/m^3. The pressure exerted by the electrons balances the inward-directed gravitational force, preventing the star from contracting any further. The most famous example of a white dwarf is the companion of Sirius. It is only about three times as big as the Earth but has a mass about the same as our Sun.
Planetary Nebula	In evolving from a red giant to a white dwarf, the gaseous outer envelope is expelled into space. The core of the red giant has collapsed into a hot planet-sized body. The star is said to be a planetary nebula*. Its temperature lies somewhere between 2.5×10^4 K and 3.5×10^5 K and its energy radiation is in the ultraviolet. The u.v. excites the outer bubble of gas causing it to radiate in the visible spectrum. The planetary nebula becomes visible. Eventually (after about 10^5 years) the nebula fades leaving behind a cooling white dwarf star.

*William Herschel, who coined the term, thought that the images of stars in this phase (viewed through his telescope) resembled the discs of planets.

Future of the Sun	When the hydrogen in the Sun's core is used up, the fusion reactions stop. Core gas falls in on itself again. As gravitation energy is liberated, heat is generated. At $\simeq 10^8$ K the pressure is so great that helium nuclei fuse to form carbon and oxygen. The outer layers of the Sun expand outwards, engulfing the inner planets (including Earth). The expanding gas cools; the yellow colour of the Sun fades to red. It is in its 'red giant' phase, becoming a planetary nebula before collapsing into a white dwarf.
Supernova	A supernova is a star that 'explodes'. Its luminosity increases so dramatically that the supernova can sometimes be seen by day. It is thought to be the beginning of the final stage in the evolution of a massive star (much bigger than the Sun). Most of the star's mass is blown away, and any remains are considered to be in the form of a very dense collapsed stellar core which may be a white dwarf, a neutron star or a black hole. The Earth and our own bodies consist of 'heavy' elements created as a result of supernova(e) combining neutrons and protons at a prodigious rate.

Neutron Star The gravitational collapse is so great that electrons and protons are compressed into neutrons. They have a diameter of only 10-20 km, a density of 10^{16}-10^{18} kg/m^3, a core temperature of $\sim 10^9$K and a very strong magnetic field. A cubic centimetre of neutron star material has a mass of ~ 250 million tonnes.

Pulsar A pulsar is a rapidly rotating neutron star. It emits *radio waves* in pulses of great regularity. The first pulsar, discovered by Jocelyn Bell in August 1967, emitted pulses every 1.33730113 seconds.

Red Shift If light from a star or galaxy is passed through a spectroscope it is split into a coloured spectrum. Embedded within are thin black lines characteristic of certain elements in the star's atmosphere (sometimes called *spectral lines*). The light of a star or galaxy receding from us appears to be of longer wavelength than if it were stationary (the Doppler effect). The spectral lines shift towards the red end of the spectrum. The size of this *red shift* is a measure of the speed of recession. A galaxy ten times further away than another recedes ten times as quickly.

Quasar Quasars look like ordinary stars when viewed through an optical telescope but are extremely strong energy sources, radiating over a wide range of wavelengths from X-ray to radio. They may be as small as 100 light-days across (our own galaxy is 70 000 light-years across) but appear to be tens of times brighter than whole galaxies. They are apparently the nuclei of active galaxies and show tremendous red shifts, which if resulting from the expansion of the universe indicates they are very old and very remote. Some quasars have red shifts so big it would appear they are on the very edge of the universe. Halton C. Arp of the Max Planck Institute for Astrophysics in Germany maintains some quasars have been found in the vicinity of nearby galaxies with small red shifts. If the quasar were connected with the galaxy, then the two objects would not be moving at greatly different speeds. This *could* mean that the red shifts (perhaps all red shifts) result from a phenomenon other than rapid recession.

Brown Dwarf Brown dwarfs are hypothetical cool stars with masses too low for nuclear reactions to occur in their cores.

Light Year A light year is the distance travelled by light in one year. It is equal to 9 460 000 million kilometres.

Parsec A parsec is 3.26 light years.

Black Holes Stars that are too massive to end their life as a white dwarf or a neutron star may form a black hole. A centre of a galaxy (where the force of gravity pulls in swirling clouds of gas and dust) could also be a candidate for a black hole. Our own galaxy, the Milky Way, *may* contain a massive black hole. The escape speed becomes greater than the speed of light and they become unobservable surrounded by a 'forbidden zone', the boundary of which is known as the *event horizon*. Inside the event horizon, the laws of physics apparently break down. Since black holes emit no light, they are very difficult to detect. However, close to a black hole we may expect to see a brilliant concentration of stars drawn into orbit around its rim – giving the black hole a 'halo'.

If a black hole is part of a binary system (two stars in orbit about a common point), we may be able to predict its presence by observing the effect of its gravitational field on its partner. It will suck in material from the other star with such force that the material emits X-rays. (At high temperatures matter radiates X-rays.)

Cygnus X-1 is a binary system in the constellation Cygnus. One of the components is an ordinary star (emitting ordinary light) of about 30 solar masses. The other (about 10 solar masses) is probably a black hole. It is so near the ordinary star that a large tidal bulge is formed. A steady stream of surface material is pulled from it, spiralling around the black hole (forming an 'accretion disc') before gradually falling in. The material, accelerated by the strong gravitational field and heated by compression, reaches temperatures up to 10^8K. Violent thermal collisions between the particles release X-rays. The characteristics of the X-ray flux suggest that the second component of the binary system is very compact (< 300 km across).

The only black holes capable of detection are those swallowing gas or dust and producing X-rays or other radiation.

Hawking has speculated that black holes *may* appear to emit radiation (Hawking radiation). Space is not a perfect vacuum. Particles and their antimatter counterparts can pop out of nothingness and mutually annihilate in a tiny fraction of a second (no laws of physics are broken provided the appearance and disappearance of the particles takes place in a *very* short time). If a particle and its antiparticle appear at the event horizon of a black hole, one of the particles could be sucked in; the other (a little further away from the event horizon) could escape. To an external observer the escaping particle would *appear* to have been ejected by the black hole. The energy given to surviving particles by the black hole would, according to Hawking, eventually lead to it evaporating. There is no positive proof that black holes exist.

The Big Bang
The big bang theory suggests that the whole Universe is expanding and that it might have started 1.6×10^{10} years ago from one place with a huge explosion.

The Age of the Universe
Imagine the following four cars setting off in different directions at different speeds *at the same time*. At a later time they have covered the distances shown.

Car	Speed (km/h)	Distance (km)
Jaguar XJ220	350	1050
Porsche 928GT	170	510
Mercedes 500SL	160	480
Bentley Mulsanne S	120	360

Using speed = distance/time, we can calculate the duration of travel for each vehicle. It will of course be the same for all of them (3 hours). We could plot a graph of speed against distance. The reciprocal of the slope of the graph would yield the time of travel.

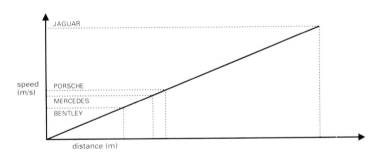

Similarly, knowing the recessional speeds of particular galaxies and their distances, and making the assumption that recessional velocity does not change with time , we can work out an approximate age for the Universe.

Galaxy	Recessional Speed (m/s)	Distance (m)
Hydra	6.1×10^{7}	37.9×10^{24}
Bootes	3.9×10^{7}	23.7×10^{24}
Corona Borealis	2.2×10^{7}	13.2×10^{24}
Ursa Major	1.5×10^{7}	9.5×10^{24}

The reciprocal of the slope of the graph yields a time of 6.1×10^{17} seconds $\simeq 2 \times 10^{10}$ years, i.e. 20 billion years.

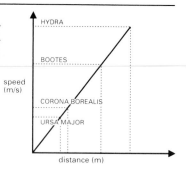

Planck Time The history of the Universe begins at 10^{-43} seconds after the big bang. This is the so called Planck time after which events can be physically described. The temperature of the mass of space and time that was becoming the cosmos at the Planck time would have been 10^{32} K.

COBE The big bang theory seems to explain the apparent recession of the galaxies and the uniform microwave background mapped by COBE (the Cosmic Background Explorer). This radiation is the fossil remains of an earlier extremely hot Universe. It has the characteristic of radiant heat – the same kind of radiant heat as emitted by a 'hot' body at a temperature of 3 K. The original hot radiant heat gradually cooled down as the Universe expanded giving rise to pockets of matter condensing into galaxies.

Critical Density The critical density of the Universe is 5×10^{-27} kg/m^3. This is the equivalent of an average of three billion (3×10^9) hydrogen atoms per cubic kilometre of space (or 3 hydrogen atoms per cubic metre!).

Omega Ω

$$\text{Omega } \Omega = \frac{\text{actual density of the Universe}}{\text{critical density of the Universe}}$$

Cosmic Matter Density and the Future of the Universe

The density of the Universe and therefore the value of Ω apparently dictates its future.

Scenario I: If the average density is less than 5×10^{-27} kg/m^3 ($\Omega < 1$), the force of gravity will never be able to stop the expansion and the Universe will expand forever. The temperature of the Universe will fall towards absolute zero (the *Big Chill*).

Scenario II: If the average density of the Universe exceeds 5×10^{-27} kg/m^3 ($\Omega > 1$), the force of gravity will not only stop the expansion but the Universe will eventually collapse back in upon itself in a cataclysmic crunch (the *Big Crunch*).

The Oscillating Universe Theory

Some astronomers believe that this contraction will ultimately result in the creation of another primeval atom which in turn will explode undergoing a new expansion phase (the *oscillating Universe* theory).

Many cosmologists believe that galaxies should be recessing at a rate that is just fast enough that the force of gravity will never quite make them stop and start collapsing in on themselves ($\Omega = 1$).

Scenario III: If the average density equals 5×10^{-27} kg/m^3 ($\Omega = 1$), the Universe will continue to expand forever but at a slower rate.

In scenarios I and III the galaxies get increasingly further apart. However the distances and dimensions *within* a galaxy do not participate in the universal expansion. Galaxies are pulled along with space as space expands.

Open Universe

In an 'open universe' ($\Omega < 1$) the density of the galaxies increases with increasing distance from the Earth.

Closed Universe

In a 'closed universe' ($\Omega > 1$) the density of galaxies decreases with increasing distance from the Earth.

Flat Universe

In a 'flat universe' ($\Omega = 1$) the density of galaxies is independent of distance from the Earth.

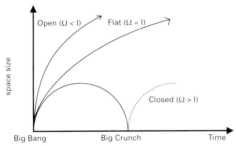

The average density of the visible Universe appears to be 10^{-28} kg/m^3 (most of the Universe is very nearly a perfect vacuum), yielding a value of $\Omega < < 1$.

Conclusions

Either 1. our understanding of the early Universe is very wrong,

or 2. most of the Universe (99%) is made up of a very strange invisible matter very different from anything we have come across. This 'dark matter' in space could consist of *massive astronomical compact halo objects* (MACHOS) – black holes or brown dwarf stars or *weakly interactive massive particles,* exotic subatomic particles (WIMPS). The hunt for this dark matter has begun!